ECOLOGY
A SYSTEMS
APPROACH

MODULE TWO

CARBON AND
ENERGY

ECOLOGY
A SYSTEMS
APPROACH

MODULE TWO

CARBON AND ENERGY

PRASSEDE CALABI

This curriculum was developed by
TERC, Inc., Cambridge, Massachusetts.
Funded in part by a grant from the
National Science Foundation.

TERC

KENDALL/HUNT PUBLISHING COMPANY
4050 Westmark Drive   Dubuque, Iowa 52002

T E R C

PROJECT MANAGEMENT: Nancy Benjamin and Sally Bindari, Books By Design, Inc.
INTERIOR DESIGN: Sally Bindari, Books By Design, Inc.
PAGE LAYOUT: Carol Keller
COPYEDITOR: Nancy Wirtes
COVER DESIGN: Scott Hancock
COVER IMAGES: © 1996 PhotoDisc, Inc.
SKULL PHOTOS: Scott Hancock and Jamil Simon

CREDITS

User's Guide
Pg. ix: CALVIN AND HOBBES © Watterson. Reprinted with permission of UNIVERSAL PRESS SYNDICATE. All rights reserved. **Pg. xi:** CALVIN AND HOBBES © Watterson. Reprinted with permission of UNIVERSAL PRESS SYNDICATE. All rights reserved. **Pg. xii:** CALVIN AND HOBBES © Watterson. Reprinted with permission of UNIVERSAL PRESS SYNDICATE. All rights reserved.

Module 2, Unit 1, Chapter 1
Module title page: Martha Cooper/Peter Arnold, Inc.; **Pg. 14:** CALVIN AND HOBBES © Watterson. Reprinted with permission of UNIVERSAL PRESS SYNDICATE. All rights reserved.

Module 2, Unit 1, Chapter 2
Pg. 22: CALVIN AND HOBBES © Watterson. Reprinted with permission of UNIVERSAL PRESS SYNDICATE. All rights reserved; **Excerpt:** "THE HAVING OF WONDERFUL IDEAS: HANK" from PIAGET IN THE CLASSROOM by MILTON SCHWEBEL and JANE RAPH. © 1973 by Basic Books, Inc. Reprinted by permission of BasicBooks, a division of HarperCollins Publishers, Inc. (Pp. 264–267)

Copyrights and acknowledgments continue on page 448, which constitutes an extension of the copyright page.

This book was prepared with the support of National Science Foundation Grant No. ESI-92-52981. However, any opinions, findings, conclusions, and/or recommendations herein are those of the author and do not necessarily reflect the views of the National Science Foundation. Any mention of trade names does not imply endorsement by the National Science Foundation.

Copyright © 1998 by Kendall/Hunt Publishing Company

ISBN 0-7872-3562-8

Printed in the United States of America

10 9 8 7 6 5 4 3 2 1

TO JIM

In praise of "imperfection"

since much of the world's richness

and all great science

stems from its exploration.

BTC

CONTENTS

USER'S GUIDE TO
ECOLOGY: A SYSTEMS APPROACH

Dear Student,

Welcome to this curriculum! You may be wondering, "Why should I take this course or use this book?" Well, science is a way of knowing based on actions you do every day: asking questions ("I wonder what's for dinner?"), observing things ("No one went shopping this week"), making predictions ("I bet we don't have anything for dinner"), and seeing if you are right ("I'll look in the refrigerator"). This curriculum is designed for you to use and sharpen those skills, to get you thinking, and to show you how much you already know and can do, even if you think you are bad at science. It does so by presenting you with data, questions, ideas, techniques, and topics in ecology (on plants, animals, ecosystems, carbon and energy, water, climate, size and shape, your behavior, tree growth and your growth, molecules, mice, moose, and more).

While it is true that we cannot make you care about ecology, we just might get you interested. And we are pretty sure you have not used a book like this before. Its focus is on you doing science, not just reading about it. Each chapter includes Explorations—work you do using data in the book or data you collect to answer various questions in ecology. Like, why are there no wasps the size of ponies? Why do more plants grow in a wetland than in a desert? What else can we deduce about the wetland and the desert from knowing that? How do we get and use energy? What ecological difference does it make whether we eat beans or burgers? Is New York City an ecosystem? Why or why not?

In this curriculum, you meet subjects you typically see in other courses—chemistry, physics, mathematics. What are they doing in an ecology textbook? Ecology is an interdisciplinary subject and includes all those subjects and then some. Ecology is about all possible interactions between and among living things and between and among living and nonliving things. So competition between pigeons for food or lions for a mate; coyotes eating mice, geese eating grass, or plants fixing carbon; and effects of climate on plant size and shape are all ecology. We need math to count, measure, weigh, or compare tulips and trees, growth, birth rates, age, size, and averages; we need physics to know how much force a bird's bill or a puma's jaws can exert; we use exponents because sometimes we need to work with very large numbers. You already have these basic skills, but you may not have applied them in these ways. We help you use those skills in new and different ways.

Actually, science is a way of knowing. By the time you finish this curriculum, you not only will know more (the aim of most courses), but, equally important, you will have learned more about how to figure things out on your own. That skill has applications for your whole life.

CONTENTS: HOW THE CURRICULUM IS BUILT CONCEPTUALLY

The curriculum consists of three Modules: **Evolution: A Natural Experiment—The Galapagos Finches**; **Carbon and Energy**; and **Water**, the latter two with multiple units and chapters. Each Module introduces key ecological concepts; the second and third Modules focus on the cycling and ecology of molecules that are ecologically important and whose cycles are subject to significant, current human perturbation. The Modules are designed to be used in sequence or separately and together provide a year's worth of material.

The first Module in *Ecology: A Systems Approach* deals with evolution by natural selection, since that is a core principle of ecology. In fact, ecology can be considered the expression of natural selection over time. Throughout the curriculum, we explore the lifestyles of many organisms and their interactions with each other and their physical environment. Many of those interactions are shaped by evolution, so it is a natural frame within which to place the rest of the curriculum.

The other two Modules build on a basic understanding of carbon compounds and water and, in successive units and chapters, relate those molecules to higher and higher levels of biological complexity. **Module 2: Carbon and Energy** and **Module 3: Water** consider their subjects at five levels:

1. the level of bonds and biochemistry
2. the individual/species level
3. the level of populations
4. the level of ecosystems/communities
5. the global level

The materials are not presented in that order, however, since it is not particularly engaging for an ecology curriculum to begin with bonds. Rather, each Module begins directly with ecological concepts and topics and considers bonds later, when you might want to understand the biochemical bases of your work with individuals, populations, or ecosystems. (Such levels and clustering of concepts also means your teacher may choose to skip around among areas or pick and choose, bypassing some areas altogether.)

Ideally, after this curriculum, when you look at a tree, for example, you will see it as a living thing that has many dimensions: It is a member of a population or species but is individually (genetically) variable; the species exists in a community or ecosystem physically (taking space) and ecologically (interacting with its own and other species—being eaten, photosynthesizing, cycling nutrients, competing); it has an evolutionary history; it is a living thing and must solve all the problems of life (getting and using energy to grow, mate, reproduce, survive).

A more traditional view of the same subject would be of boxes: the tree box, the photosynthesis box, the competing-for-sunlight box, the water box, the herbivore box. We try to break down the walls of all those boxes to show that everything is connected and cannot be put into boxes, especially in ecological studies.

GROUP WORK

We believe that a science class runs on the same principles as a science lab: doing science, learning science, collaboration, and reflection. We have considered the first two, and reflection runs throughout the curriculum, especially the Integrations. Now, let's focus on collaboration.

Most of the curriculum involves work in small groups, which has several advantages. Often learners do better in a situation of equality and shared responsibility; it is easier to take risks and chance being "wrong" if others participate in the decision.

Group work also fosters collaboration rather than competition—thinking together, with each of you contributing. It broadens the resource base, since each of you brings different skills, perspectives, and ideas.

Group work needs work in order to succeed, however. The same differences that can broaden your group's resources may also lead to friction.

You are going to have to try to be a "good citizen" as a member of your group. Keep an eye out for problems—one person dominating, lack of interest, serious differences of opinion among members—and try to help balance things or ask your teacher for help. People are not born with group skills, but they can learn those skills. Indeed, the ability to work well as the member of a team is one thing employers look for in employees and is a skill that will stand you in good stead no matter what career you choose.

TECHNIQUES

Unlike typical science techniques, the ones in this book have been carefully designed to illustrate the underlying principles. They are not "black box" procedures to be carried out obediently but without understanding. When you burn stuff using the technique of calorimetry, you see that energy is released by combustion as heat; you see that the heat is captured by water; you see that the temperature of the water rises. No black box here.

CALVIN AND HOBBES © Watterson. Reprinted with permission of UNIVERSAL PRESS SYNDICATE. All rights reserved.

Because we deliberately try to present a different angle or perspective, one major difference in your work with this curriculum is that you take on that new perspective, too. Some students have found it exciting; we hope you do, too. Again, welcome.

If you have suggestions or comments, please send them to Dr. Prassede Calabi, care of Kendall/Hunt Publishing Company. Your feedback will be extremely helpful for any curriculum revisions. Thank you.

ACKNOWLEDGMENTS

An effort such as this curriculum reflects input of different kinds and degrees from numerous people. All their contributions are important but are so various they are hard to compare. How does a key phone call of just a few minutes compare with months of development, testing, or evaluation effort? Yet all are essential. Here goes.

First, special thanks to Brian Drayton, project director, for important conceptual, logistical, and development work, especially throughout the first phases of the project. His background complemented my own and lent balance to the total picture. He is co-author and primary developer of specific pieces, as noted, and contributed supporting prose and scientific or pedagogical content throughout.

Thanks to Dan Perlman for conceptual and development work, especially (but not only) **Module 2, Unit 2**. To Marsha Pomeroy for all her work on **Module 3**, and for being so easy to work with. William Spitzer, Sylvia Weir, J. Stephen Lowe, and Jane Ceraso helped develop aspects of the whole and contributed to individual pieces—thank you. Thanks also to Tasha Morris, first Administrative Assistant to the project, and to Alison Paddock for balancing this project with a second one and with most of the immediate world.

Thanks to Amy Schulman Weinberg for evaluation and rooting out opacity, and to Deborah Levine for evaluation and assessment.

To Donald Humphrys, Ivo Lindauer, and M. Patricia Morse (at the National Science Foundation) and Alan Vincent (at Kendall/Hunt) for believing in the project.

TEACHERS AND STUDENTS

This text is the better for input from all the teachers and students who used versions of it; to them all—thank you!

Thanks to our local **in-house pilot test students** for their enthusiasm, honesty, and trust in us.

Rachel Bauer, Somerville High School
Marianne Bowers, Somerville High School
Paolo DiFablo, Somerville High School
Peter French, Winchester High School

Antonio Hernandez, Hull High School
Carlos Hernandez, Hull High School
Susanna Hollister, Brookline High School
David Hood, Winchester High School
Eric Hood, Winchester High School
Rachel Megerman, Brookline High School
Sergio Serpa, Somerville High School
Jeff Tahnk, Winchester High School
Dee Wolfe, Hull High School

Our **pilot test teachers** were especially important in testing and helping shape our rough draft materials. Thanks to:

Mark Dewart, Park Tudor School (Indianapolis, IN)
Steve Case and Brad Williamson, Olathe East Senior High School (Olathe, KS)
Peter McLean, St. Andrews School (Middletown, DE)
Susan Oleszko-Szuts, Governor Dummer Academy (Byfield, MA)

Special thanks to our **observation site field test teachers** for their time, energy, and willingness to step into another world with us.

David Chuckran, Bridgewater-Raynham Regional High School (MA)
Charles DeLeo, Weaver High School (Hartford, CT)
Joseph Donager, Hull Environmental High School (MA)
Sarah Fogerty, Lincoln School (RI)
Vicki Goldburgh, Brimmer and May (MA)
Susan Olesko-Szuts, Governor Dummer Academy (MA)
Tad Sudnick, Cambridge Rindge and Latin High School (MA)
Alan Weinstein, Cambridge Rindge and Latin High School (MA)

Special thanks to Sarah Fogerty, Susan Olesko-Szuts, and those who tested both first and second drafts of these materials.

Thanks also to our **other field test teachers and their students** for feedback, good will, and commitment.

Jules Adam, Oak Glen High School (New Cumberland, WV)
Peter Auger, Falmouth High School (Falmouth, MA)
Linda Baker, Davis High School (Davis, CA)
Scott Battaion, West Valley High School (Cottonwood, CA)
Leslie Beaulieu, Shore Country Day School (Beverly, MA)
Donalda Cas, Bridgewater-Raynham Regional High School (Bridgewater, MA)
Debbie Coates, Shore Country Day School (Beverly, MA)
George Collins, Mariemount High School (Cincinnati, OH)
Joseph Donager, Hull Environmental High School (Hull, MA)
David Form, Minuteman Technical High School (Lexington, MA)
Elizabeth Hedgepeth, Mount Arat Junior and Senior High School (Topsham, ME)
Timothy Hoshal, Grand Ledge High School (Grand Ledge, MI)
Thomas Hudson, Garfield High School (Seattle, WA)
Mary Bishop Kennedy, Texas Military Institute (San Antonio, TX)

Phyllis Olson, James Bowie High School (Arlington, TX)
Mary Priestly, Franklin County High School (Winchester, MA)
Melissa Schermer, Souhegan High School (Amherst, MA)
James Sullivan, Hatboro-Horsham High School (Horsham, MA)
Charles Tarleton, Lunenburg High School (Lunenburg, MA)
Lou Verner, Elm Lea Farm (Putney, VT)
Peter Weis, Wachusett Regional High School (Holden, MA)
Michael Vandenberg, Willow Creek High School (Willow Creek, MT)
Christopher Wells, Melbourne High School (Melbourne, FL)

Our **Advisory Board** was especially helpful with comments on pilot materials, and some also in reviewing manuscript—thank you all; and special thanks to S. J. McNaughton.

Steve Case and Brad Williamson, Olathe East Senior High School (Olathe, KS)
Mark Dewart, Park Tudor School (Indianapolis, IN)
Scott Eddleman, Fenway School at Bunker Hill Community College (Charlestown, MA)
Daniel Goroff, Derek Bok Center for Teaching and Learning, Harvard University (Cambridge, MA) and National Research Council (Washington, D.C.)
Robert Harriss, University of New Hampshire Institute for the Study of Earth, Ocean and Space (Durham, NH)
Kelly McConnaughay, Bradley University Biology Department (Peoria, IL)
Peter McLean, St. Andrews School (Middletown, DE)
Samuel J. McNaughton, Biological Research Labs, Syracuse University (Syracuse, NY)
Susan Oleszko-Szuts, Governor Dummer Academy (Falmouth, MA)
Douglas Ryan, U.S. Forest Service (Washington, D.C.)
Alan VanArsdale, Northeast States for Coordinated Air Use Management (Boston, MA)

Many teacher participants in another National Science Foundation–funded project developed by this author (Calabi) also used parts of this curriculum and gave us comments—our warm thanks to them (Teacher Enhancement in Pedagogy through Ecology TE 92-53280).

OTHER GREAT FOLKS

To Books By Design: Nancy Benjamin, Sally Bindari, Carol Keller, and Nancy Wirtes for professionalism, clarity of design, top-quality work, and grace under pressure.

To Sally and Carol especially for appreciating the vertical line, design, and patience.

For his exceptional generosity, our heartfelt thanks to Bill Watterson for permission to leaven the text with his inimitable wit of Calvin and Hobbes.

Warm thanks also to Gwilym S. Jones, Director of the Center for Vertebrate Studies, Northeastern University; Fred Sibley and Paul F. Whitehead, Peabody Museum of Natural History, Yale University; and Jane Winchell, Peabody Essex Museum of Salem, MA, for their generous loan of bony skulls (**Module 2, Unit 2, Chapter 1**), no strings attached.

Thanks to Catherine Alexander for her drawings (chickadee, hyrax, squirrel) and to M. S. Quinton for his photo (bobcat meets muskrat).

To the indexing party: Kevin Flick, Monica Kearney, Alison Paddock, Kristen Rooney, Paul Rooney, Marsha Pomeroy, Rachel Skiffer, and James Wilkinson.

To Jane Nielson for critical paperwork; to Jim Terrell for a key address; to Patricia Dupree, John Foster, Kevin Flick, Monica Kearney, Barbara Sampson, and Robert Tinker for support at critical moments.

To Rachel Skiffer for her combined skills as typist, bloodhound, and etcetera; Ellen Archer for typing and bibliographic research; Robin Brown for exceptionally careful work on copyright permissions, especially from Tunisia, England, and Outer Mongolia.

For fighting the good fight—and winning the war if not the battle—thanks to Sally Bindari and Scott Hancock.

Special thanks to Scott Hancock for beautiful art, hard work, and easy grace; to Alison Paddock for being there; and to CBB for believing and insisting.

CARBON AND ENERGY

MODULE TWO
OVERVIEW

The movement and transfer of energy within and among parts of an ecosystem are the foundation underlying all other ecological processes.

This Module describes how energy is stored and moved in the global carbon cycle. It considers energy transfer in communities and trophic pyramids via photosynthesis, feeding, predation, decomposition, competition. It explores questions such as: What is energy, biochemically and biologically? Why is food "relative," that is, why is grass energy for a cow but not for a cat? (And what differences in lifestyle go with that: how animals are built; their size; how they move; who or what they eat and digest; how they get what they eat; how many of them can live on 10 hectares?) How do desert- and water-living plants differ in energy needs and use (shape and size; how they fit into their ecosystem)?

The energy "Big Picture" (the global and ecosystem scale or level) is drawn by integrating smaller-scale energy pictures (although any complex picture is more than the sum of its parts). Thus this Module helps you explore energy at various scales—from the biochemical to the global scale—so you can develop tools and building blocks both to understand each scale independently and to integrate those blocks into an ever widening, cross-scale picture, ultimately yielding a Big Picture.

1

GROUPINGS AND WHAT THEY MEAN

GROUPINGS AND WHAT THEY MEAN

UNIT 1

CONTENTS

UNIT 1 OVERVIEW

GROUPINGS AND WHAT THEY MEAN

Ecology, asking questions, thinking, and thinking about thinking—those are the main points of this Unit. They take various forms: grouping organisms; figuring how many cows are used by a burger chain; exploring some key ideas in ecology; designing and doing a research project outdoors; and discussing ideas you and others have about science, questions, thinking, and learning.

Sometimes students think science is boring. And whether you will like this unit, we cannot say. But we doubt that you will be bored.

THE "NATURAL LOOK" IS MANY-FACETED

CHAPTER ONE

Exploration 1 (Homework)
GROUPING: PLANTS, ANIMALS, AND OTHERS

Below is a set of organisms. Each of them has things in common with or shares relationships with some of the others. What are some such relationships?

Materials
- **Organism names** and **pictures**

Procedure

1. **Making relationships.**
   After you have read the following list, select several sets of organisms that are somehow related. Describe their relationship(s) and arrange them (either their names or their pictures) in a diagram, chart, or list that shows the relationships you have in mind. Please specify the relationships and describe your reasoning in your notebook.

kangaroos	vultures	prairie dogs	trees
ants	millipedes	bushes	termites
ravens	fungi	rabbits	emus
foxes	dingoes	bacteria	badgers
grasses	earthworms	owls	fleas

   Bring your organism list and diagrams to the next class, as well as any other groupings, questions, and comments, so you can refer to them if you want.

emu

badger

rabbit

vulture

fungus

termite

ant

millipede

fox

owl

flea

bacteria

kangaroo

raven

earthworm

dingo

prairie dog

10

Exploration 1 (Class)
GROUPING: PLANTS, ANIMALS, AND OTHERS

Reconsider the set of organisms you used for a homework activity. Some of these organisms share ecological relationships; others do not. See if you can rearrange some organisms in groupings in which the organisms interact with one another in some way.

Materials
- **Exploration 1 (Homework) list, illustrations**, and your **homework**
- **Reference materials** from your teacher

Procedure

1. **Ecological relationships: Within teams, compare and discuss your homework results.**

   Reconsider your homework. Working in teams of three to five students, choose and arrange some organisms in another kind of grouping, specifically, groupings in which the organisms interact with one another in some way. Since the network of possible relationships between organisms has several layers, this task has a couple of rounds. So you may find that you have second—and third!—thoughts. Before you begin, read Step 2, on having productive discussions.

2. **Notes on productive discussions.**

   Life is complicated, and relationships are even more so (as you may already know). Any ecological study includes a stage in which you try to "see" the question from as many angles as possible. Because organisms are related in many ways, as you think of possible relationships, and especially as you discuss each others' suggestions, you will come up with lots of questions. That is a sign of productive conversation—indeed, your success with this work can be partially measured by the number of questions your team has.

   A question can be the beginning of understanding and exploration. Any question is fair game, and it is no disgrace if someone's question catches you off guard or raises something you had never thought of.

   The questions can be questions of fact: "Doesn't an eagle mostly eat little things?" "Do those animals actually live in the same areas?"

   Or the questions may be of a different sort: "Does it make sense to group things that way?" "Well, why not?"

   Some ways of grouping things are mostly for human convenience, like arranging things in alphabetical order. Some ways of grouping have to do with actual characteristics of organisms and their lifestyles—these are groupings by function. Others, like yours here, can be about relationships among organisms. Some groupings may seem arbitrary and then reveal deeper meanings as you keep thinking about them, say, arranging organisms by their kind of mouth or mouth parts. Each kind of grouping is useful in its own way; its value depends on the kind of questions you are asking and how best to answer them.

3. **Teams reorganize the organisms and their relationships.**
    Have your team choose six to eight organisms that you think interact with each other. How do those organisms relate to one another? Make a diagram or other illustration showing the relationships and be ready to describe or explain the relationships.

4. **Note questions and ideas.**
    Have one or two members of your team record the questions any team member raises during your work. Answers to some of these questions may come out in class discussions; others will emerge as you progress through the Module; still others you may want to pursue further in class or out.

5. **Team reports and class discussion.**
    Now each team puts its diagram up on the board, describing and explaining the relationships. Does everyone agree with the groupings? Not all organisms occur (live) in the same places. Identify a few pairs that do not occur in the same place, and a few pairs that do. How can you tell?

    Did teams come up with the same types of relationships? Do you think these are all the possible kinds of relationships among living animals? Why or why not? Which (if any) have been left out?

CASE STUDY
SOLVING MYSTERIES: EVERYTHING HAS MANY NAMES

All mysteries (say, the typical <u>Star Trek</u> episode) have the person "who dunit." But at first that person is not named or pointed out. Rather, as the mystery unfolds, the audience becomes more and more informed about that person, until we put together the pieces of information to name the "bad guy," the one "who dunit." How do we do that?

Each bit of information adds a role, a dimension, or a characteristic to the person. We keep adding these bits to see a more complex person, a more complete or accurate picture of that person.

THE CONNECTION

At some point we get a piece of information that clicks and makes us say, "Aha! the guilty one!" That very friendly person who is knowledgeable about the desert (or some distant galaxy) turns out to have that knowledge from having been in prison there—which means she and the drug runner <u>were</u> in the same place at the same time. So that person's roles include being friendly, being knowledgeable about a certain place, and being a former prisoner who thus is likely acquainted with the drug runner—a crucial combination for this mystery.

THE TOOL OF RENAMING

Such renaming or building more complex pictures by adding roles (or names) is one of several simple but powerful mental tools or habits you can get from studying ecology. It can also be used in nearly everything else.

Use yourself as an example. What are some of your "names" and roles? You are a student (you are using this text!), maybe you are an employee somewhere, a member of some school group(s), and an individual with various characteristics. Each of these roles can be described in more detail. You might be a different kind of student in this class than you are in English or social studies, hating one and loving the others. You could also have several roles in your own family unit, such as ward, son/daughter, niece/nephew, brother/sister, aunt/uncle, oldest/youngest, and so on.

DESCRIBE A FLOWER

Consider a flower. In your notebook, write down and describe three roles for it. In the next class session, you will briefly discuss those roles.

MATH PROOFS ARE ESSENTIALLY RENAMING THINGS

So what good is this, and what does it have to do with solving mysteries, or with ecology, or with anything for that matter? Renaming is a powerful tool and one you likely remember from math proofs. By renaming things and substituting different names, you can get somewhere quite different from where you began. Here is an example. Let's prove that multiplication distributes over subtraction. In mathematical terms, that means for any real numbers x, y, and z,

$$x\,(y - z) = xy - xz$$

Start with one of the two equations in your original terms and proceed from there:

$x\,(y - z) = x\,[y + (-z)]$	**"Rename" subtraction as addition of a negative.**
$= xy + x\,(-z)$	**Distribute multiplication over addition.**
$= xy + (-xz)$	**Positive times negative is negative.**
$= xy - xz$	**"Rename" addition to change back to subtraction.**

And look—in four steps we have substituted and calculated to demonstrate that the two initial equations are equal. This demonstration, or proof, would not be possible without using other names or roles of terms already in the equation. Renaming and using other properties of organisms, people, whatever, allow us to see and understand them in more complex and richer ways.

THE VALUE OF MULTIPLE ROLES

Throughout your work with this book, you will often find yourself renaming things—actually adding names or roles. Each time you do, you expand your image or understanding of that organism and how it fits into a particular ecological scene or interaction—you will have a clearer idea of "who dunit."

The power of this renaming tool lies in how it expands your thinking or image of whatever you are thinking about. That expansion enriches your knowledge about or understanding of the thing, and that gives you more to work with, more angles or aspects with which to solve the mystery.

Renaming becomes a spiral, which keeps growing outward. In fact, the power of this "multiple roles" way of looking at things might be more apparent if you consider its absence. Have you seen one of your teachers outside school and had trouble recognizing him? Chances are your image of him is so tied up with his role as teacher and his physical placement at school that you literally have no role or image of him outside school. You can be sure that he has a life outside school, with many other roles: town council member, basketball player, parent, spouse, and so on. Yet you think of him in just his teacher role. See how flat and limited your picture is?

Exploration 2
ENERGY RELATIONSHIPS

Materials
- **Exploration 1** and all your work with it
- **Reference materials** from your teacher

Procedure

1. **Who eats whom/what/why?**
   Suppose we change the task slightly and ask specifically for a diagram of energy relationships, that is, who eats whom or what. Would your team diagram change? Why?

   Does this include everything that the organisms need to survive? Is there anything missing?

2. **Energy relationships: Team reports and class discussion.**
Compare team results by putting them on the board and discussing differences between relationships and the relative numbers. Does it clarify anything to consider these relationships as energy relationships? What happens to energy? What is missing from the picture?

READING
ANSWERS IN THE BALLPARK: USEFUL APPROXIMATIONS

Practically all the time, people are involved in making observations and developing expectations or predictions. (For example, you observe that your pet comes running into the kitchen at the sound of a can being opened, and you begin to make predictions about why. Is it because of the sound? The smell?) **Much progress in science happens because someone decides to test a prediction or expectation.** For instance, the Greek philosopher Aristotle made two interesting observations. He noticed that (1) the shadow of the earth on the moon, during a lunar eclipse, was always circular, and (2) the North Star looked lower in the sky when the observer was near the equator than when the observer was in northern regions. From those two observations, Aristotle predicted that the earth is spherical, not flat (it is likely that other cultures came to this same conclusion earlier, and he was simply unaware of it). Aristotle published his ideas in 340 B.C., and they were verified by experiments conducted by Eratosthenes later that century and driven home by Magellan's circumnavigation of the earth some 1,700 years later. Part of the art of science lies in discovering just what your expectations are and then making the comparison with what is really out there.

Although at some points in your research you need to be very precise in your numbers or calculations, like when weighing a dried plant for carbonometry, at other points you do not need to or cannot even get the "right" answer. At a time like that, "right" means "within an order of magnitude," that is, between, say, 10^4 and 10^5.

FERMI PAINTED WITH BROAD STROKES

Such calculations are often called "Fermi calculations," after the physicist Enrico Fermi. Because he thought about Big Picture things like what you get when you break atoms into smaller and smaller parts and how to make atomic bombs, Fermi had to do a lot of (very) educated guessing and estimating. In beginning to think about a problem, he would often challenge his students and colleagues to solve the problem "roughly," that is, within an order of magnitude. Such rough calculations are especially useful during early stages of solving problems, when they produce rough predictions that may help you see where your investigation might go. In other words, these rough answers give you a "ballpark" idea of where the answers lie, numerically speaking. And you can build on and refine those ballpark figures or decide that the rough answer tells you that the problem is not interesting. For example, if you estimate that a particular nesting site for flamingos ought to support about 10,000 pairs, you would probably lose interest in looking at the numbers if you found 15,000 or 20,000 pairs. On the other hand, if you counted only 1,000 or as many as 100,000 pairs, you might be really curious to know what is actually going on and why your original estimate was so different.

In ecology such calculations are exceptionally useful because so many ecological events happen on a vast scale or are things that are impossible to measure accurately, such as the global movement of nutrients like carbon or water or the numbers of invertebrates in the ocean. There is just no way to get a precise measurement of how many diatoms are floating around in the oceans!

COWS AND BURGERS

Here is an example of a Fermi problem. Without using any reference materials, estimate how many cows it would take to serve a billion people at a burger joint. How would you go about it? The following notes are from one attempt.

Ground Beef

First, how much ground beef do you need to serve a billion people? Well, how much might each person eat? We do not really know, but let's say that each person eats a quarter pound of beef per visit. Some people probably eat less, and others more, but let's go with that number for now. That means that the burger joint would need 1×10^9 people $\times$ .25 lb per person = 2.5×10^8 lb of ground beef.

Cows

How many cows do you need to get 2.5×10^8 lb of ground beef? Think of how much a cow weighs. Maybe we would guess no more than 800 pounds. How much of that is meat versus bone and organs? Maybe a cow is 50% meat. Now, not all that meat gets ground up for burgers—let's say half of that gets sold as steaks and ribs and such. That means that you get 800 lb/cow $\times$ 50% meat/cow $\times$ 50% ground beef/all meat = 200 lb ground beef per cow, more or less.

OK, the burger joint would need 2.5×10^8 lb ground beef to serve a billion people at about 200 lb ground beef per cow:

$$= 2.5 \times 10^8 \text{ lb ground beef} / 200 \text{ lb ground beef per cow}$$

$$= 2.5 \times 10^8 / 2 \times 10^2$$

$$= 1.25 \times 10^6 \text{ cows (1.25 million)}$$

Reality Testing: The Farm

We have made a lot of assumptions here, of course, which we would need to test to make our estimate much closer to reality. In fact, if you call somebody who knows about cattle farming, you can test our reasoning. The Fermi or order-of-magnitude way of saying our prediction is that you will find in the range of 1 million to 1.5 million ($1–1.5 \times 10^6$) cows, rather than 100 times that many ($1–1.5 \times 10^8$) cows.

HOW DOES THIS RELATE TO ECOLOGY?

This answer is actually pretty remarkable, given how little real information we had to go on. The fact is, in very many cases of ecological studies, we are at almost that much of a loss for firm information. There are two important situations in which this can be true.

Vastness, or "Big Pictureness"

Say the phenomenon we are studying occurs on too vast a scale. For example, later on in this Module, you will consider how to estimate plant matter for a forest study site of 100 square meters (100 m²). Suppose we want to find out how much above-ground plant matter exists on all continents. (That is another way of describing the total amount of energy and nutrients now available from plants in all terrestrial ecosystems.) We cannot do it by cutting down all forests, mowing all grasslands, harvesting all cacti and mosses, and then drying and weighing everything! No, we take some measurements and then do order-of-magnitude calculations. That gives us a basis on which to refine the numbers by doing experiments or by more detailed studies of particular systems (including some cutting, mowing, and weighing).

Serious Lack of Information

The second case would be if the phenomenon is so little understood that you must make some educated guesses about its size, as a way to begin probing. For example, we do not know how important salamanders are to the forest ecosystems of eastern North America, that is, what role or roles they might play, how many there might be, or other similar information. In fact, it seems absurd at first to ask the question, "Do salamanders play a role in the global carbon budget?" After all, salamanders are so small and seem not to be numerous—you walk in the woods, and you hardly see any at all.

Yet, Dr. Rick Wyman at the Huyck Reserve Biological Field Station in New York has found a reason to ask that "absurd" question. When he first counted salamanders in some study sites, he found more than he expected, far more. Thus, even though they are small, if there are a lot of them, they might actually have a large effect. After all, salamanders are predators, and as such play some role in the cycling of nutrients and energy.

Dr. Wyman performed an order-of-magnitude calculation, starting with his study data. He had been finding salamanders at a density of about two per square meter. So his calculations went like this: "If salamanders occur at about 2 per square meter, and there are about N square meters of forest, and each salamander weighs about 3 grams. . . ." By the time his calculations were done, Wyman's numbers led him to propose that salamanders might be major players in the global climate system. His rough numbers are convincing others, and the National Science Foundation is funding more research to test his ideas. They may turn out wrong when he looks more closely; more likely, he will discover new, perhaps related surprises.

We need this kind of probe as a first step, because Earth is a largely unexplored, unknown planet, and such rough data help us find and grasp important pieces of the Big Picture.

Exploration 3
RELATIVE POPULATION SIZES

KEEP THOSE NUMBERS STEADY!

So far, you have considered a still picture—a snapshot of a group of organisms and their relationships at one moment in time. What if you wanted to revisit the group a few times in the future, say, at yearly intervals for ten years? How many of any type of organism is necessary to keep the picture "steady," or constant? For the populations to continue and survive over time, what other aspect of organisms' lives must we include? In other words, what mechanism(s) that change (increase or decrease) animal numbers have we left out?

Materials
* **Results** from Exploration 2
* **Reference materials** on organisms in groupings

Procedure

1. **Approximate population sizes: Numbers and mechanisms.**
    Working in your teams, think about how many individuals of each organism might be in a functional group such as you developed. Let each team prepare a chart with its organisms and their "guess-timated" population sizes. In thinking about this question of population sizes, ask yourself questions like these:

    * "How many rabbits does a dingo eat in a day, a week, or a year?"
    * "How much plant material does a rabbit eat?"

    Are there patterns to your answers? What are they? (Refer to the Reading on approximations, if that helps.) Be ready to explain the reasoning for your numbers.

    What mechanism for changing organism numbers have we left out of our static picture? We have considered death, that is, an organism being eaten by other species. But how does the population size of one species increase?

2. **Class discussion of teamwork.**
    Let each team prepare a chart with its organisms and their relative population sizes. As a class, prepare a chart on the board with headings like "Organism," "Eats," "Is Eaten By," "Population Size," and others if you need them. For each organism, fill in what different teams have come up with. Consider and discuss both similarities and differences among team answers. Resolve as many differences as possible using the reference materials; mark the others for future consideration.

3. **Other questions.**
    Are there patterns to your answers? What could they mean? Write down questions or predictions that come out of this discussion. Save them for future reference. Some questions will answer themselves as you progress through this module; you will gain tools with which to answer others.

4.   A comment and moving on.

All organisms that live in a given area are related energetically, directly or indirectly. The next weeks will be spent on examining these kinds of relationships in order to better understand where energy comes from, and how organisms get it, use it, and transfer it to other organisms.

GETTING HOOKED THROUGH FIELDWORK

CHAPTER TWO

OVERVIEW

Ecology is everywhere, even in the urban or suburban areas in which most of us live. But we tend to be quite ignorant about the natural world, and the study of urban ecology especially is in its infancy. Television helps bring the natural world to us, but to study ecology, we need to be outside—any kind of outside. Here, we go outside to discover what's there and to think about it ecologically. You will be surprised how much you see and how much you already know.

Exploration 1
YOUR LOCAL SITE: ECOLOGY IS EVERYWHERE

Because ecology encompasses living things, nonliving things, and the interactions among them (as shown by the diagram below), it can be seen anywhere. Today, you will demonstrate that to yourself.

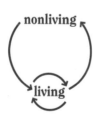

Materials
- **Blank paper**
- **Pencil**
- **Watch**

Safety

> **WARNING**
>
> Before the field trip, visit the site and note possible safety issues, such as broken glass, abandoned buildings or wells, cliffs, hornets' nests, and plants such as poison ivy or poison oak.

> **WARNING**
>
> If you have any allergic reaction to plants or insect bites or stings (especially bee stings), take precautions as necessary. Bring along any medications if you might need them.

> **WARNING**
>
> Use the buddy system. Although you do the first part of this Exploration by yourself, always stay in sight of someone else from the group, so you neither get lost nor are ever actually alone.

Procedure

1. **Seeing what is around you.**
   Following your teacher's instructions, spread out so you can work alone but stay in sight of someone else from the group. Try to see what is around you.

2. **Questions.**
   On your paper, write down 21 questions about what you see. All kinds of questions, any kind of questions.

   When you have finished or 30 minutes are up, whichever comes first, return to the spot designated by your teacher.

3. **Round robin of questions: In the field or in class.**
   Each of you will have a chance to raise at least one of your questions for the group's consideration. So pick your most burning questions—something that really caught your attention or interested you (like, "why am I being bitten by so many mosquitoes?" or "why are plants growing out of that trash?").

4. **Considering other questions.**
   Since everyone gets to ask a question, you will be considering other students' questions. If you have questions or comments about someone else's question, speak up. You may be helping that person think, just as comments on your question may help you think.

5. **Answering questions.**
   Part of the discussion will include how to go about answering some questions. What next steps might you take? How might you take them?

6. **Your research project.**
   If possible, you will be using your own or another equally interesting question as the focus of a group research project. You may want to use the Integration worksheet to help organize your ideas. Even if you do not actually carry out the research, it is important to discuss how you might do so.

CASE STUDY

CONFESSIONS OF A TERRIFIED SCIENCE LEARNER

"I was sure my questions were real dumb. I've always been bad in science and now everybody would know. Then some other kid asked a question I had. Hey! maybe I wasn't so dumb after all!"

Feel familiar? This reaction is from someone who had participated for the first time in the process of 21 Questions to Conclusions, just as you did today. So where do we get the idea that asking questions means we are stupid? Actually, probably from several places.

QUESTIONS AS STATEMENTS OR EXCLAMATIONS

People often ask questions they do not really mean or use questions to make an observation or statement—like Calvin's mom.

It seems pretty clear what Calvin is doing, which is why he is asking her what she really means. Is she actually asking a question? What kind of answer do you think she is expecting? What do you think she is saying?

OFF-LIMITS TOPICS

Can you think of a time you asked a question that made someone uncomfortable or got you in trouble? There are whole topics about which people often do not want questions asked—like sex, religion, politics, or whatever makes them uncomfortable. If you have been shut up before, it makes it hard to ask questions again, doesn't it?—even about other topics.

FACTS ARE "IT"

Another reason people might not like to ask questions is because we can be a "know-it-all" society, where facts count more than thinking, and right/wrong answers are what learning is about.

Remember your work in **Chapter 1**, in which you grouped plants, animals, and other things? Remember that an answer might be right or wrong depending on context? (Although dingoes do not eat prairie dogs because the two live on different continents, dingoes are carnivores, which typically eat herbivores like prairie dogs.) Or that an answer can be partly right and be a helpful and even necessary stage toward finding a more complete answer? ("Herbivores eat grass." Actually some herbivores eat grass; others eat both grass and other plants; some never eat grass.)

We may be inhibited from asking questions because we are afraid of not knowing, of giving the wrong answer, of showing our ignorance. But not asking a question is a huge handicap, especially in doing science. How are you going to find out about stuff it you do not ask—and answer—questions? Science is a process, a way of learning or finding out. And along that way you need to ask questions. In fact, the whole "scientific method" (which you probably have heard about so often that your eyes are glazing over right now) starts with a question. Just as you did at your field site today.

SCIENCE COMES OUT OF QUESTIONS

Einstein, Curie, Edison, Priestley, Pasteur, Margolis, Goodall, Salk, Newton, Boyle, Levi-Montalcini, Darwin—all these scientists asked questions, lots of questions. Indeed, their work began out of and developed with questions. They not only admitted their ignorance, they considered it a challenge and a tool. Questions are a beginning, not an end. (Interesting biographies exist for most of those scientists; even more interesting is their work. You should be able to find some in any library, either in books or in journals like Scientific American.)

Let's consider a small example. Two sisters are examining a rhododendron bush they had bought and planted at their parents' house several years earlier. Both notice that the flowers are a different color than in previous years, but the sisters have completely different reactions. One thinks there might be some reason—for example, it was overcast most of the past week, and perhaps bright sunlight brings out different chemicals in the flowers, which affects their color. The other sister is amazed even to think that such a question could be asked. To her, bushes just "are." A rhododendron's behavior is incomprehensible, not something that can be understood or is even worth trying to understand. (It turns out that, in fact, the amount of sunshine does affect flower color.) But the interesting thing is the sisters' different attitudes. To one, the observation raises questions; to the other, it raises a blank.

Doing science is like solving mysteries or riddles. For more, see the **Technique: Introduction to Research**—just the first section for now—about mysteries.

EXCERPT
"The Having of Wonderful Ideas," by Eleanor Duckworth

"Hank"

It is a truism that all children in their first and second years make incredible intellectual advances. Piaget has documented these advances from his own point of view, but every parent and every psychologist knows this to be the case. One recurring question is, why does the intellectual development of vast numbers of children then slow down? <u>What happens to children's curiosity and resourcefulness later in their childhood? Why do so few continue to have their own wonderful ideas? I think part of the answer is that intellectual breakthroughs come to be less and less valued. Either they are dismissed as being trivial . . . or else they are discouraged as being unacceptable</u> [emphasis added]—like discovering how it feels to wear shoes on the wrong feet, or asking questions that are socially embarrassing, or destroying something to see what it's like inside. The effect is to discourage children from exploring their own ideas and to make them feel that they have no important ideas of their own, only silly or evil ones.

But I think there is at least one other part of the answer, too. Wonderful ideas do not spring out of nothing. They build on a foundation of other ideas. The following incident may help to clarify what I mean.

Hank was an energetic and not very scholarly fifth grader. His class had been learning about electric circuits with flashlight batteries, bulbs, and various wires. After the children had developed considerable familiarity with these materials, the teacher made a number of mystery boxes. [This activity is from the Elementary Science Study's <u>Batteries and Bulbs</u>. This and the other ESS units are currently available from Delta Education, Nashua, New Hampshire.]

Two wires protruded from each box, but inside, unseen, each box had a different way of making contact between the wires. In one box the wires were attached to a battery; in another they were attached to a bulb; in a third, to a certain length of resistance wire; in a fourth box they were not attached at all; and so forth. By trying to complete the circuit on the outside of a box, the children were able to figure out what made the connection inside the box. Like many other children, Hank attached a battery and a bulb to the wire outside the box. Because the bulb lit, he knew at least that the wires inside the box were connected in some way. But, because it was somewhat dimmer than usual, he also knew that the wires inside were not connected directly to each other and that they were not connected by a piece of ordinary copper wire. Along with many of the children, he knew that the degree of dimness of the bulb meant that the wires inside were connected either by another bulb of the same kind or by a certain length of resistance wire.

The teacher expected them to go only this far. However, in order to push the children to think a little further, she asked them if they could tell whether it was a bulb or a piece of wire inside the box. She herself thought there was no way to tell. After some thought, Hank had an idea. He undid the battery and bulb that he had already attached on the outside of the box. In their place, using additional copper wire, he attached six batteries in a series. He had already experimented enough to know that six batteries would burn out a bulb, if it was a bulb inside the box. He also knew that once a bulb is burned out, it no longer completes the circuit. He then attached the original battery and bulb again. This time he found that the bulb on the outside of the box did not light. So he reasoned, rightly, that there had been a bulb inside the box and that now it was burned out. If there had been a wire inside, it would not have burned through and the bulb on the outside would still light.

Note that to carry out that idea, Hank had to take the risk of destroying a lightbulb. In fact, he did destroy one. In accepting this idea, the teacher had to accept not only the fact that Hank had a good idea that even she did not have, but also that it was worthwhile to destroy a small piece of property for the sake of following through an idea. These features almost turn the incident into a parable. Without these kinds of acceptance, Hank would not have been able to pursue his idea. Think of how many times this acceptance is not forthcoming in the life of any one child.

But the main point to be made here is that in order to have his idea, Hank had to know a lot about batteries, bulbs and wires. His previous work and familiarity with those materials were a necessary aspect of this occasion for him to have a wonderful idea. David Hawkins has said of curriculum development, "You don't want to cover a subject; you want to uncover it." That, it seems to me, is what schools should be about. They can help to uncover parts of the world that children would not otherwise know how to tackle. Wonderful ideas are built on other wonderful ideas. In Piaget's terms, you must reach out to the world with your own intellectual tools and grasp it, assimilate it, yourself. All kinds of things are hidden from us—even though they surround us—unless we know how to reach out for them. Schools and teachers can provide materials and questions in ways that suggest things to be done with them; and children, in the doing, cannot help being inventive.

There are two aspects to providing occasions for wonderful ideas. One is being willing to accept children's ideas. The other is providing a setting that suggests wonderful ideas to children—different ideas to different children—as they are caught up in intellectual problems that are real to them.

HOW ORGANISMS (EXCEPT PLANTS) ACQUIRE AND USE ENERGY

How Organisms (Except Plants) Acquire and Use Energy

U N I T

2

CONTENTS

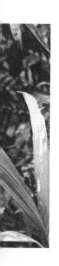

UNIT 2 OVERVIEW

HOW ORGANISMS (EXCEPT PLANTS) ACQUIRE AND USE ENERGY

Energy: cats, cows, and calories. Energy: Who needs it? What is it? How do you get it? How do you use it or lose it? In this Unit, you explore those questions and the following.

When is an activity not an activity? How are death, energy, and carbon related? What do a mouse, moose, millipede, and you have—and not have —in common? Why are there no wasps the size of ponies?

You compare cheetahs and dung beetles, build food chains, calculate the energy you and other organisms take in, use, and waste, and you discover who the real energy giants are.

BONY SKULLS
HOW ANIMALS ACQUIRE ENERGY

CONTENTS

CASE STUDY
FEEDING AND EATING

As we saw in the **Evolution Module**, getting and eating food are essential to survival. While that may seem obvious, in fact it is an extraordinarily important aspect of ecology. How and whether a creature gets food, plus how and whether it reproduces successfully, are central to ecology and evolution. Those two aspects of an organism are major aspects of the organism's lifestyle—of "how it makes a living."

The variety of ways in which creatures get food is astonishing and ranges from the familiar (cows eat grass) to the esoteric (hummingbirds feed their young aphids) to the nearly unbelievable (fishers specialize in eating porcupines; some ants eat fungi that they grow themselves and tend as carefully as human farmers do their cornfields). Here are a few more examples; some of them may be familiar to you; you may know others we have not mentioned.

The angler fish is so-called because, like an angler or a fisherman, it uses a wormlike lure to catch fish to eat. But the lure does not come from a bait shop; it is a special wormlike growth that dangles from the roof of the angler fish's mouth. When the angler fish sits with its mouth open, the "lure" wriggles temptingly, attracting small fish straight into the angler fish's mouth and down its hatch.

Then there is the sea otter, which floats comfortably on its back while eating. It uses its chest as an "anvil" and a rock as a "hammer" to crack open the sea urchins and other shellfish on which it feeds.

The polar bear waits motionless by a hole in the polar ice for up to an hour. The hole is likely a seal breathing hole. If a seal emerges to breathe

while the bear is waiting, a lunge and a mighty swipe can pull the seal up onto the ice to become the bear's dinner.

A large tropical fish species closely related to the intensely meat-eating piranha eats mostly fruits that drop into the river from overhanging trees. This is especially interesting because there are few vegetarians among fish, and this species is also quite large to be eating fruit (adults weigh about 3 kilograms).

The familiar yellow jacket wasp collects protein, dead (from your picnic or a dead animal) or alive (it kills some caterpillars with a sting). It brings the protein to its nest, and in each comb it also lays an egg. Once the eggs hatch, the mother wasp frequently replenishes the protein, which serves the newly hatched insects as food until they mature and leave the nest.

The Australian butcher bird also stores food, piercing dead animals such as small lizards onto long thorns in thorny trees. The thorns also help keep other animals from getting at the stored food.

Migrating animals often have odd food habits, such as not eating for long periods of time or completely changing what they eat depending on where they are. The blue whale essentially does not eat for the 8 months it spends traveling to and living in the warm tropical oceans, where it mates. During the other 4 months, spent in the colder polar seas, it feeds on tons and tons (literally!) of tiny shrimp-like sea creatures. Caribou feed on grasses when they can and lichen in winter when they cannot get grasses.

Fishing spiders specialize on small fishes that get caught in webs spun across streams.

Caterpillars and locusts are among the many insects that eat plant material. Locusts also migrate but, unlike whales, they eat throughout their migration. They are still considered a plague because they can be so numerous that they can strip an area clean of vegetation, down to the very last leaf and blade of grass. Robber flies and dragonflies, in contrast, prey on other insects. They sit motionless on a leaf or twig until they see another insect fly by and then swoop out to nab and devour it.

Garter snakes eat primarily earthworms, insects, and even sticky slugs.

There are many, many species of nematodes, most of which are specialized to one thing, such as vinegar, mammal tears, and soil-living micro-organisms.

One of our favorite examples is a mite that feeds on ant "blood." The mite attaches itself to a hind foot of an army ant soldier and is actually walked on by the ant—in effect being used as an artificial foot but with no apparent signs of discomfort by either the ant or the mite. And so the mite is well positioned to insert its mouthparts into the foot-joint of the ant and to suck out the small amounts of liquid it requires.

Nearly all living beings (except plants) require six things to survive: water, vitamins, minerals, carbohydrates, proteins, and fats. The last three items are carbon-containing compounds. All living and once-living things, including plants, contain those same three carbon-containing compounds. So what's the big deal about carbon?

Carbon can be combined biochemically with other common elements, especially hydrogen and oxygen, in bonds that can carry a great deal of energy. Since getting food means getting energy, it also means getting carbon. This Unit explores carbon: carbon as food and as a carrier of energy in and through creatures and ecosystems. The finches in **Module 1** are a good example of the importance of getting enough energy and of being the "right" size or shape to do so successfully.

In the next class sessions, we will examine animal heads—their skulls, jaws, and teeth—as a start to thinking about how particular animals get food and energy.

Here are a few questions to consider. Write your answers in your notebook and be sure to bring them to class.

- Except for plants, nearly every living things eats other things. Why?
- How do plants get their energy?
- How is that genuinely different from how other organisms get energy?

Exploration 1
GROUPING BONY SKULLS

Cat versus cow—an animal's head reveals a great deal about the animal's ecology, biology, and even evolutionary history. Here we begin to explore these aspects of animals by studying some bony heads—or particularly their skulls, jaws, and teeth.

Materials

- **Skull photo cards** (from your teacher), 1 set per team. (A few skulls have cracks, broken bones, or a missing tooth. These skulls are natural specimens; no animals were killed for these photos. The specimens are from museums and include zoo animals that died of age or illness.)

Procedure

1. **Study and group photographs.**
    In teams, study the pictures, illustrations, and skulls before you and in the following pages. Think of ways in which they differ or are similar; think of what they might tell you about the original animal. With your team, group the set of skulls before you in some way that reflects your thinking and makes sense to you. If you are using real skulls, be gentle, especially when opening and closing the jaws.

    Be ready to explain to someone else how and why you grouped the skulls as you did. Do not hesitate to move a skull from one group to another if you see something new about it and change your mind.

2. **Write your results and thoughts.**

   Write down your final reasons with the key characteristic(s) of each group you make. Keep track of questions that come up along the way.

   Once you have groupings on which your team more or less agrees (be sure to write down why any team member may prefer an alternative grouping), generate a list of questions about a group—that is, what would you like to know about the animals represented?

3. **Discuss with another team.**

   Another team of your classmates has a set of photos identical to yours. Discuss whether you have come to the same conclusions about the skulls. Why or why not? Can each team show the other things they might not have noticed? Does one team think some things are important that the other team does not? Can you tell each other why?

4. **Teams present to the class.**

   Now all teams present and describe their original groupings, so the whole class can see each team's results.

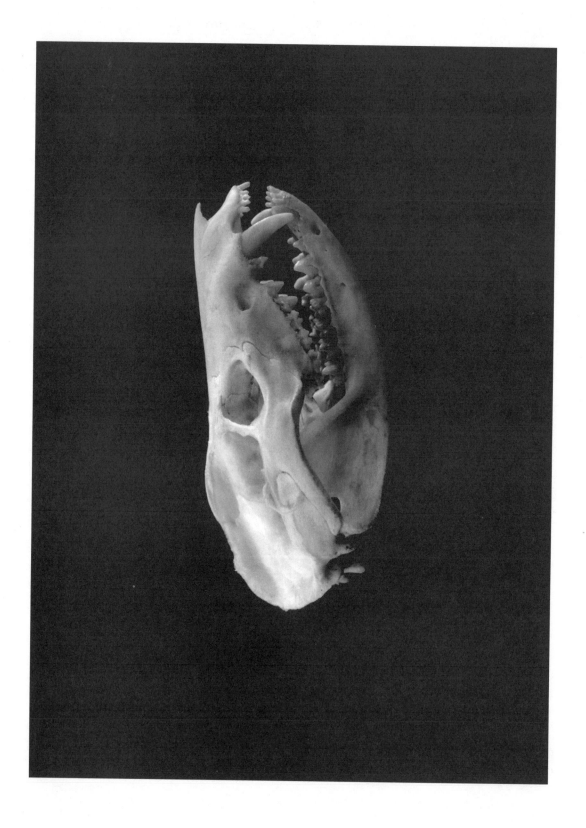

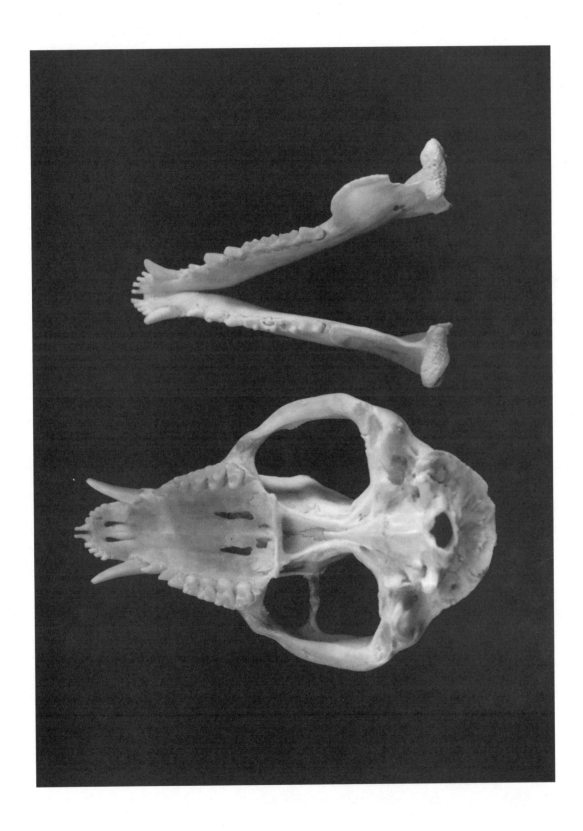

A1

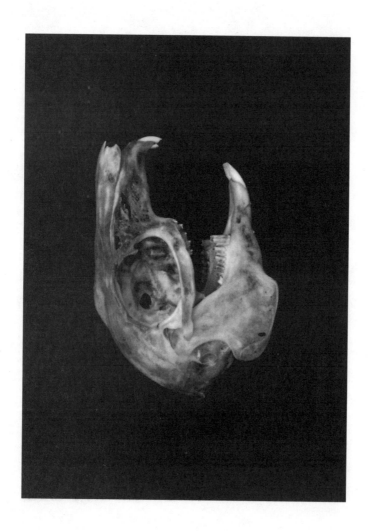

A2

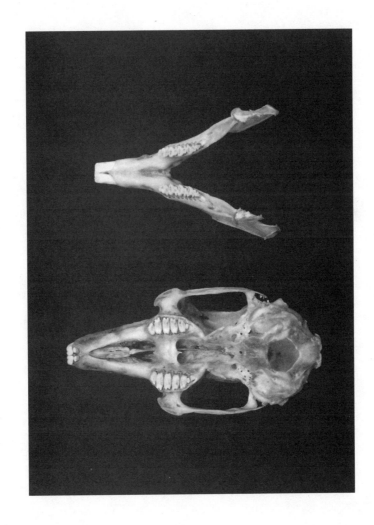

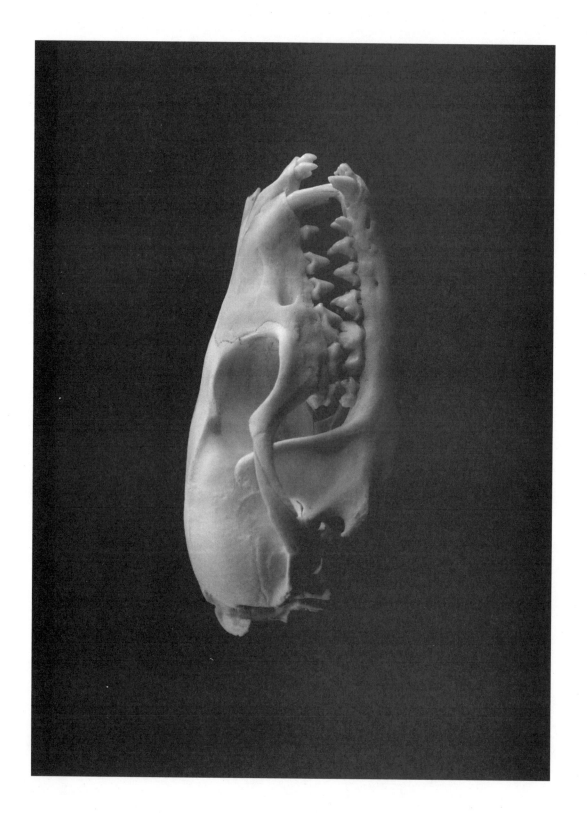

A3

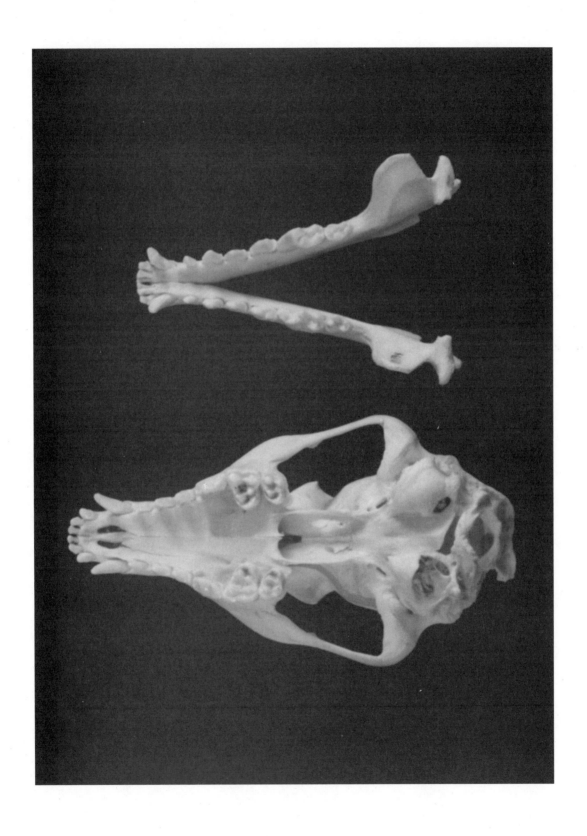

A3

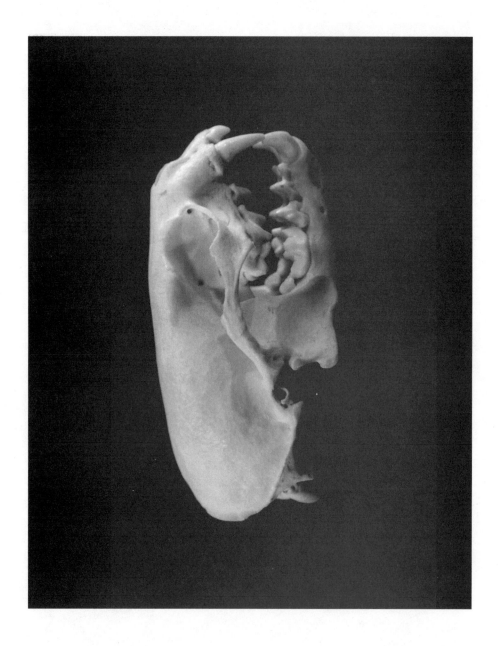

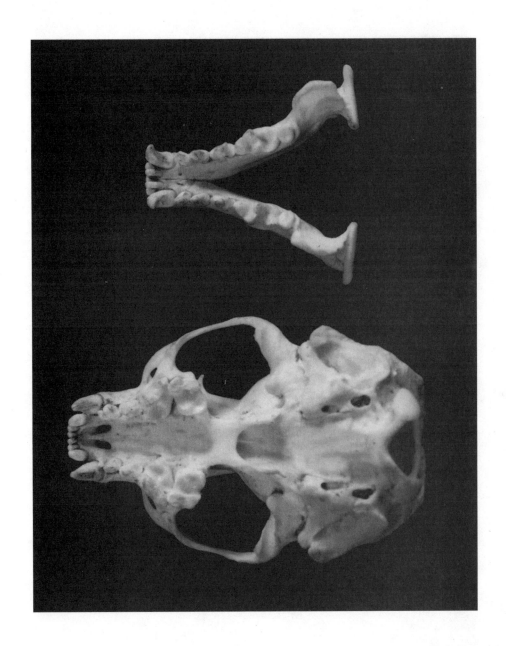

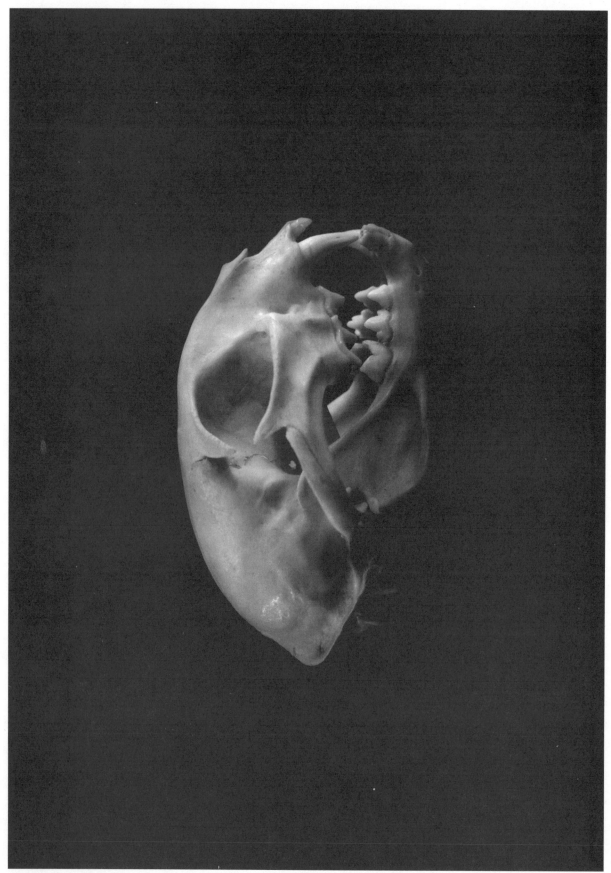

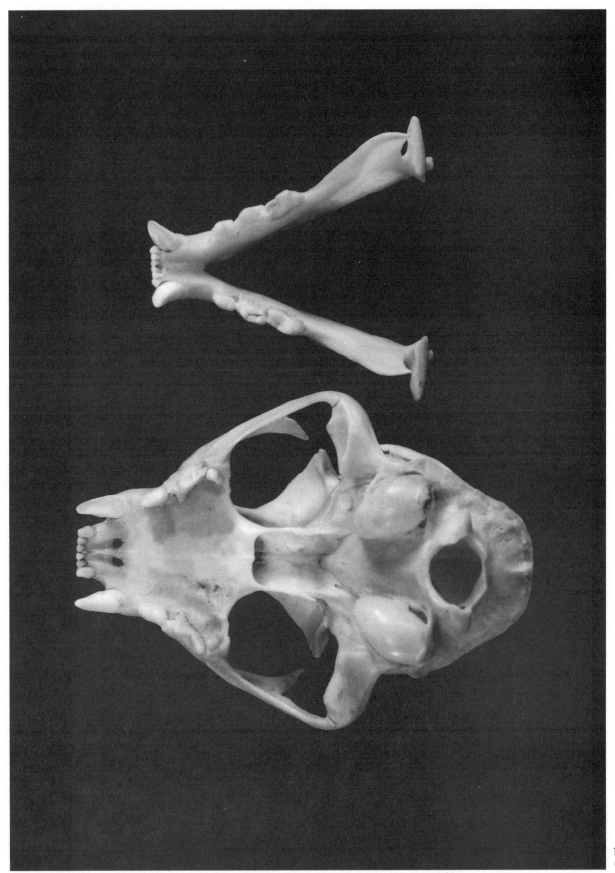

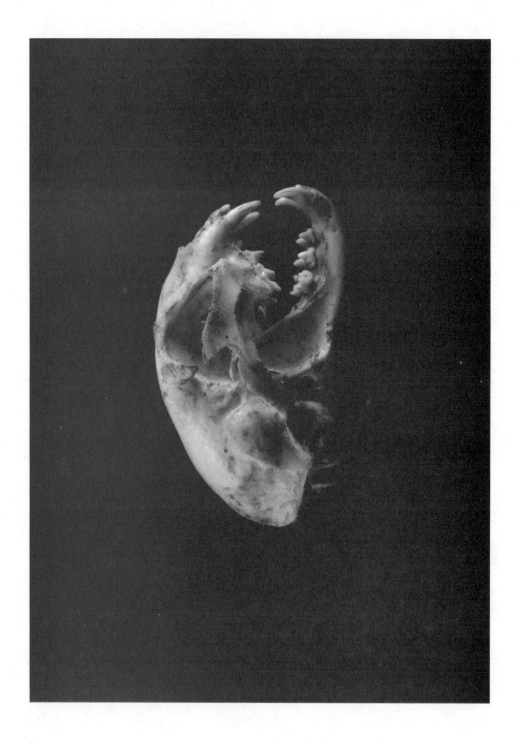

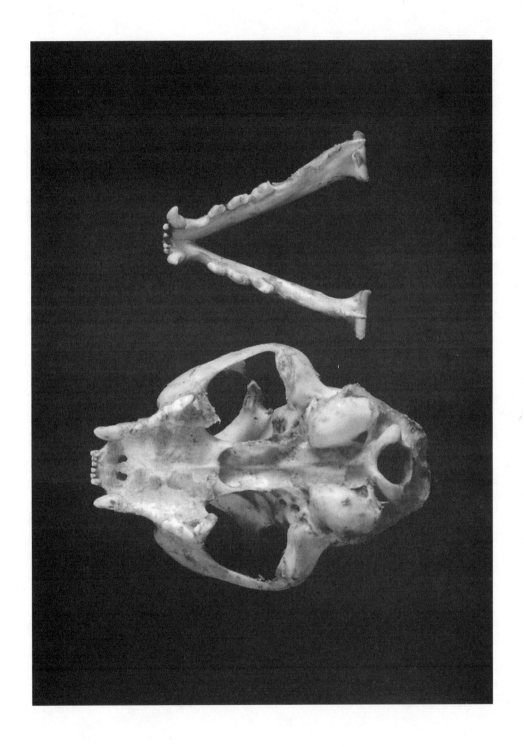

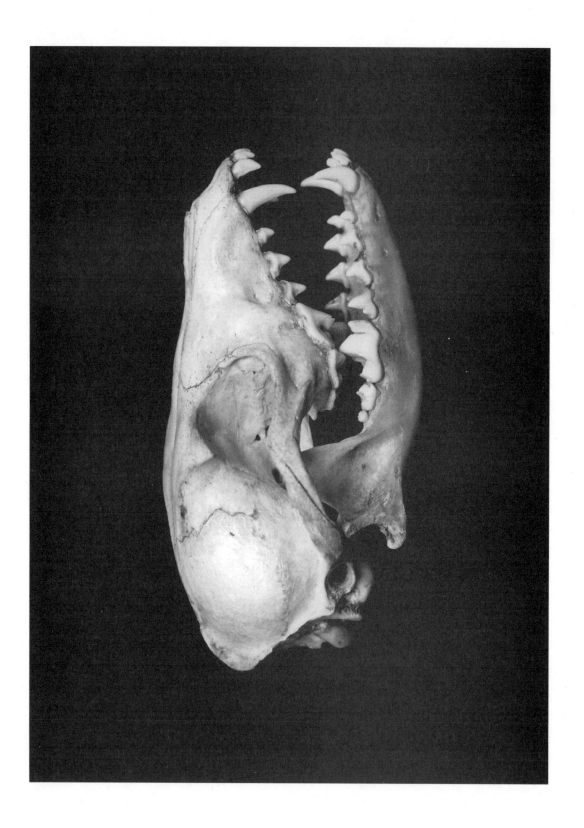

A7

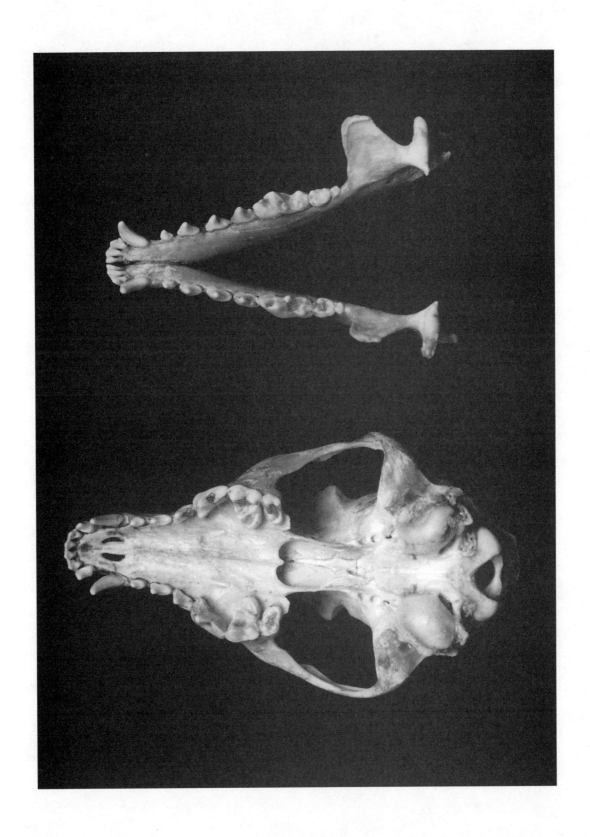

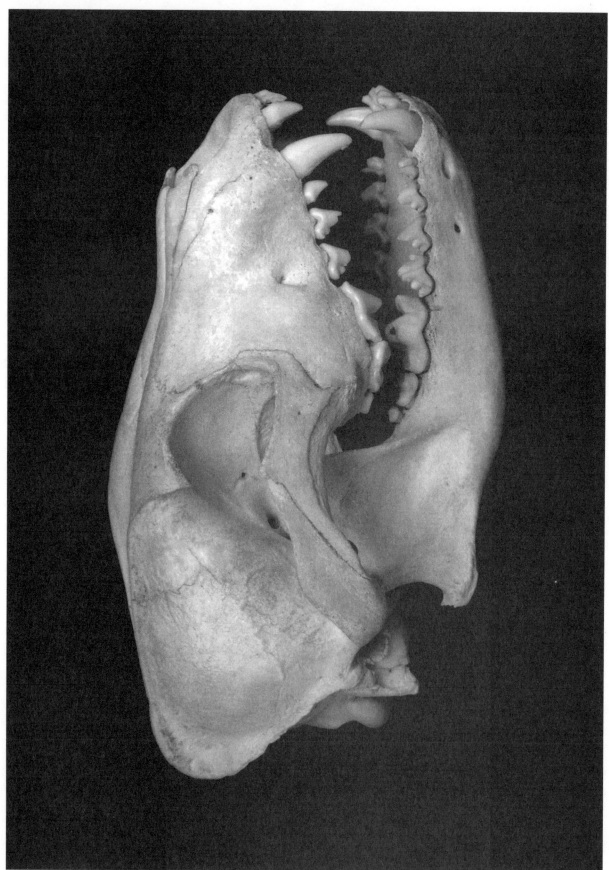

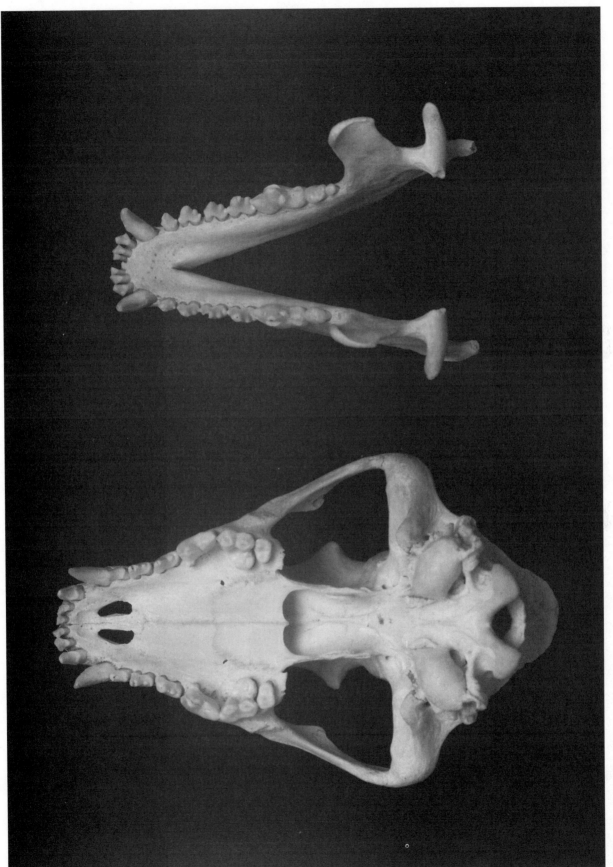

A8 (70% of actual size)

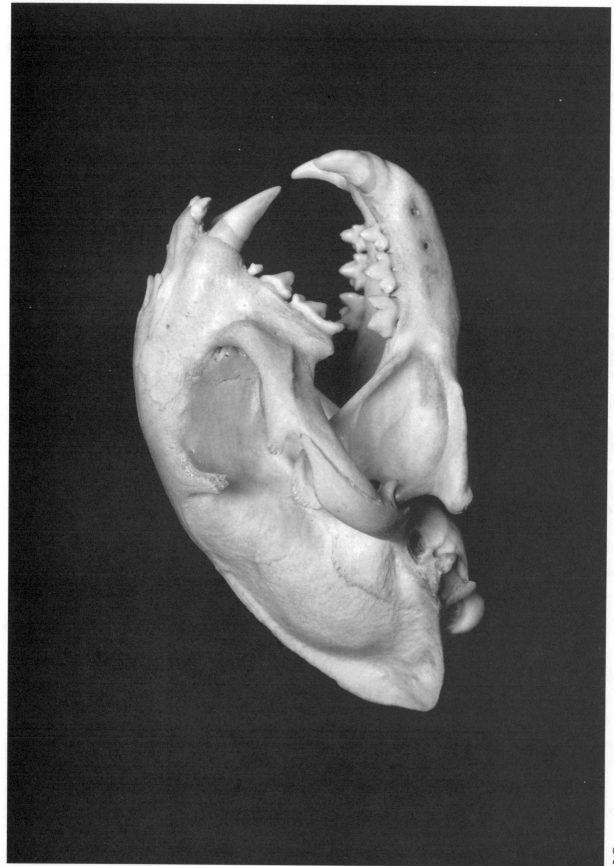

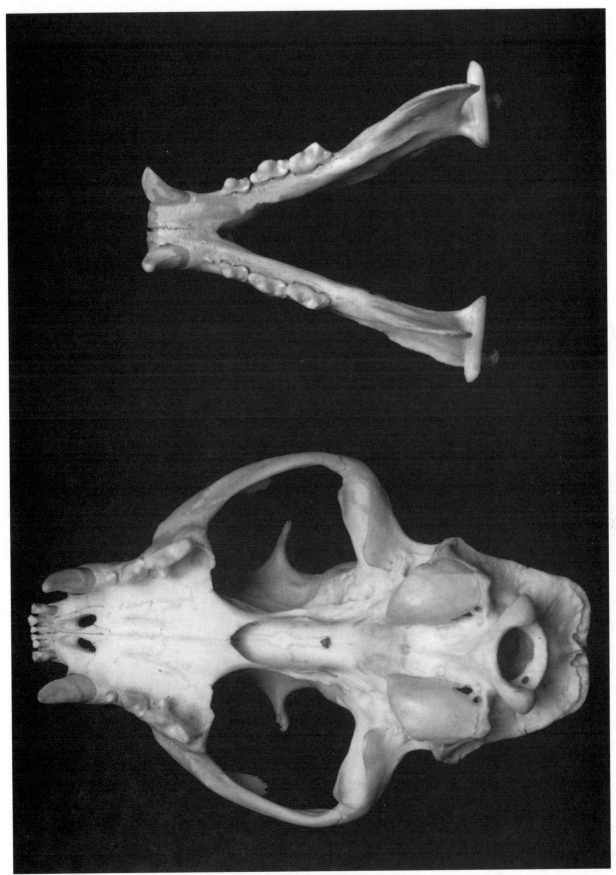

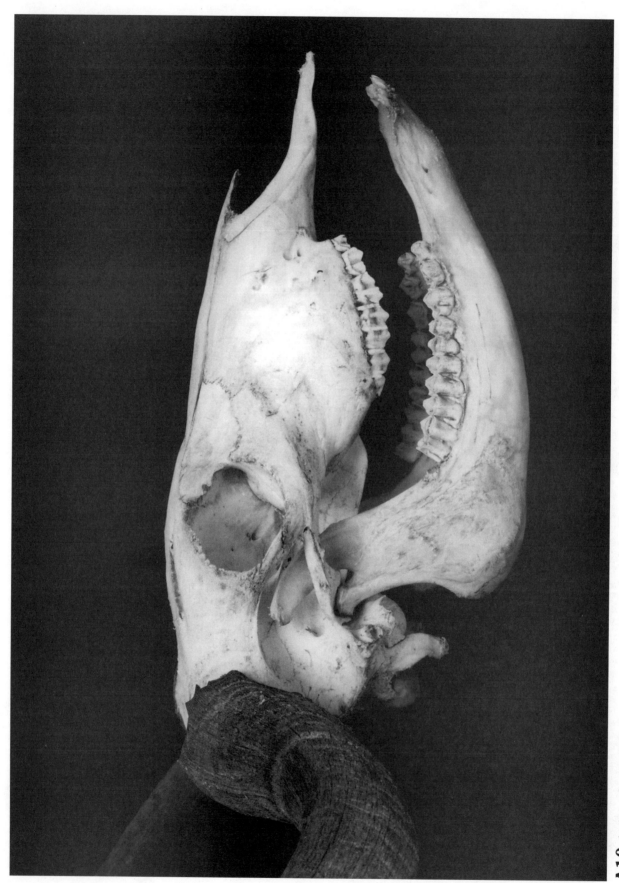

A10 (45% of actual size)

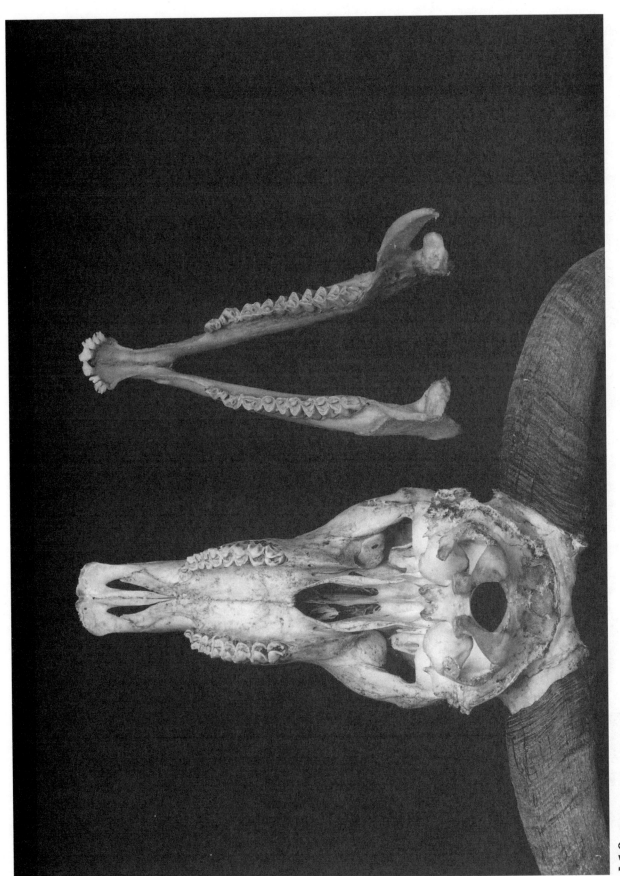

A10 (35% of actual size)

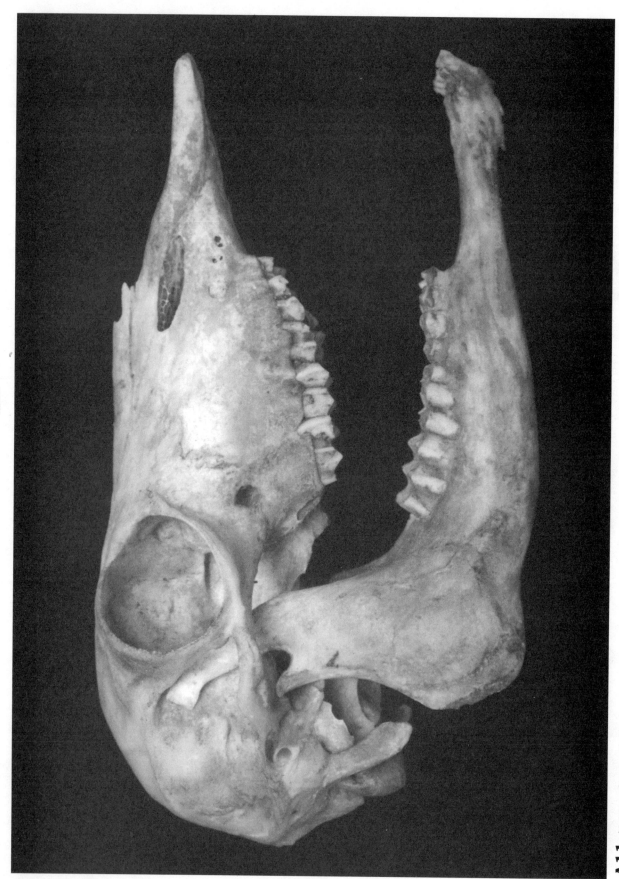

A11 (90% of actual size)

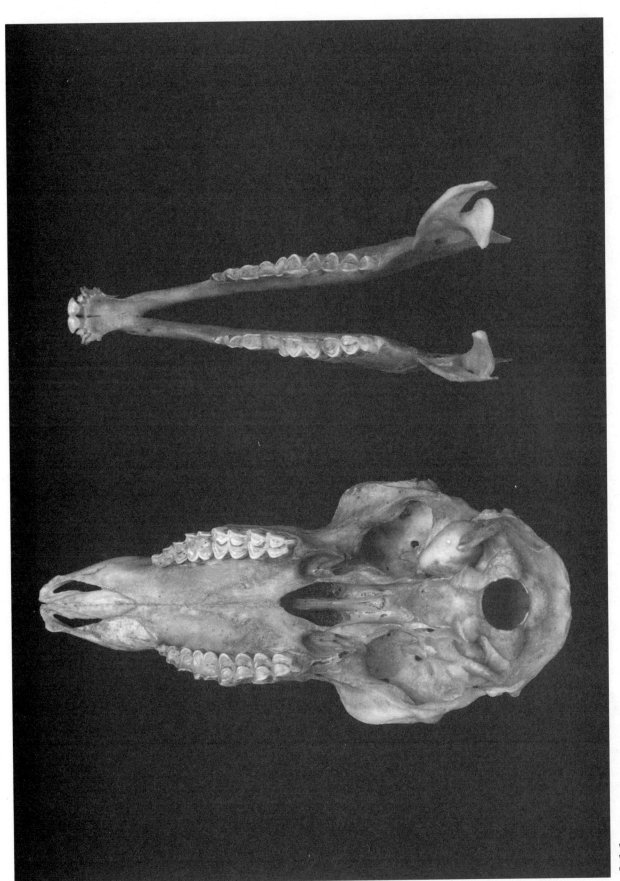

A11 (60% of actual size)

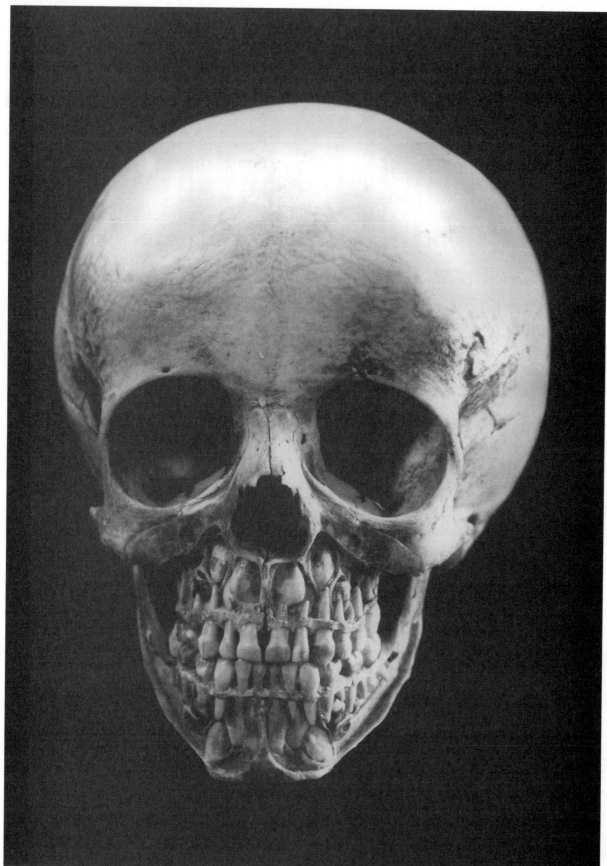

Notice the double rows of teeth on the skull and jaws of the head to the left. Why do you think they are there? (**HINT:** Normally the uppermost and lowermost rows would be covered with skin and muscle; the two middle rows would be covered by the lips.)

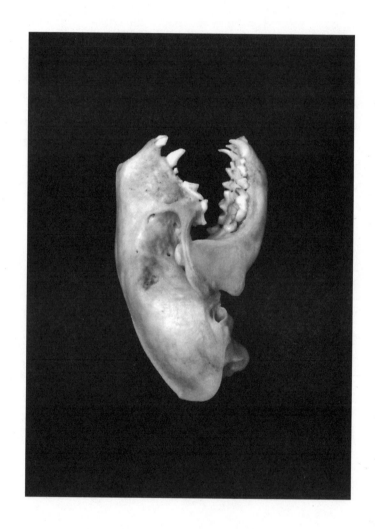

A13

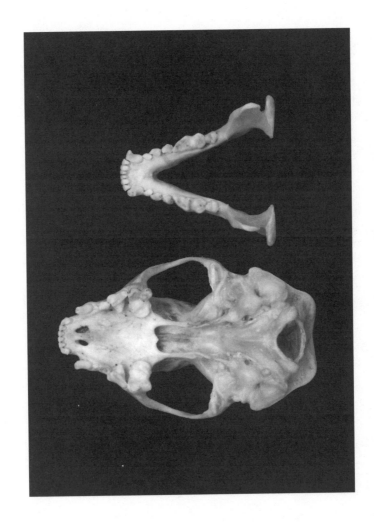

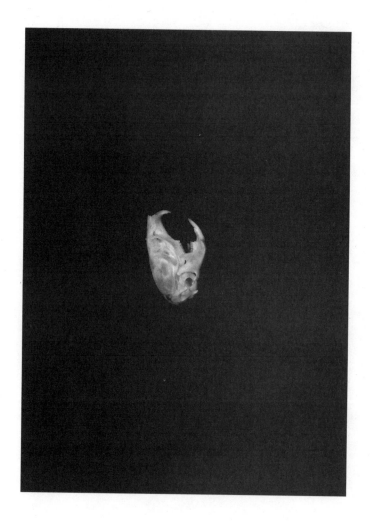

A14

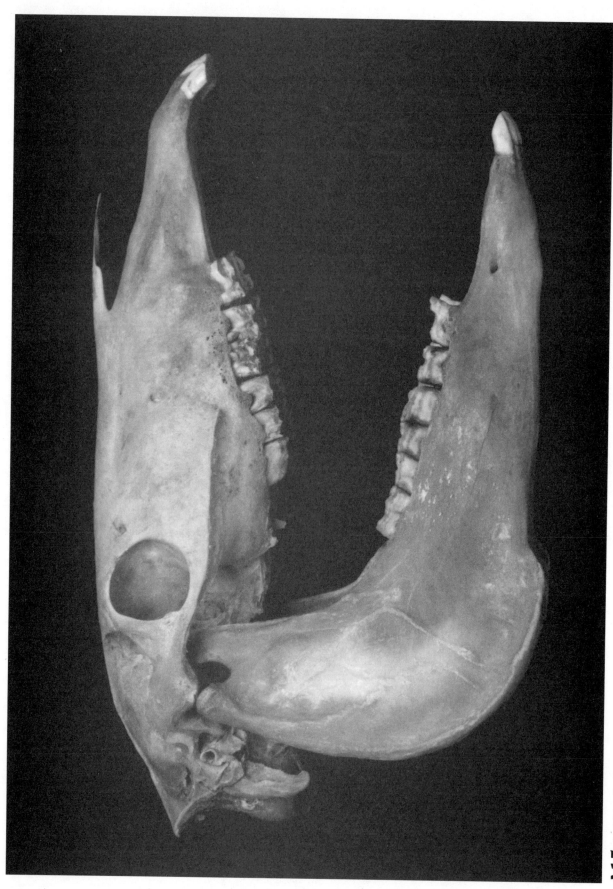

A15 (40% of actual size)

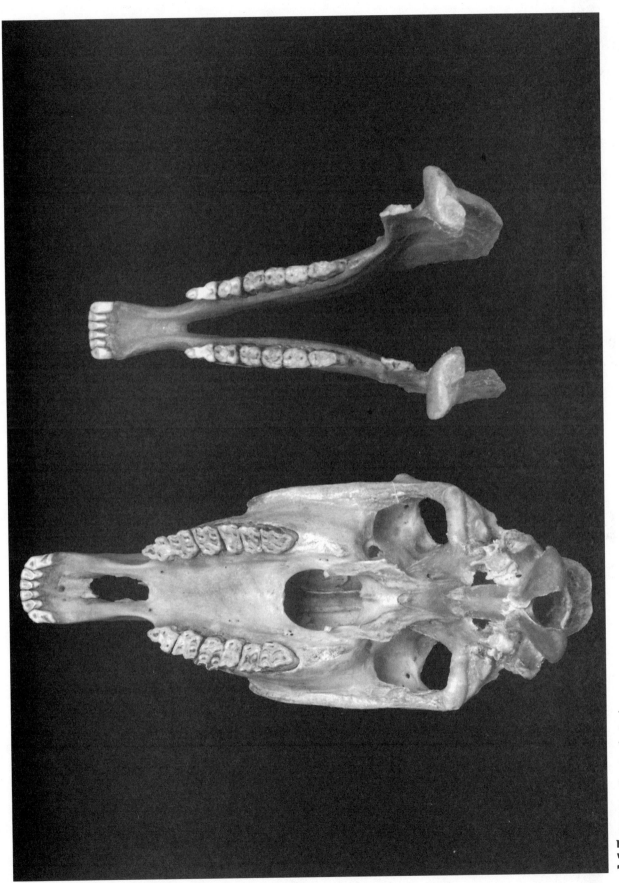

A15 (30% of actual size)

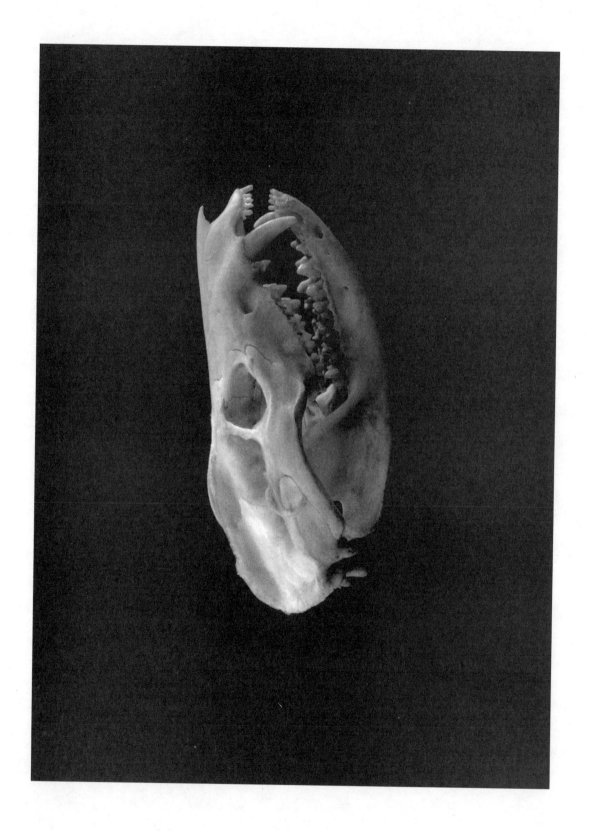

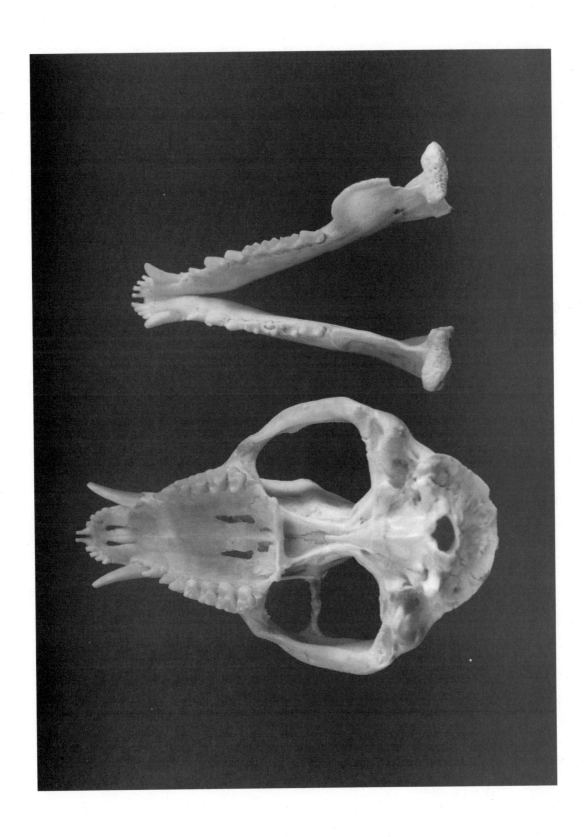

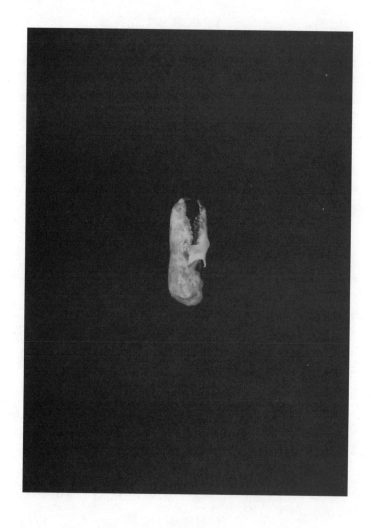

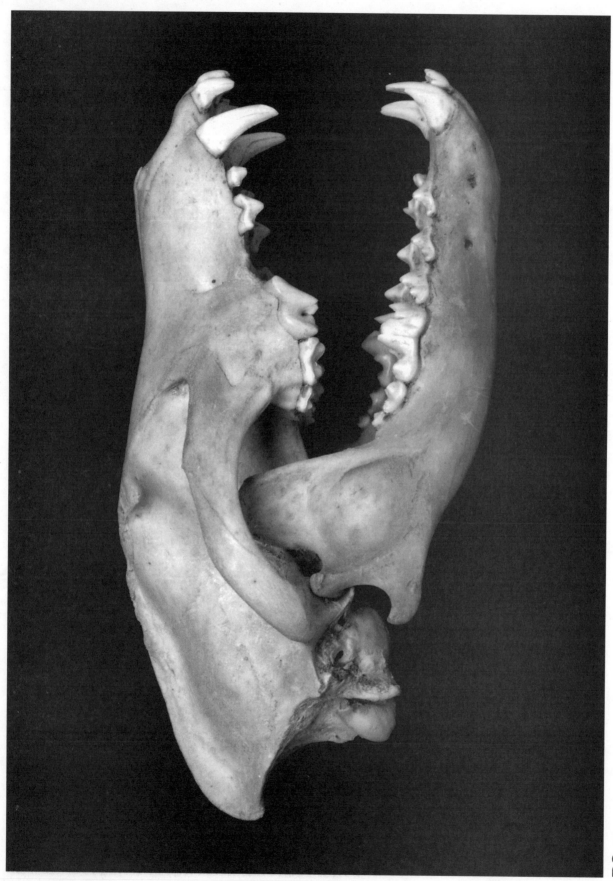

B3 (80% of actual size)

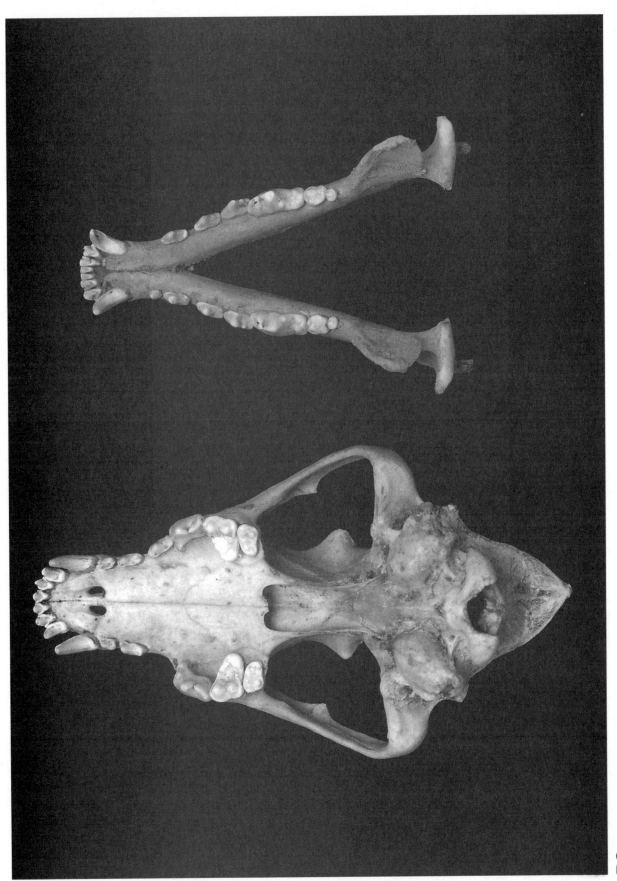

B3 (60% of actual size)

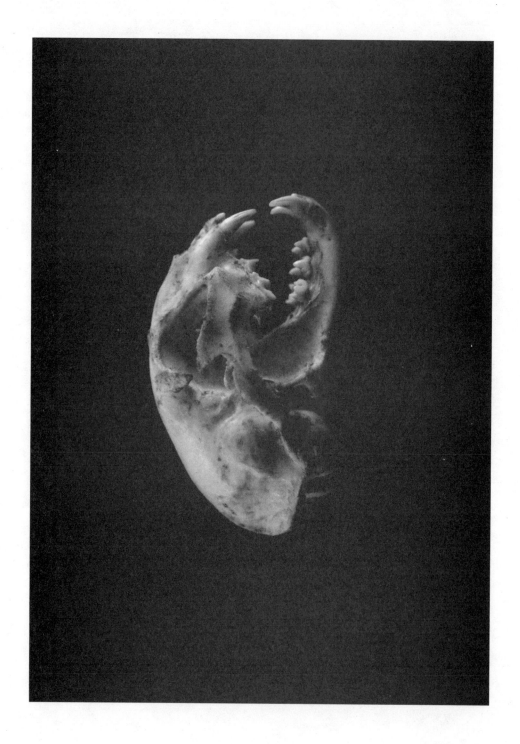

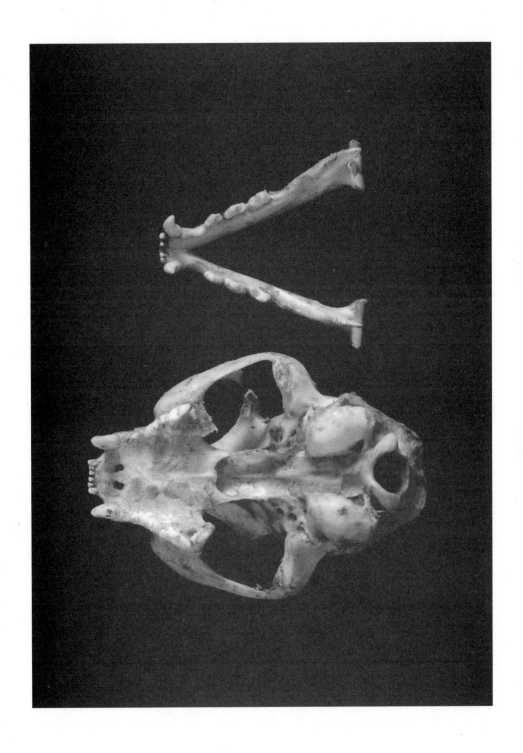

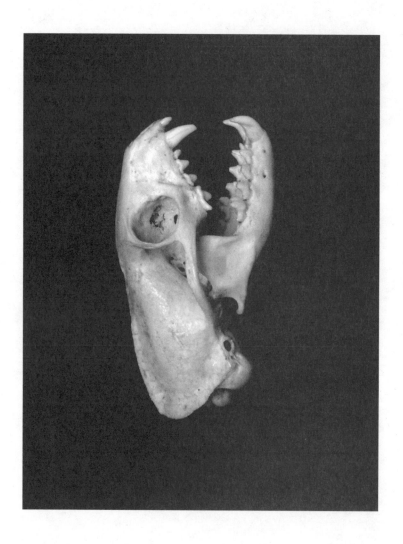

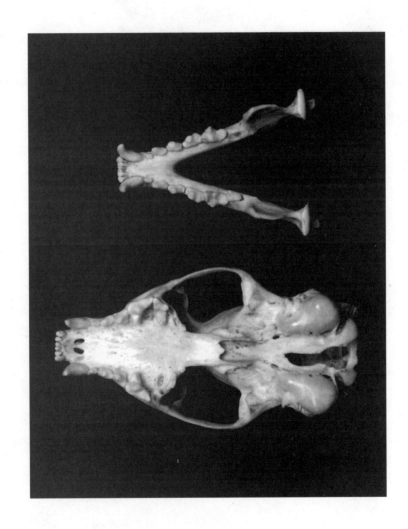

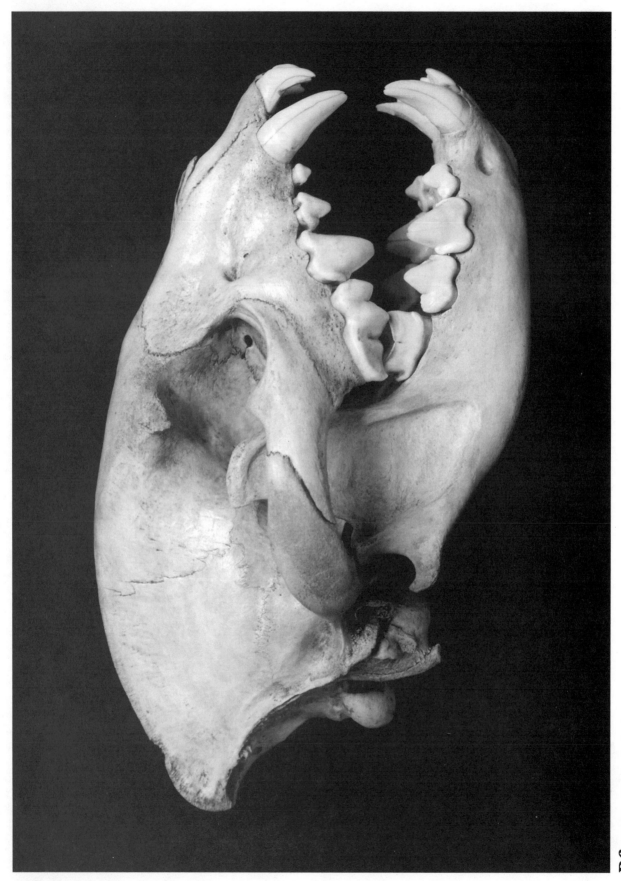

B6 (85% of actual size)

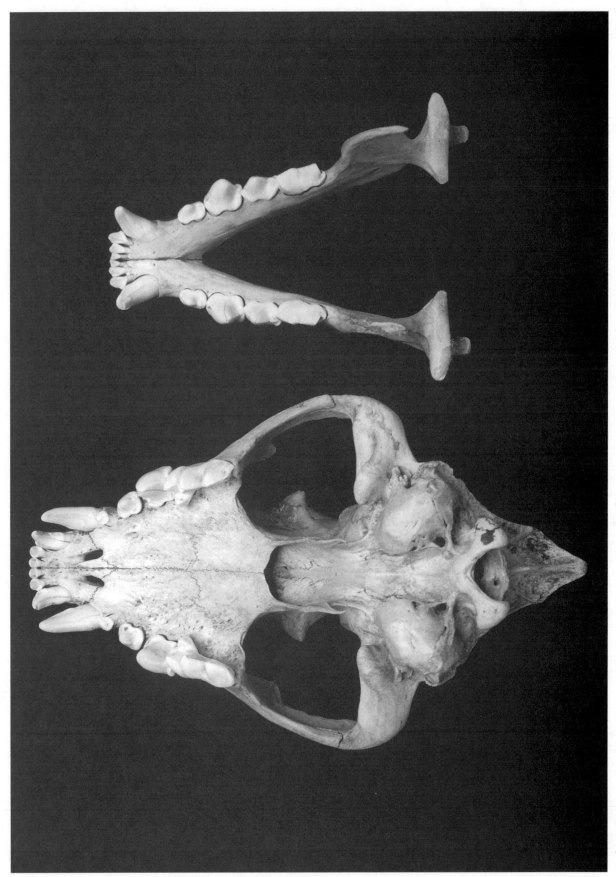

B6 (65% of actual size)

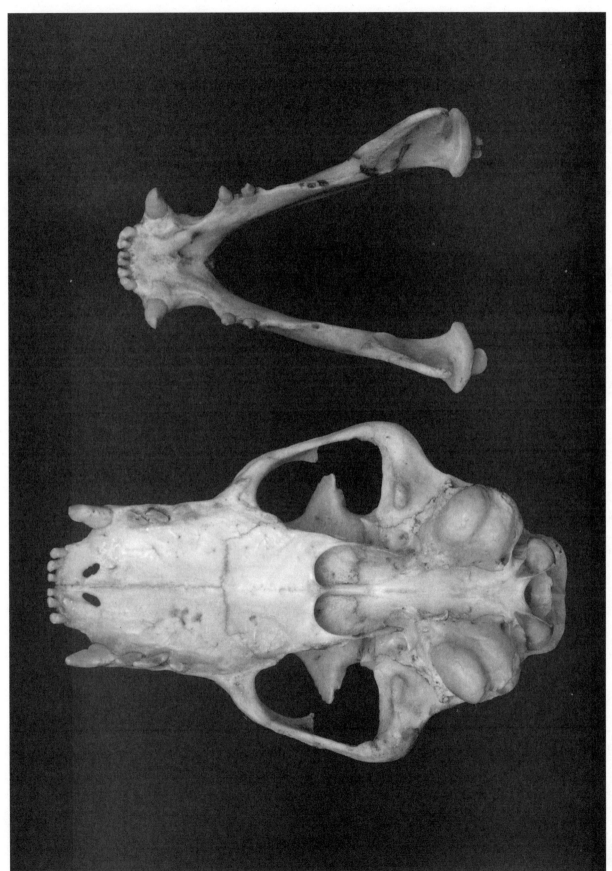

B7

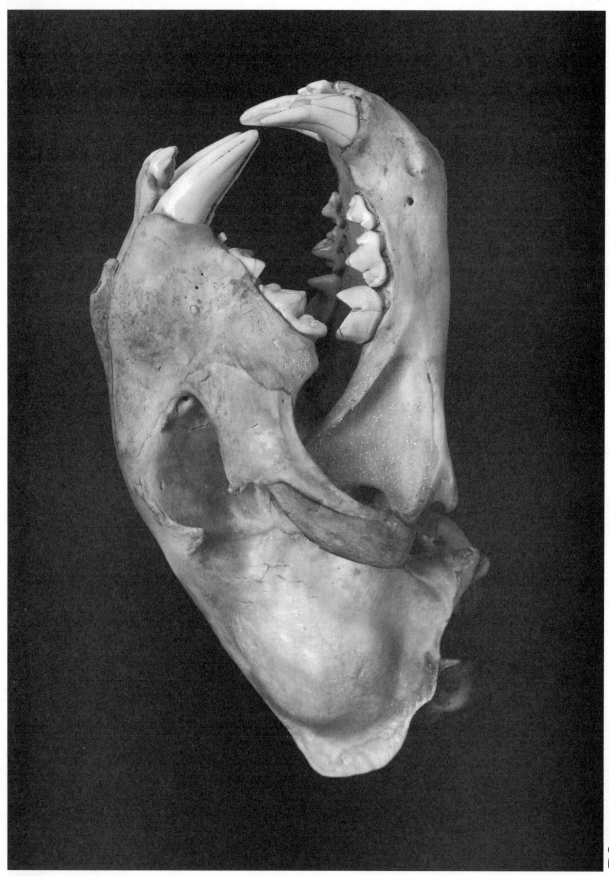

B8 (75% of actual size)

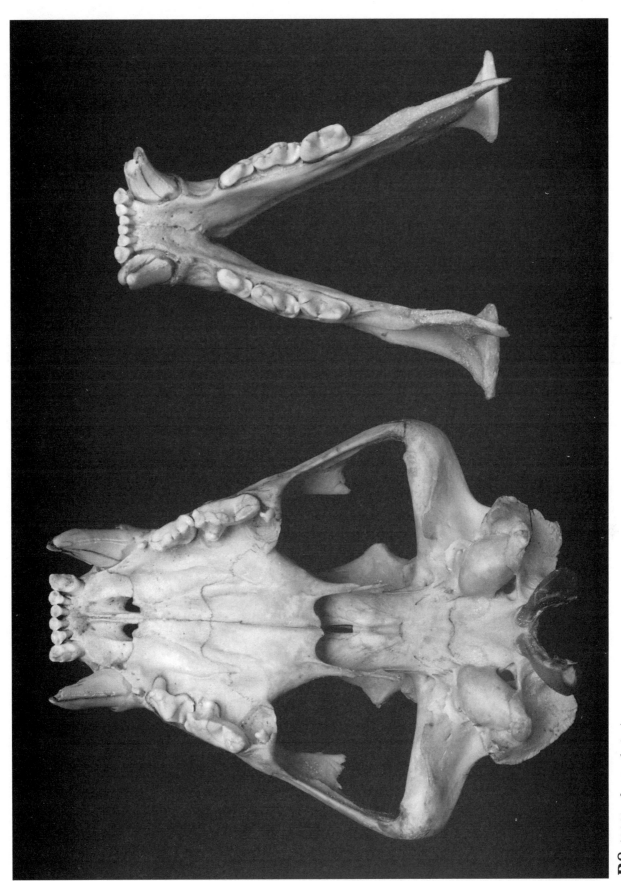

B8 (60% of actual size)

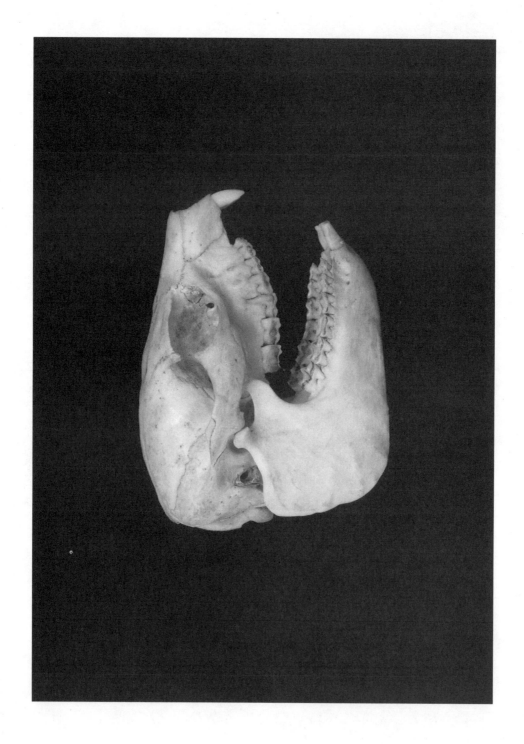

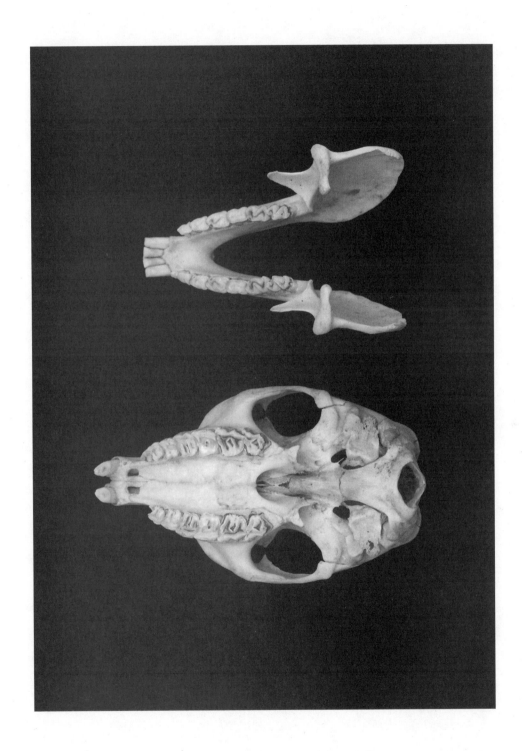

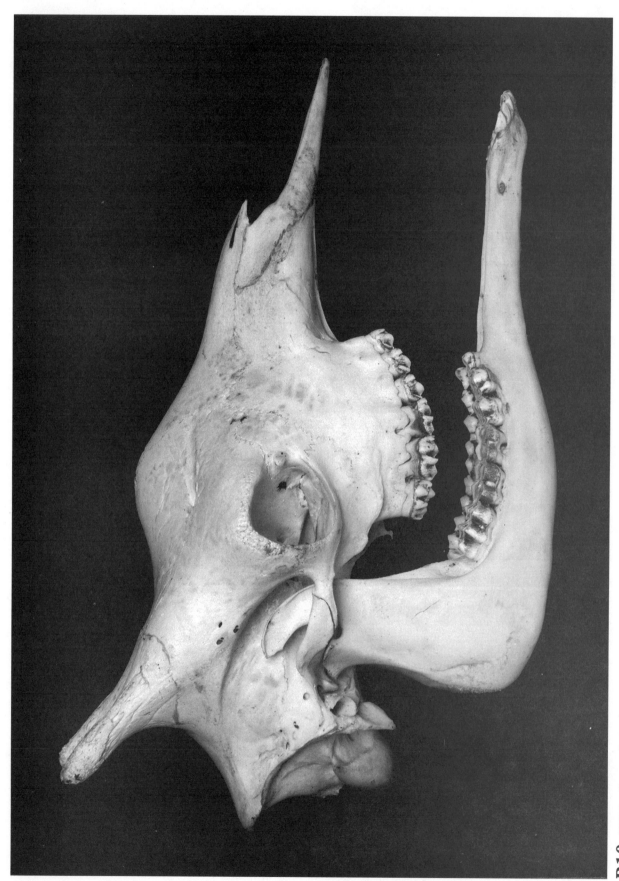

B10 (35% of actual size)

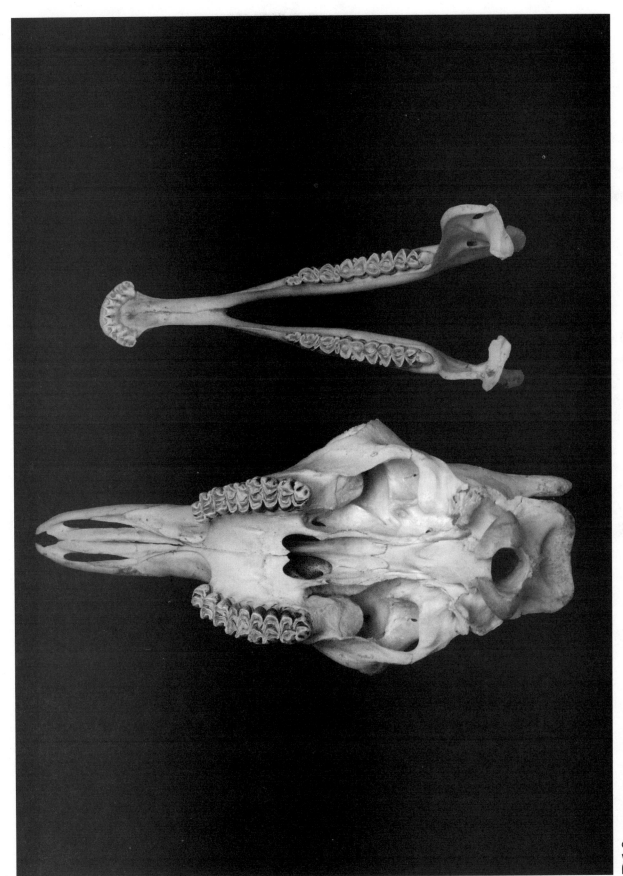

B10 (25% of actual size)

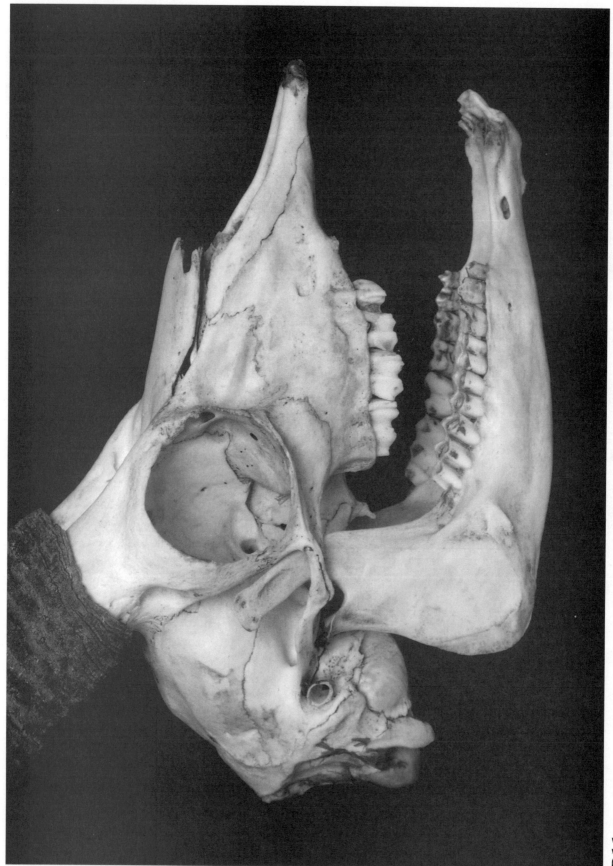

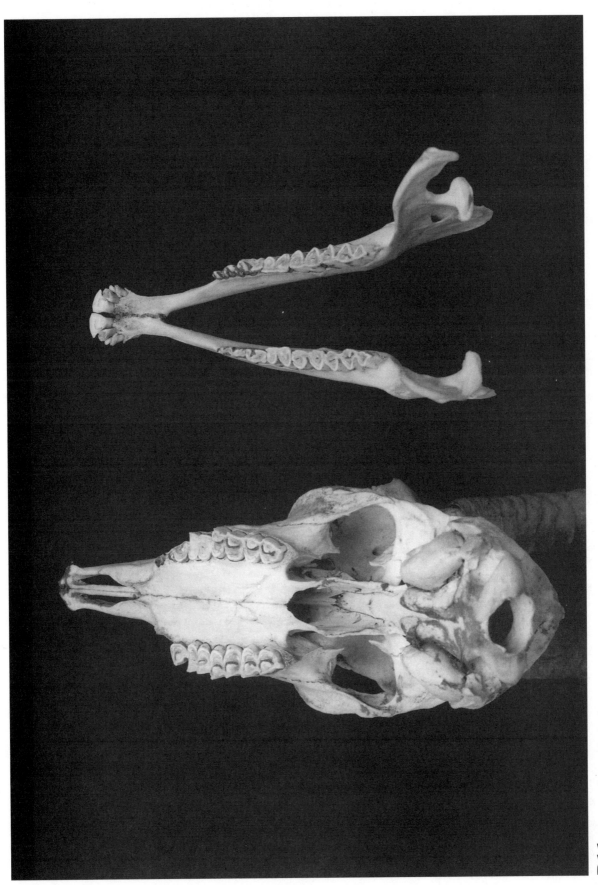

B11 (70% of actual size)

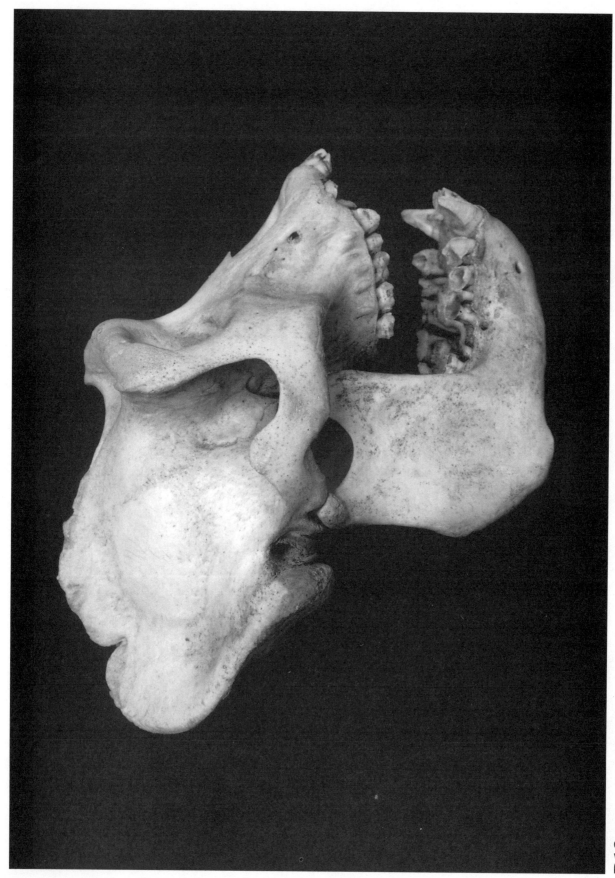

B12 (50% of actual size)

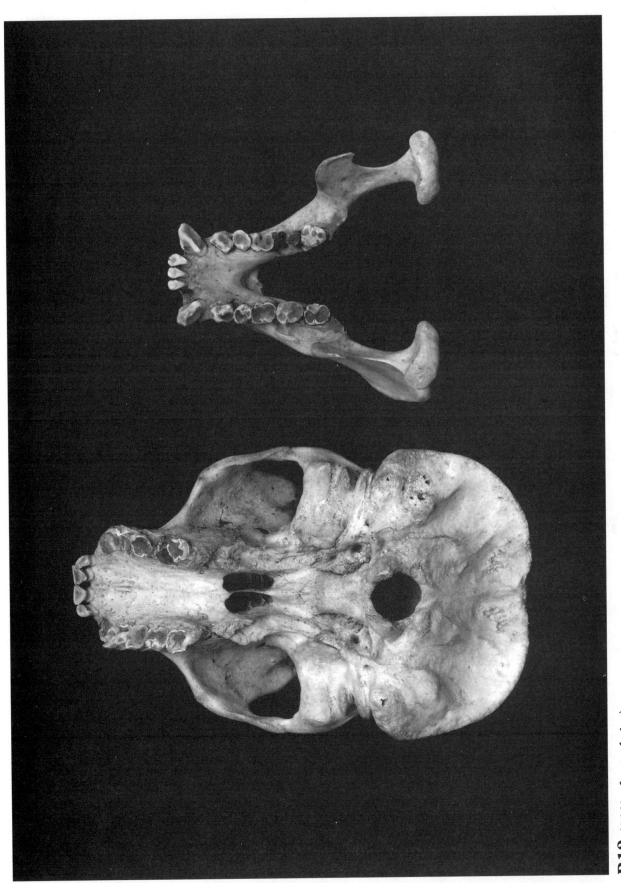

B12 (40% of actual size)

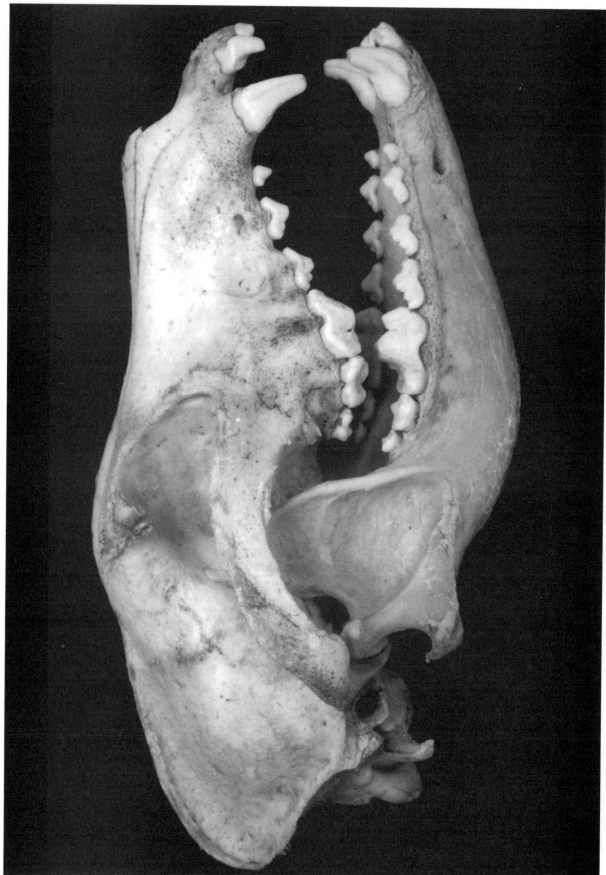

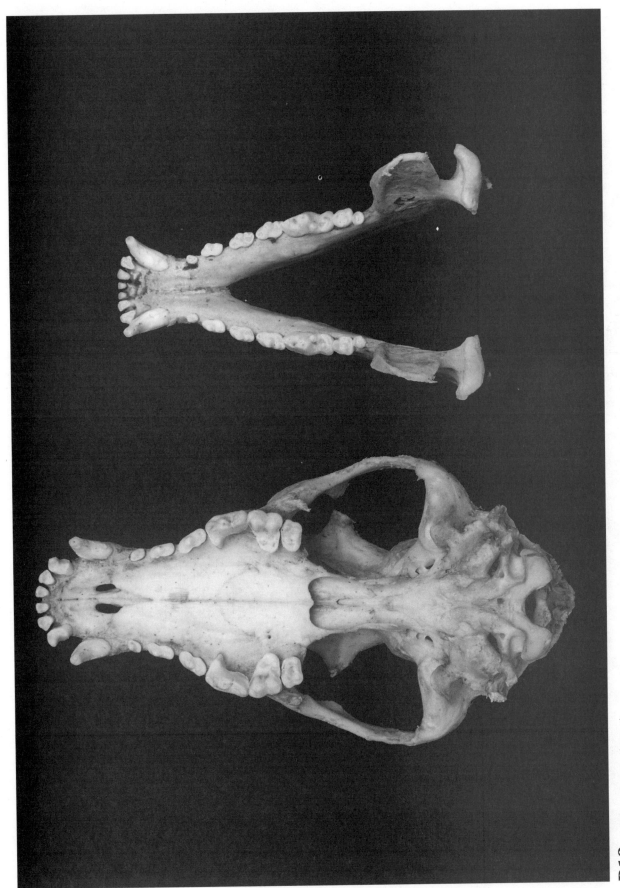

B13 (65% of actual size)

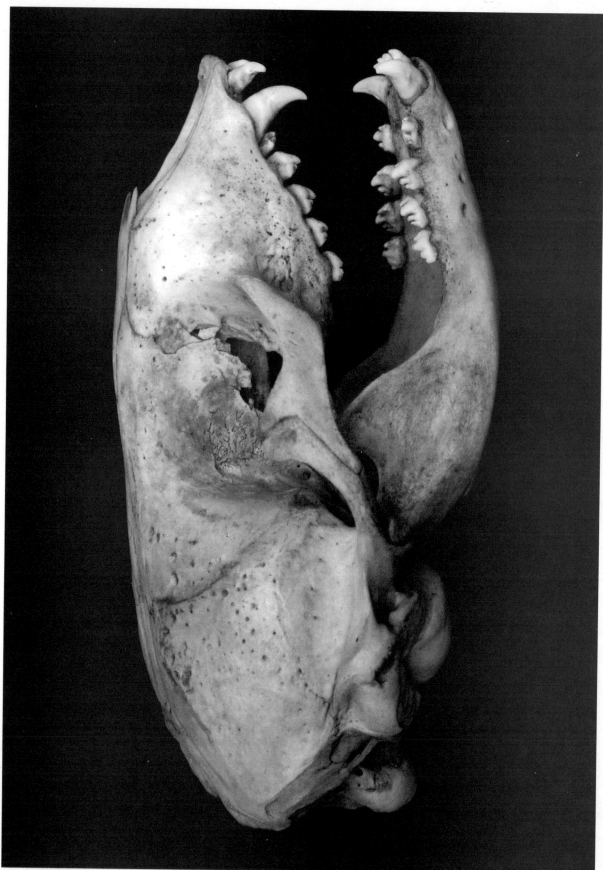

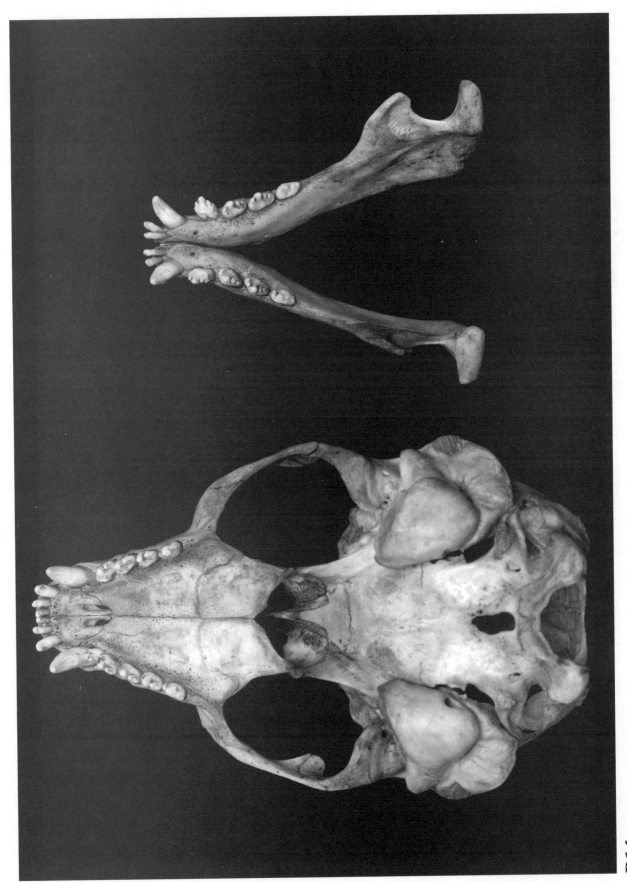

B14 (75% of actual size)

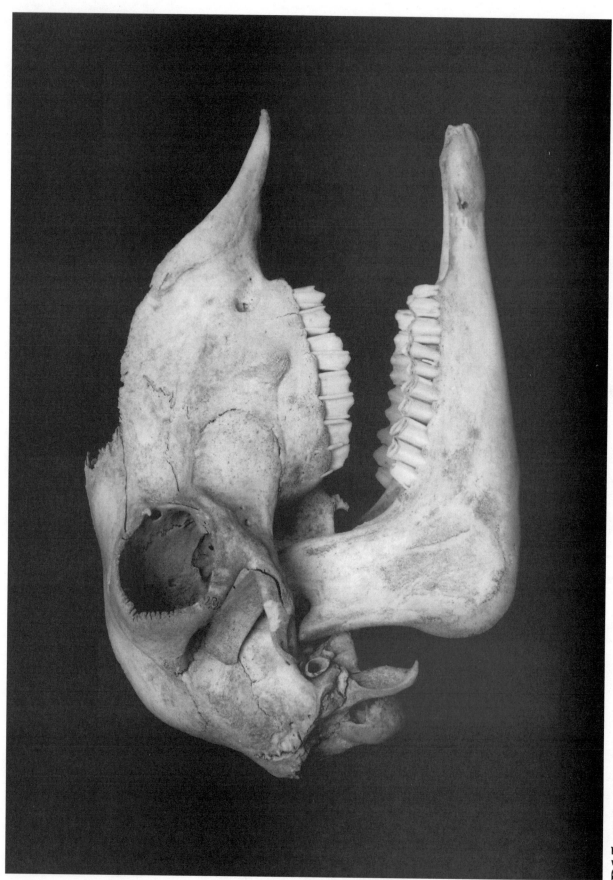

B15 (75% of actual size)

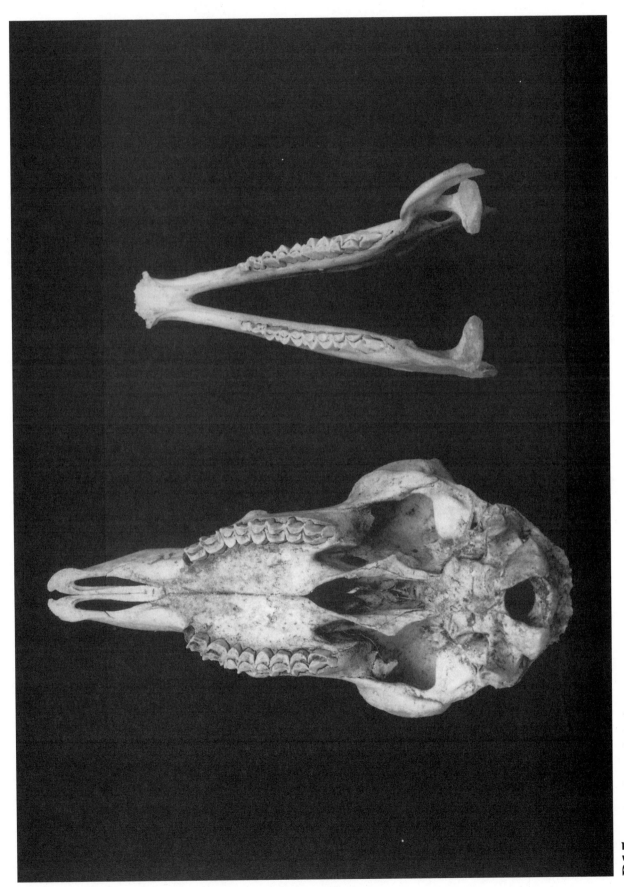

B15 (60% of actual size)

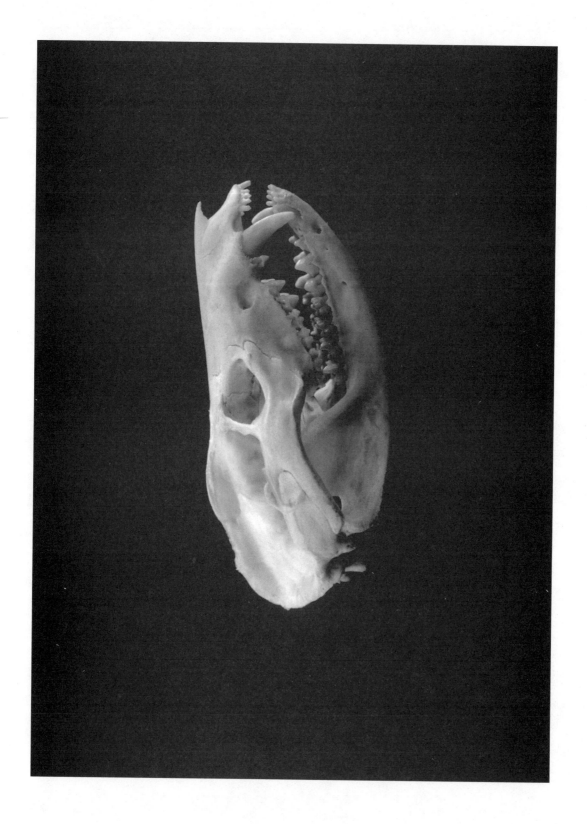

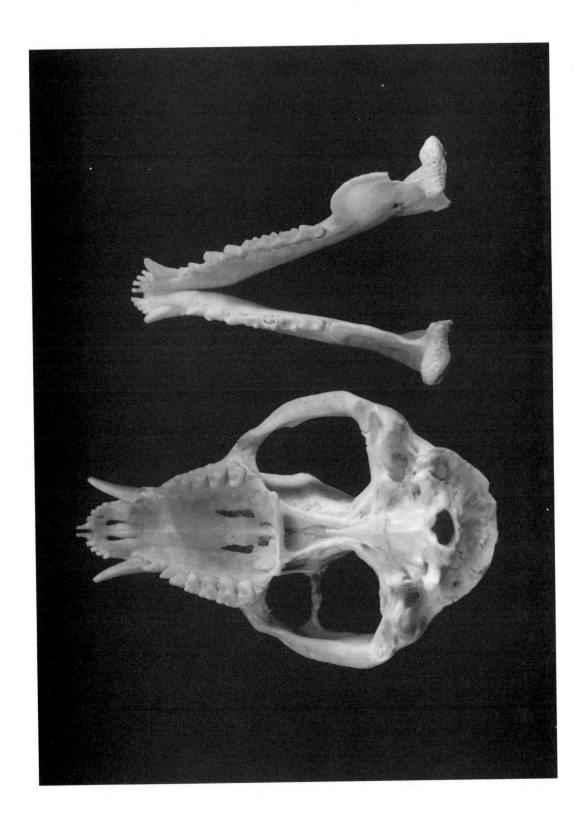

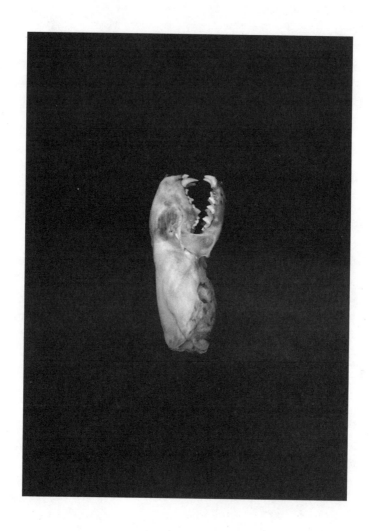

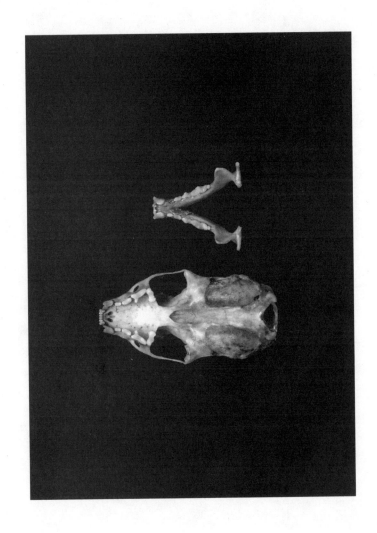

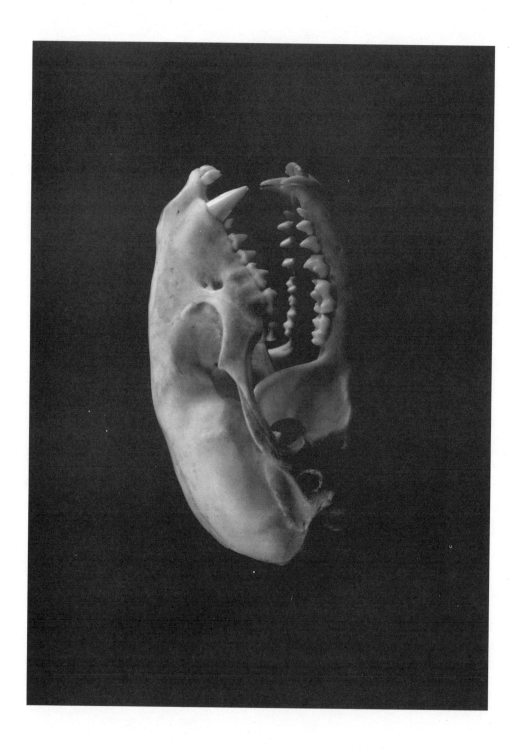

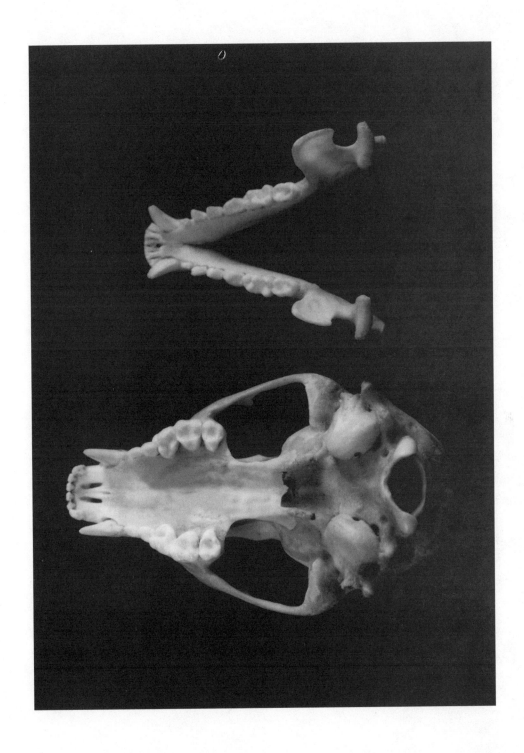

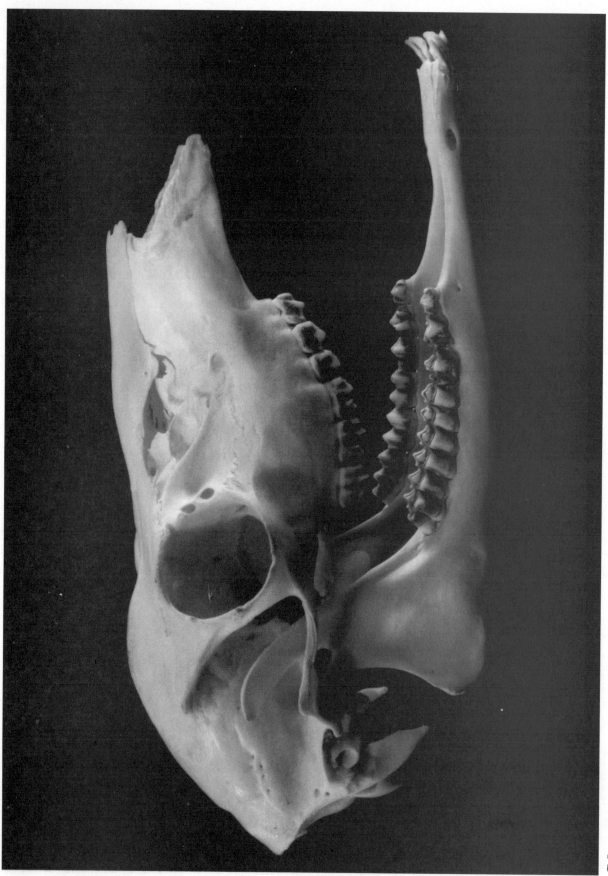

C4 (70% of actual size)

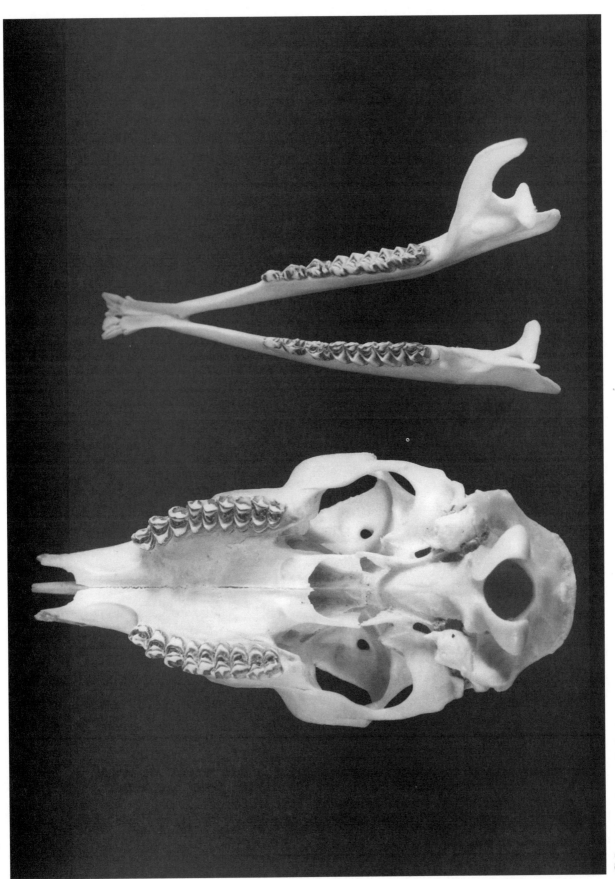

C4 (55% of actual size)

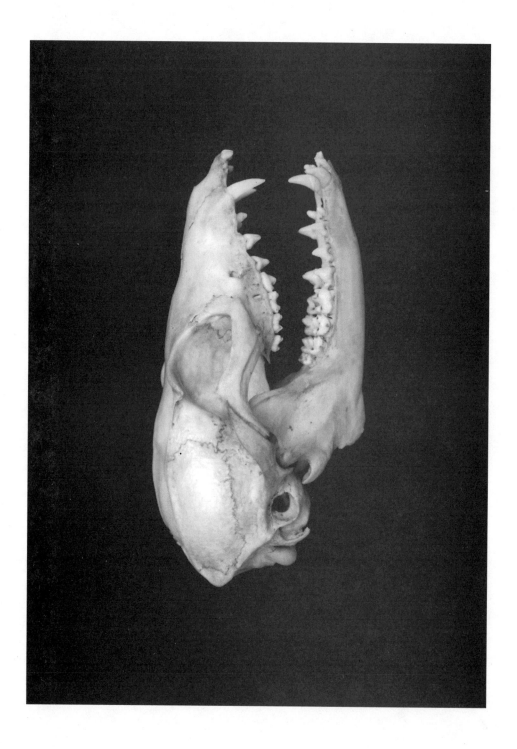

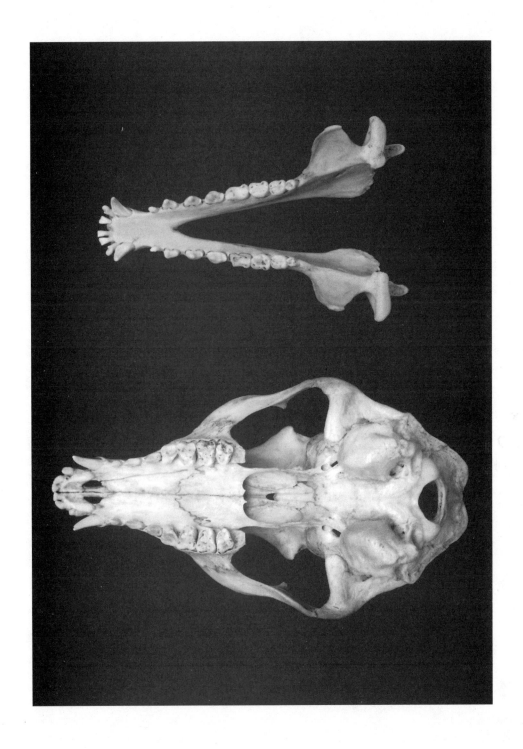

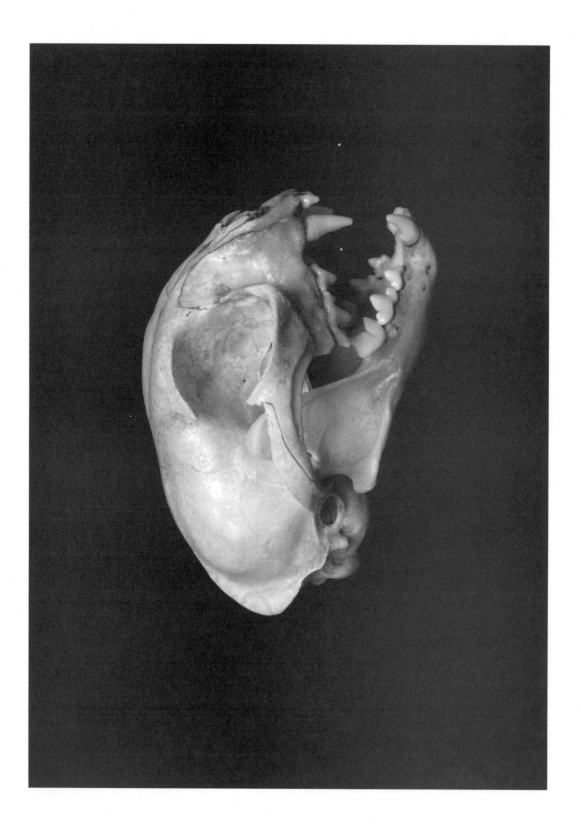

C6

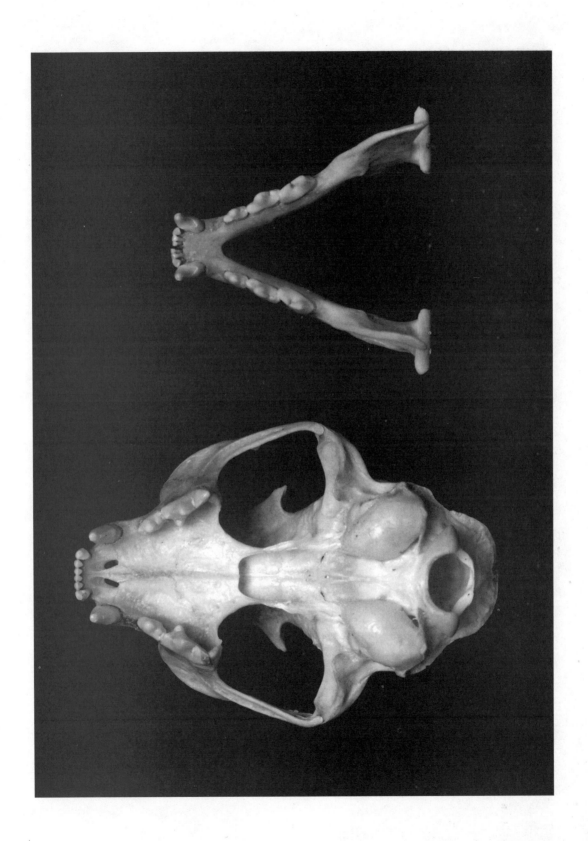

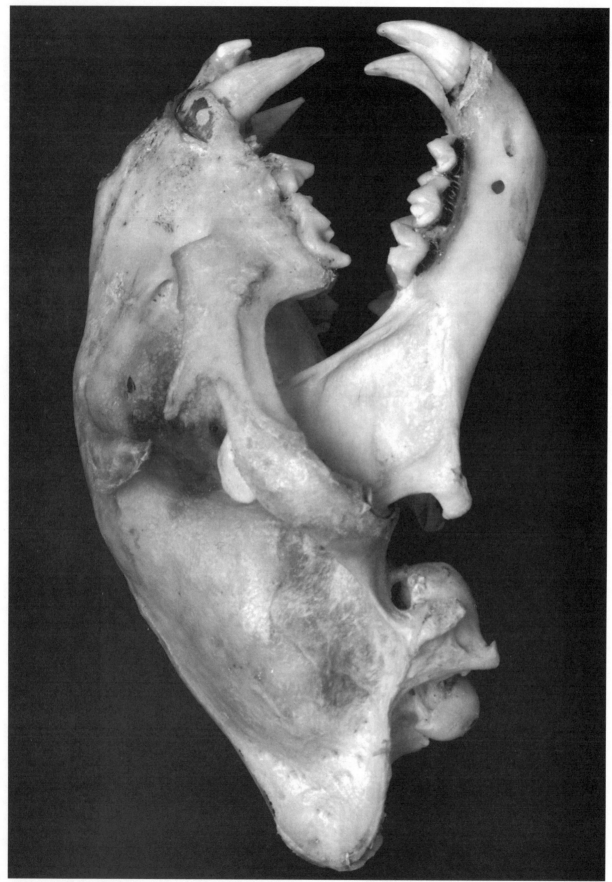

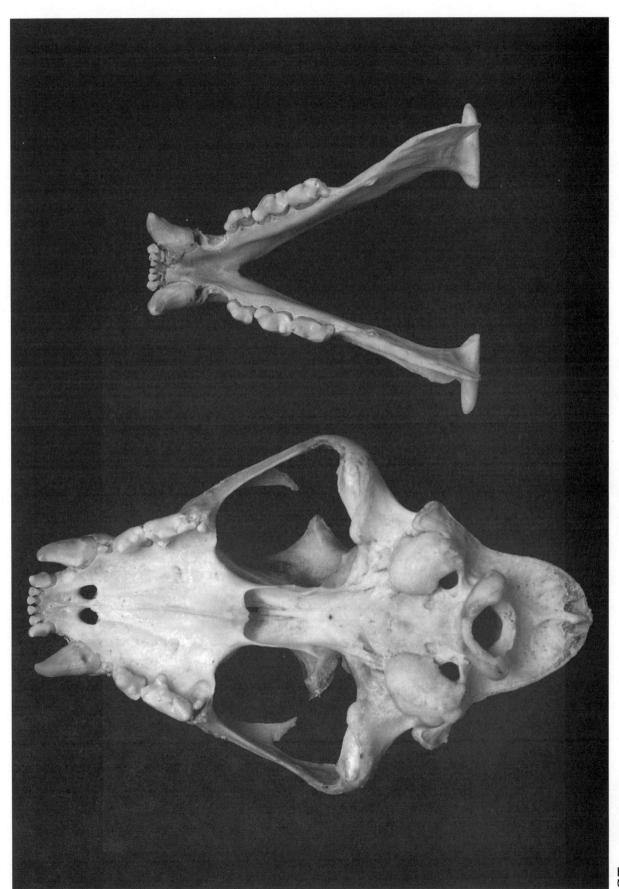

C7 (70% of actual size)

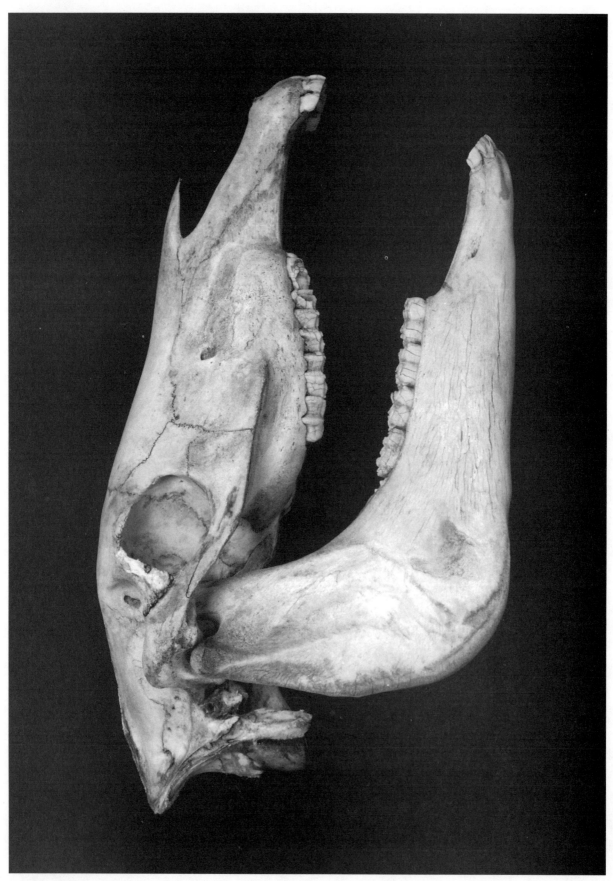

C8 (45% of actual size)

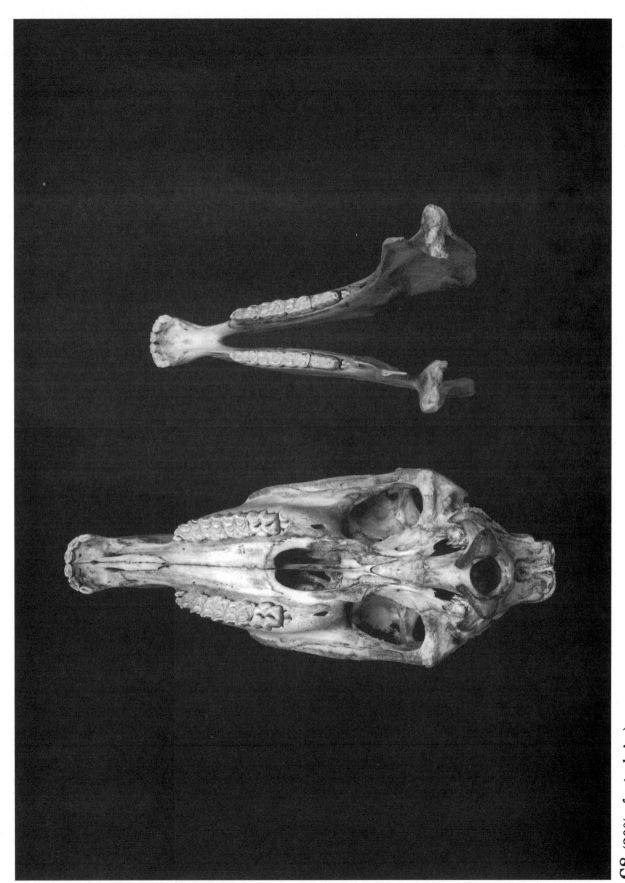

C8 (30% of actual size)

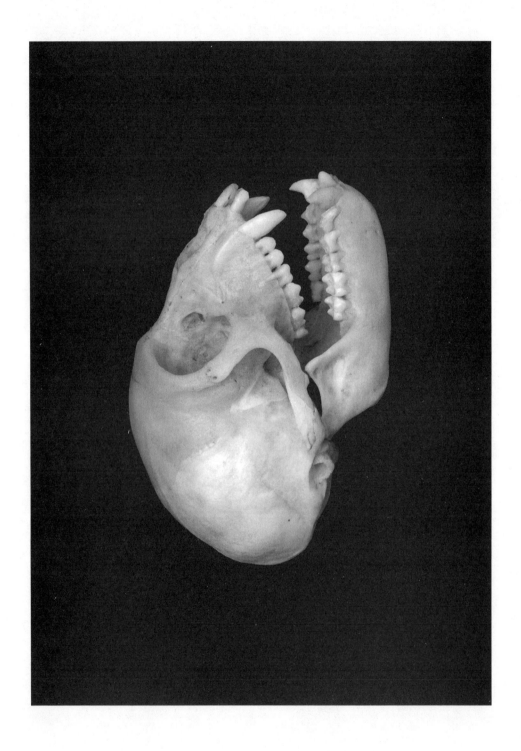

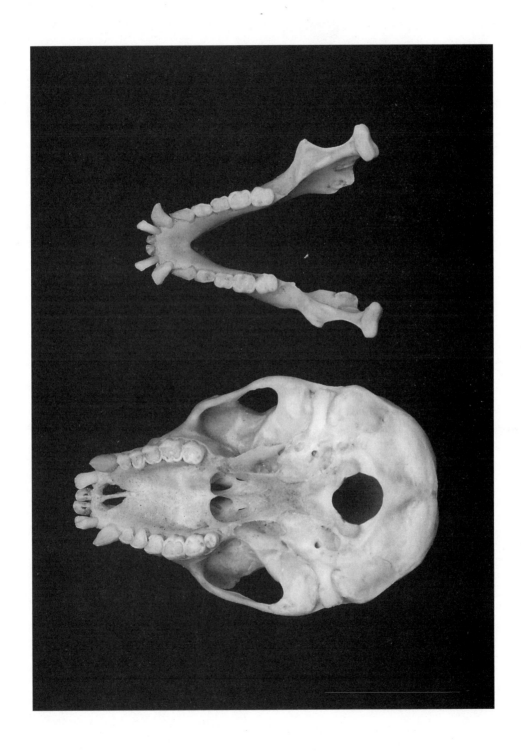

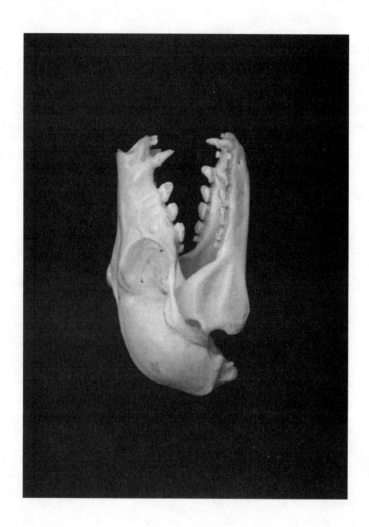

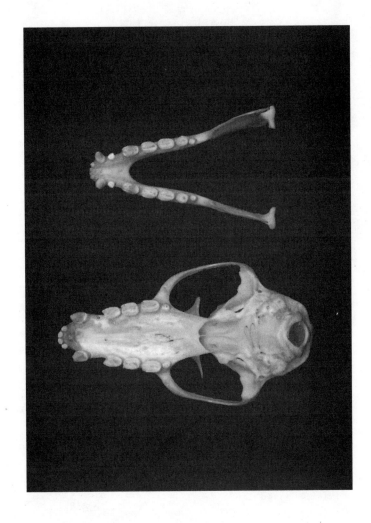

C11 (60% of actual size)

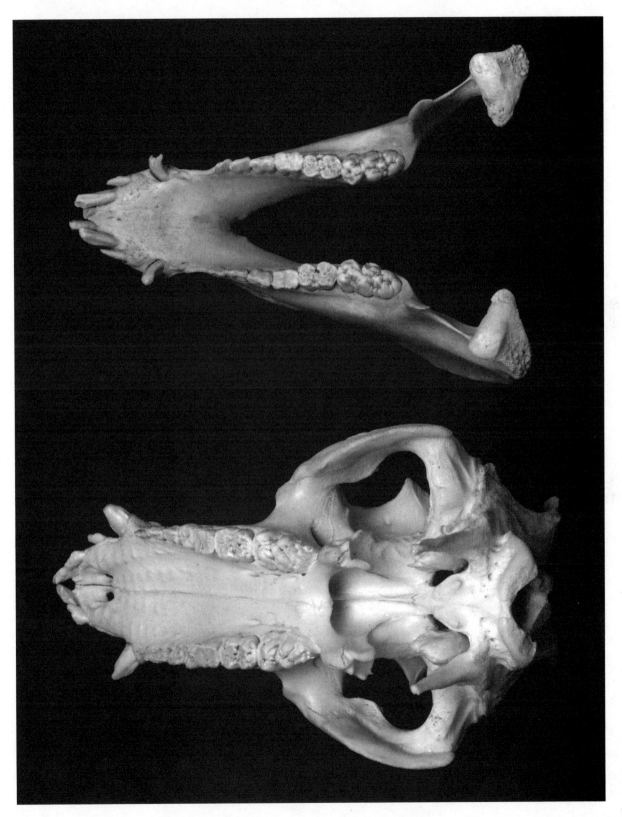

C11 (50% of actual size)

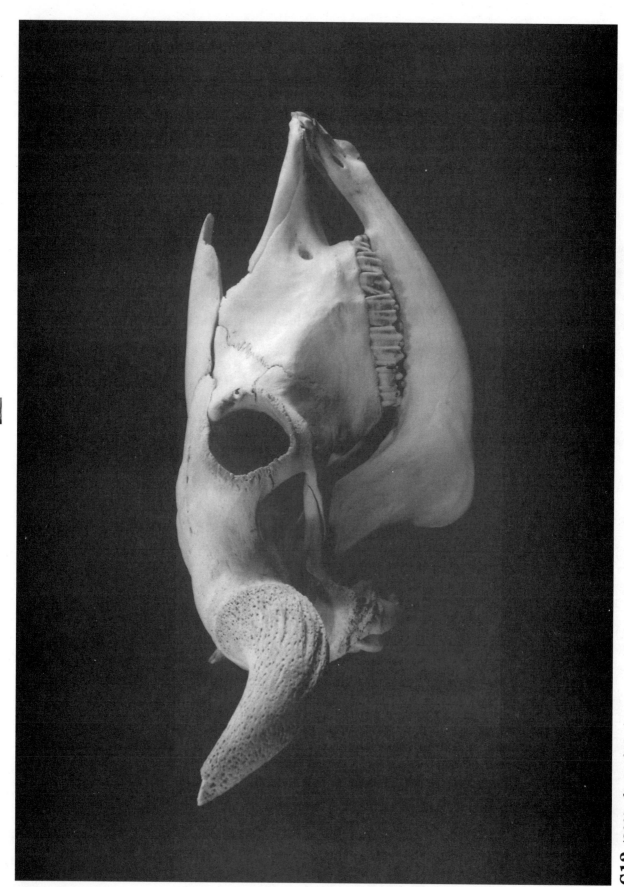

C12 (30% of actual size)

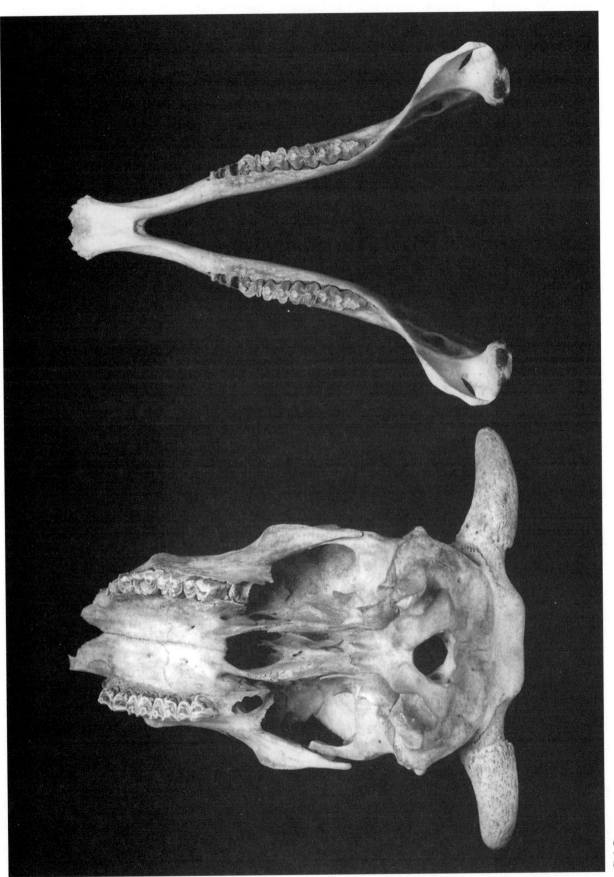

C12 (25% of actual size)

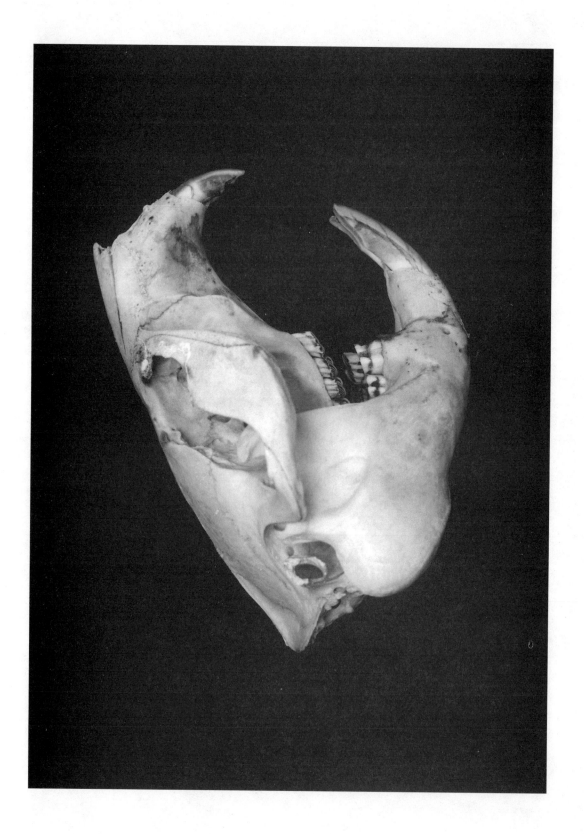

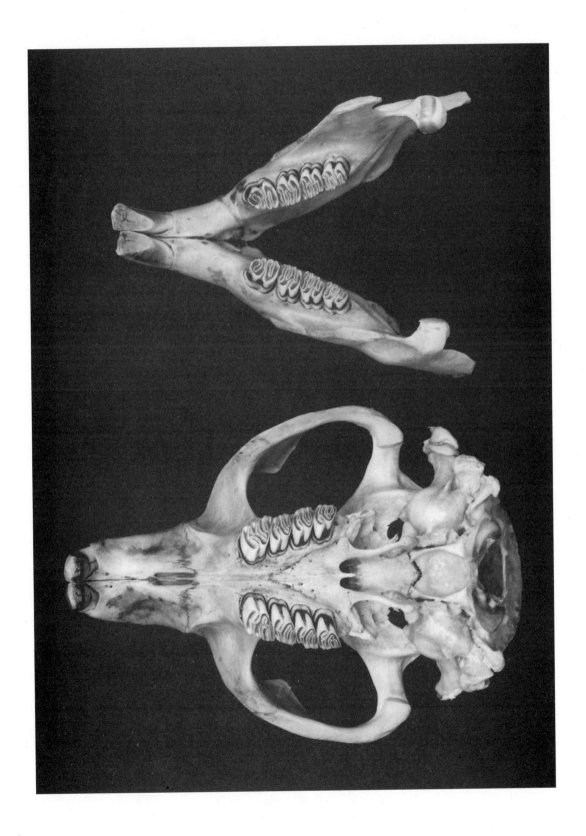

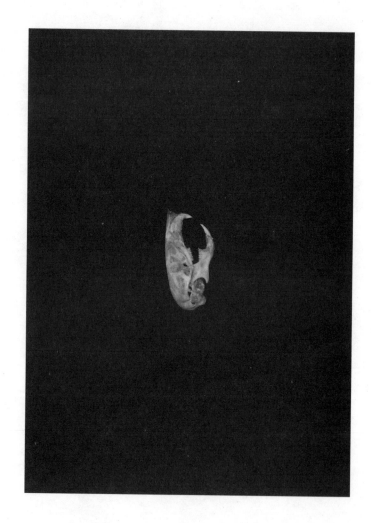

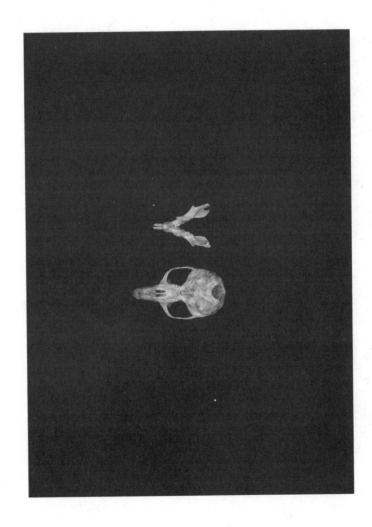

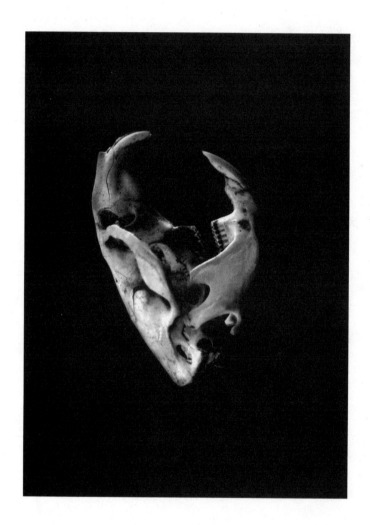

READING
SKULLS AND FEEDING

Based on <u>Hyman's Comparative Vertebrate Anatomy</u>, edited by Marvalee H. Wake.

FEEDING

Food Gathering

Most mammals (humans are a notable exception) use their heads as organs of prehension or grasping. However, the physical demands of prehension vary greatly according to the type of food eaten.

The cat skull illustrates features typical of mammalian carnivores. The pointed canines serve to grab, hold, and kill prey. While strain to the skull and lower jaw of a domestic cat while grabbing prey may be slight because of the small size of its usual prey, in other carnivores, such as the large felids (lion, leopard, etc.), which prey on large animals, these strains are substantial. The skull and lower jaw must be able to withstand impact that may tend to force the open lower jaw back against the skull: they must also be able to withstand the effects of the weight and struggles of the prey that may pull the lower jaw forward and rotate it downward. **Note that the jaw joint of a cat is much more secure than that of a sheep.** Forces that drive the lower jaw back against the skull are resisted by a well-developed joint at the back of the jaw. Forces that pull the lower jaw forward are resisted to some extent by the direction of pull of the relatively large temporalis muscle (identifiable from the relatively large temporal fossa on the skull). It is appropriately directed to resist forward and downward displacement of the lower jaw.

In contrast, the sheep is a grazing animal that pulls up grasses. The absence of enlarged canines in sheep reflects total lack of predatory behavior: it also reflects the development of types of competitive and defensive behavior that do not employ canines either for display or for actual biting. Furthermore, the loss of large canine teeth is also a consequence of the development of considerable transverse movement of the lower jaw when chewing. It should be apparent that the physical demands of food procurement are much less on the skull of a grazing or browsing animal than on a carnivore; insofar as food procurement is concerned, a large temporalis muscle and a relatively secure jaw joint are thus not needed by noncarnivores for procuring food.

Chewing

Unlike the great majority of other vertebrates, most mammals chew their food. The effect of chewing is to reduce food items to a size suitable for swallowing, as in carnivores, or to reduce great amounts of tough plant material of low nutritive value to small bits in order to break down nondigestible or poorly digestible cell walls, and to increase the surface area available for digestive juices to work on.

In carnivores, flesh is cut into pieces mainly by the shearing action of the carnassial teeth (last premolar above, first molar below). Demonstrate

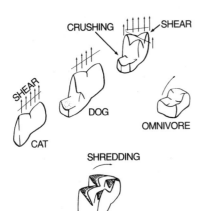

CRUSHING
SHEAR
SHEAR
CAT
DOG
OMNIVORE
SHREDDING
UNGULATE HERBIVORE

on a cat skull with lower jaw in place that the shearing action mostly involves upward rotation of the lower jaw. Slight transverse (side to side) movement of the lower jaw to the side on which food is being cut probably also occurs in order to press the cutting surfaces of the carnassials tightly together and ensure effective shearing. Note that the jaw joint of the cat will allow upward rotation of the lower jaw and slight sliding from side to side. It will not readily allow forward and backward sliding of the lower jaw, for reasons already considered in relation to prehension (grasping food).

Chewing in the sheep, on the other hand, employs a highly mobile jaw joint. The ridges on the lower molars and premolars move sideways across the ridges on the upper teeth. The intervening food is ground and cut to pieces in the process. To accomplish this, the lower jaw swings (rotates) and slides from side to side: actions which involve forward, backward, and transverse movements of the jaw articulating joints. As is typical of mammalian herbivores, the relatively large size of the lower jaw reflects the fact that the masseter and internal pterygoid muscles are the dominant jaw adductors. The temporalis muscle is much smaller, as indicated by the small size of the temporal fossa. The masseter and internal pterygoid muscles also have a substantially larger lever arm than the temporalis because the jaw joint is raised far above the level of tooth row. (Note that in carnivores the temporalis muscle is the largest and also has the greatest leverage.) The former muscles are those mainly responsible for the chewing movements described.

INTER- AND INTRASPECIFIC AGGRESSIVE AND DEFENSIVE BEHAVIOR

In addition to procuring and processing food, the head is important in defensive activities against enemies and in aggressive activities toward members of the same species for space (territory), social position, or mates.

Carnivores typically display their well-developed canines, exhibiting them as potential weapons of aggression or defense. When actual fighting occurs, either within or between species, biting is common. This type of fighting, involving the teeth and jaws, utilizes the same adaptations that carnivores possess for bringing down prey; qualitatively, at least, the physical demands on the skull and lower jaw are similar. It also appears that those herbivores that retain conspicuously developed canines (e.g., gorillas, pigs) do so for their value as threat or weapons in combat.

Sheep represent herbivores that have eliminated canines (in this case, by modifying the lower canines to function as incisors) and that utilize head-to-head butting as the major method of intraspecific combat, especially among males competing for mates. In the domestic sheep, some bone modifications for this type of behavior can be seen. Note the great breadth of the frontal bone in the eye region. In the adult male (especially in some wild species) this region is massively developed and expanded through development of sinuses within the frontal bone itself. This region forms the structural base for support of the horns, which may be subjected to great impact forces. Also, note the downwardly rather than backwardly facing foramen magnum, which is oriented so that when the head is lowered and the horns and frontal region are facing forward, the forces created by the impact of butting are directed into the neck, which therefore forms a buttress against these forces.

VARIANTS OF MAMMALIAN SKULLS AND TEETH

Primitive Therians: The Opossum

The primitive therian (marsupial) mammal skull is much like that of the opossum: both the snout and temporal region are long, the braincase is rather narrow, and the zygomatic arch is complete and well-developed. The lower jaw possesses a large joint piece, slender body, and an articulation slightly above the level of the teeth. Canines are large, incisors small and unspecialized, premolars simple, and molars suited both for shearing and grinding: the entire dentition is adapted for a generalized carnivorous-omnivorous diet. From this type of skull, that of all later therian mammals is probably derived.

Insectivores

Primitive insectivores, like hedgehogs and tree shrews, are similar to the opossum in general skull morphology; most groups show an enlargement of certain incisors and reduction of the canines.

Carnivores

The long-snouted skulls of generalized fissiped carnivores, such as civets and dogs, differ little in appearance from that of the opossum. In the cats and weasels, the facial region is extremely shortened. The jaw articulation of most carnivores lies close to the level of the lower tooth row. All fissipeds are characterized by large canines and by the specialization of the last upper premolar and the first lower molar as a set of enlarged flesh-shearing blades called carnassials. In extremely carnivorous forms, such as cats, the number of molars is greatly reduced: in more omnivorous forms, like the bears and raccoons, the molars are expanded for grinding and the carnassials are reduced.

In the fish-eating pinniped carnivores (seals, sea lions), the skull is usually similar to that of fissipeds, but the cheek teeth are simpler and all alike and there are no carnassials. The skull of the mollusk-eating walrus is extremely massive: the cheek teeth are flat-crowned crushing surfaces, and the upper canines are greatly elongated to form the "clam-rake" tusks.

Edentates, Pangolins, and the Aardvark

The endentates (armadillos, sloths, and anteaters) are a diversely adapted group characterized by the degeneration of the teeth, which are simple pegs lacking enamel in armadillos and sloths and are entirely absent in anteaters. Incisors are lacking; sloths have enlarged anterior teeth. In some armadillos the number of teeth is greatly increased over the usual number for placental mammals. Except in sloths, the skull is long and tubular, especially in the giant anteater. The distantly related pangolins and aardvark are convergent upon true anteaters because of their similar ant- and termite-eating habits. Pangolins are toothless, but the aardvark (which may be derived from primitive ungulates) possesses peculiar enamelless cheek teeth.

Rodents and Lagomorphs

These two groups are characterized by the absence of canines and the possession of an enlarged pair of rootless, ever-growing upper and lower incisors separated from the cheek teeth by a space (diastema); otherwise, they are quite different and are not at all closely related. Lagomorphs (rabbits, hares, and pikas) are easily distinguished by the possession of a second pair of small upper incisors behind the enlarged pair and by numerous perforations (fenestrations) of the snout. Chewing (mastication) is by side to side movements of the jaws, and the skull and mandible therefore resemble those of ungulates in proportions (see below). The skull of rodents tends to be low and little arched, unlike that of rabbits, and the lower jaw has a small joint. Anterior premolars are lost and those present are usually molarlike: the cheek teeth have complicated morphology with well-developed cross ridges. Chewing is by fore-aft movements of the mandible.

Cetaceans

Perhaps the most remarkable variants of the mammalian skull are seen among the whales and dolphins. The cranial region is short and broad, and the face has a beak or rostrum formed by elongated maxillae and premaxillae. The external nostrils have moved far back and open upward by way of the "blowhole"; the very reduced nasals lie behind them. The bones surrounding the blowhole of toothed whales are asymmetrical in size and shape; this is most pronounced in the sperm whale. Toothed whales possess conical teeth that may greatly exceed the normal placental number and that do not undergo replacement. In the sperm whale they are confined to the lower jaw. The whalebone whales are completely devoid of teeth; instead, there is along each side of the upper jaw a series of frayed horny plates (the "whalebone" or baleen), which hang vertically and are used to sieve plankton from the water.

Ungulates

Ungulates are the herbivorous hoofed mammals of the orders Perissodactyla (horses, tapirs, and rhinos) and Artiodactyla (pigs, hippos, camels, deer, cattle, and a great variety of other "cloven-hoofed" types). In all, the cheek teeth tend to become square and the cusps tend to become complicated. In the perissodactyls, the premolars become molarlike and the cheek teeth develop ridges connecting the main cusps; this is called a lophodont pattern. The most complicated pattern of lophs is seen in the horse. Primitive artiodactyls, like pigs and hippos, have molars with separate bulbous cusps—a bunodont pattern. Advanced artiodactyls, the ruminants, possess molars in which the cusps are crescentic—a selendont pattern. In artiodactyls, the premolars tend not to be fully molarlike.

The skulls of most ungulates share a number of common features that are related to the way plant food is procured and processed. With few exceptions, the face is elongated and very deep and the cranial region is short: the eye orbit is closed behind: canines are reduced and incisors are specialized for cropping (in advanced ruminants, the lower canine has the morphology and function of an incisor): there is a space (diastema) in front of the cheek teeth: the lower jaw has a deep angle, a small joint, and an articulation elevated well above the tooth row: weapons are often developed on the skull, solid keratinous horns in rhinos, bony antlers in deer, true horns (keratinous sheath covering a bony core) in cattle, antelopes, and their allies. Only a few ungulates retain enlarged canines that serve as weapons: the curved, ever-growing tusks of pigs and hippos and the saber-like upper canines of tragulids and musk deer.

Primates

The higher primates—monkeys, apes, and humans—are characterized by skulls with a large, rounded cranium, a relatively short face, the complete separation of the forwardly facing orbits from the temporal fossae by a bony wall, and the shift of the occiput and foramen magnum to a more ventral position below the braincase. The molar teeth of apes and humans are bunodont, suitable for an herbivorous or omnivorous diet. The teeth of Old World monkeys are somewhat lophodont. There are only two, instead of the usual three, incisors. The canines are enlarged in male apes and monkeys, usually small in females: in humans, they are small in both sexes. The apes and humans are characterized by extensive fusions of the skull bones.

Exploration 2
NAME THAT ANIMAL

Animal heads come in a wonderful diversity of shapes, sizes, and specializations. Teeth and jaws are especially diverse—"all the better to eat you with" (in the words of Little Red Riding Hood), whether "you" happen to be leaf, wood, nut, insect, bird, clam, whatever. You have just spent some time thinking about any sort of differences or similarities among skulls. Now we will concentrate on functional differences and similarities.

The shape, size, and function of an animal's skulls, jaws, and teeth are tightly linked to the kinds of food the animal eats, and how it obtains and starts to process that food. What an animal eats is a major part of its ecology or "way of life"; thus, by studying an animal's skull, teeth, and jaws, you can learn a great deal about that animal. Teeth are especially durable, so they last for a long time after an animal has died and make good fossils. Teeth are, in fact, often the sole or major fossil remains of long-dead organisms (which has given rise to feeble jokes among scientists who study fossils: "Give me a tooth and I'll design you the animal.") Without going that far, there is much to be learned by examining teeth and the jaws and skulls that hold them.

Materials
- **Skull photo cards** (from your teacher), 1 set per team
- **Groupings lists** from previous class session
- **Rulers**
- **Reference materials**

Procedure

1. **Who eats what?**

    As before, in teams, examine the skulls, jaws and teeth while specifically considering their function. What might each group eat? Why do you think so? Use these ideas to help you find out who the animal is in step 2.

2. **Identify the family of one skull.**

    Have each team member pick a skull. Using the reference materials, try to identify its taxonomic family. That is, is it from the family Felidae, Canidae, Mustelidae, Bovidae, What-idae?

3. **Name your skull.**

    Once you tentatively have identified a family, can you tell which species you have? Either way, bring your skull and its family name to your teacher and match the skull number to the master list to find your animal name.

4. **Literature research and writing about your skull.**

    Still working individually and using the reference materials, learn more about how your beast "earns a living." (Did you make some accurate predictions about its food types? What made you think so?) Prepare a brief paragraph about your animal—what it eats, where it lives, what sort of social life it has, maybe something about its relatives. (Look at the "family trees" for ideas.)

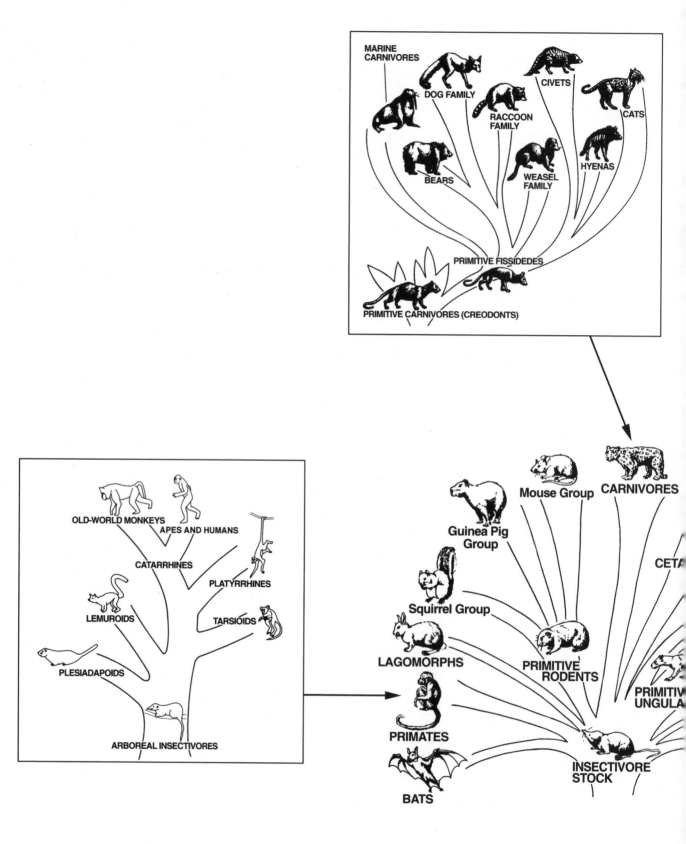

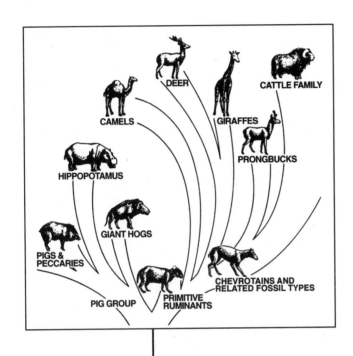

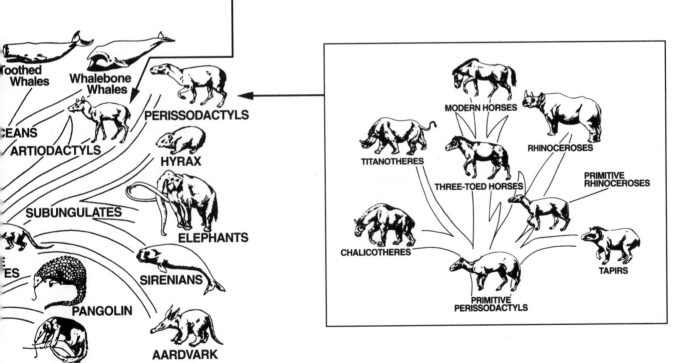

WHAT YOU EAT AND HOW YOU SPEND ENERGY

CHAPTER TWO

OVERVIEW

Animals get energy by finding and eating food. This is in contrast with plants, which get their energy through photosynthesis—catching sunlight. Once an animal has eaten its food, how is the energy in the food used, or "spent"? What determines how much food an animal needs anyway? We have just considered bony animals and their foods, especially what they eat as reflected in their teeth and skulls. In the next few chapters, we explore ways in which animals use the energy in their foods, starting with <u>you</u> as the research animal.

CASE STUDY
TWO LIFESTYLES

THE THREE-TOED SLOTH

You are moving through the wet forest of Costa Rica. The light is dim and greenish, filtered by the layers upon layers of tree boughs high above you. The variety of plant forms is dazzling, but you are on the lookout for animals. You know the place is teeming with creatures you have never seen, from tiny mites to lumbering tapirs—half-horse, half-pig—and jungle cats.

You hope that, with care and luck, you will meet some of these fascinating strangers on their home turf.

A quiet noise sounds above you in a cecropia tree—you look up and get a glimpse of the most successful mammal in the Central American jungle. You freeze and hold your breath, but you are forced to exhale and breathe in before the animal moves again. The three-toed sloth takes no notice of you, but hangs there biting off leaves and slowly swallowing them. Nothing in the picture changes much for minutes at a time; the animal's slowness is emphasized by colorful birds shooting by and the passing of a troop of monkeys.

Sloth

Sloths do move slowly, although they change trees as often as once a day, moving among trees in a home area that more than one sloth may share. Once a week, they climb to the base of a favorite tree to urinate and defecate, covering the deposit sketchily with kicks from their hind feet as they begin the long climb to the canopy again. The round trip may last a half-hour.

The sloth's very name means "slowness," and its lifestyle is designed for economy of effort and energy use. It has no social life to speak of: mating is brief, adults do not stay together or raise their young together; and a mother cares for the single offspring for a few months before she leaves her young in her own home territory and moves "next door" to start a new territory.

Sloths are little preyed upon and have few conflicts with other sloths. Each sloth has its own favorite foods, which means that several sloths may share territory, since each uses different resources within the area. The most frequent interactions a sloth has with other organisms involve the community of algae, insects, and other small creatures that inhabit its fur. In fact, its greenish tinge is due to algae in the fur.

The sloth moves slowly through the trees, and its body works slowly at every level. It is a mammal and thus maintains its core body temperature within a certain range through metabolic activity. That is unlike, say, a reptile (a turtle or a snake), which regulates its core body temperature by external means, such as sunlight, and can get too sluggish to move if surrounding temperatures become too cold. The sloth, while maintaining a constant core temperature, does even that more "slowly," that is, at a lower rate than a typical mammal of the same size (6–10 kg). Sloth core temperature is around 31°C to 33°C (87°F to 91°F), while other same-size mammals are typically about 38°C (100°F).

The sloth eats low-quality food, with relatively few usable calories per amount or weight of food. It keeps its temperature within the critical range by living in an area without real temperature extremes and by basking often in the sunny, upper reaches of its food trees. It moves slowly, spending most of its time browsing or resting. The sloth spends little of its energy on warming up or cooling off, avoiding predators, defending or even marking its territory, or chasing its meals, which are on the trees surrounding it. The females do not build nests, and they give birth to few young, which are weaned early and can soon feed themselves.

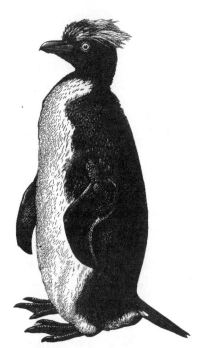

Emperor penguin

THE EMPEROR PENGUIN

Go about as far south as you can, to Antarctica, and you will find the emperor penguin. Actually, you will not find just one, because they live in colonies of thousands, spending the short summers fishing along the edge of the ice pack and the long winters laying their eggs and raising their young.

The emperor is the largest penguin species and one of the largest of birds, standing up to 1.2 meters tall, and weighing as much as 40 kilograms. Like all penguins, they are flightless swimmers, chunky in shape, and very social. They pursue their prey actively in the sea and are pursued along the edges of the ice and in the water by leopard seals, which are powerful and effective hunters.

Emperor penguins do all their eating in the summer. When winter comes, and the pack ice thickens and stretches out to sea, the penguins walk far away from the coast to their breeding areas. There the mated pairs choose a nesting spot, and the female lays a single egg.

With the temperature generally far below freezing, a penguin egg could not survive unheated for more than a few seconds, so the female keeps it on her feet, covered by her feathers. She then passes it to the male, who keeps it covered on his feet. They take turns for the next 2 months at protecting the egg; each turn lasts weeks.

When it is the male penguins' turn to keep the eggs warm, the females head off to gather food. To reach fishing grounds they have to walk and slide as much as 100 kilometers to the sea, across land and the ice pack. There they fish, gorge, and then walk the same distance (or more) back, in the subzero cold and wind.

Meanwhile, the males stand in a crowd of thousands, each holding an egg on his feet. The wind chills reach far below 0°C and there is no sunshine to speak of, so the birds spend all their energy keeping warm. They cannot feed, and their mates will not return with supplies for weeks. All during that time, the birds keep themselves and their eggs warm, at about 38°C to 40°C (99°F to 104° F), using only energy stored in the fat they put on during the previous summer.

Finally, the females return with their crops full of fish for the now hatched chicks. The males, in turn, walk the many kilometers to the shore and recover from their long fast. They return with food for the chicks, then the females again take a foraging trip. The mates take turns like this until the chicks are old enough that the whole colony can move to its summer grounds by the sea. A few weeks are spent at the shore, basking in what summer sun there is. Then winter moves in, and it is breeding season again. The chicks are now young adults and on their own.

Consider These Before You Go On . . .

1. How, or on what, do sloths and penguins spend energy?

2. How much energy do you think sloths versus penguins need to gather to survive and reproduce?

3. Would a sloth make a good penguin, or a penguin a good sloth? Why? How? What are some important differences between the energy needs and uses of the two animals?

Write your thoughts in your notebook (remember to bring it with you to class).

In the Explorations coming up, you will construct an intake and activity budget—an account of the energy <u>you</u> take in and use. You will ask similar questions about your own energy use.

Exploration 1
YOUR INTAKE AND ACTIVITY LOG: DATA COLLECTION

How organisms get, use, and transform energy is a key part of all ecosystems. What "role" does each species play, energetically? A "role" means how an animal finds and digests food, interacts with others of its kind, avoids predators, reproduces, and copes with changes in the physical environment. All these activities require, release, or change the form of energy. We will consider the sum of these metabolic, biological, and behavioral activities, which are each animal's contribution to the energy flow of its ecosystem.

Let's start by using you as a sample animal and take data with which you can describe your energy intake—the energy you take in as food—and your energy expenditure—how you make use of the energy in the food you have eaten. Building on this experience, later you will construct similar energy budgets for other animals.

The research includes work outside and inside class: data collection outside class and analysis in class. You will collect data on two things: what you eat and drink, and your activities. You will convert all those data into units of energy called calories. And then you will look for patterns in who used how many energy units and how the units were used. (If you prefer to observe someone else, you may do so. But that will be difficult, since you are not likely to be with that person for 24 consecutive hours, so your data may be incomplete.)

Materials
- Data sheets from the teacher: your **Activity Log** and your **Intake Log**

Procedure
Record intake and activity for 24 hours. Before starting, plan how you might collect the data.

On Your Activity Log
1. **Note time spent.**
Note how long you spend on each activity; estimates are okay if they are not too wild. It will simplify things if you record activities in 10- or 15-minute units of time and round off if the amount of time is close to the unit you have chosen. So you might call 8 or 12 minutes of TV a 10-minute estimate.

If, however, you have much shorter bursts of some activity, such as walking between classrooms, record those individually. (What would happen to your data if you rounded off several 2-minute activities to 10 minutes each?) Later, when you analyze the data, add shorter times for one type of activity to get the total activity time.

For example, if you spent a little over a minute walking slowly from class to class, and you switched classrooms seven times, you might record "walking slowly to class" eight times, and then add that up for an estimated total of 10 minutes of slow walking.

2. **Record everything.**
    Be sure to record the time you spend sleeping, sitting on a bus, taking a shower—everything. How does this relate to "being alive"? Why? What do we mean by "activity"?

3. **Note how "hard" or energetically you did the activity.**
    With an activity like sitting in front of the TV, this doesn't make sense, but with, say, bike riding, the amount of effort makes a real difference. For example, if you rode your bicycle for 30 minutes, you would use more energy riding hard than if you rode in a slow, relaxed way.

    On Your Intake Log

1. **Record all your food and drink.**
    Note everything that you consume during a 24-hour period.

2. **Types and amounts.**
    Note both the types of food eaten (peanut butter sandwich, whole milk, skim milk) and the amounts of food eaten. It is okay to use everyday measures (number of sandwiches, cups of milk, etc.). Such estimates may mean that on some points your data will not be completely precise, but they probably will be accurate enough not to change the final data. (This is another sort of "rounding off," right?)

3. **Nutritional information, especially kilocalories.**
    If you consume already prepared or packaged food (chips, cookies, yogurt, soda, etc.), you might find it handy to cut out or copy the nutritional information on the side of the package. This will provide you with calorie information (and also something about the amount of fats, carbohydrates, and protein in the food).

4. **Bring all your data to class.**
    Bring your data to class, to calculate your energy intake and expenditure for your sample day. For Exploration 3: Patterns in Intake and Activity Data, also find and bring in the following: your current weight, height, and shoe size and your height, weight, and shoe size last year.

Exploration 2a
YOUR ACTIVITY LOG: DATA ANALYSIS

As is often true when doing research, you have lots of data, in various units: amounts of food and drink, time spent on various activities, calories, kilocalories. Now we will "boil the data down," into one set of units (kilocalories) and just two numbers. What do you think those numbers represent? In this Exploration we consider your Activity Log data; in Exploration 2b, we consider your Intake Log data.

Materials
• Your **Activity Log**
• The **Energy Expenditure Table**, below

Procedure

1. **Converting time spent on activities into kilocalories.**
    Do any additions you need to get a total amount of time spent on each activity—add up all time walking, all time sitting, and so on. Then use the Energy Expenditure Table to calculate how much energy you used during the sample 24 hours.

2. **Activities not listed in the table.**
    You may find that some of your activities are not listed. Try to find a listed activity that is roughly similar, and use its value (or adjust as seems appropriate). For example, baseball is not listed, but soccer is. Given the many pauses in the action of baseball versus the continuous running in soccer, it probably would be best to choose a value near the lower end of the soccer range to use for baseball playing. Just be sure to note that this energy-use value is an approximation. Alternatively, try to find the activity in other references your classroom may have for this kind of study, such as exercise books or the little calorie-use booklets sold in supermarkets.

3. **Energy per unit time.**
    Energy expenditures are expressed in kilocalories per kilogram per hour (kcal/kg/hr). Why are they expressed like this? We must include a measure of energy, since we are talking about energy, hence, the unit kilocalorie. For some activities, a single energy expenditure value is given, while for others, minimum and maximum values are listed. In many potentially strenuous activities, you may spend more or less energy depending on how actively you participate. For example, in a pickup basketball game, you may play very hard or only casually; your energy spent depends on the intensity of your game. The most/least energy values for each activity are often quite different, so try realistically to assess your participation level (e.g., bicycling ranges from 3 to 14 kcal/kg/hr). (The kilocalorie is useful as both a measure of energy expenditure and of energy intake.)

    You also need to account for the time spent on an activity, since the longer you do something the more energy you use. In fact, since the equation is units per hour, express your times in hours. If you sat for 30 minutes, convert 30 minutes to 0.5 hour.

Energy Expenditure Table

| | KCAL/KG/HOUR | |
ACTIVITY	MINIMUM	MAXIMUM
Sleeping	1.0	
Resting in bed	1.0	
Sitting	1.1	
Lying quietly	1.2	
Classwork, lecture	1.5	
Conversing	1.6	
Writing	1.6	
Driving a car	2.5	
Aerobic dancing	5.0	10.0
Basketball (game)	7.0	12.0
Basketball (nongame)	3.0	9.0
Bicycling (outdoors)	3.0	14.0
Bicycling (stationary)	1.5	14.0
Jogging 5 mph (12 min/mile)	8.0	
Jogging 6 mph (10 min/mile)	10.0	
Running 7 mph (9 min/mile)	12.0	
Running 8 mph (7.5 min/mile)	13.0	
Running 10 mph (6 min/mile)	15.0	
Skating, ice or roller	4.0	8.0
Soccer	5.0	12.0
Swimming	4.0	12.0
Walking 2 mph (30 min/mile)	2.0	
Walking 3 mph (20 min/mile)	3.0	
Walking 4 mph (15 min/mile)	4.5	

4. "Per kilogram."

What is the role of the term "per kilogram"? Imagine two people about to take a run together. One person weighs 50 kg, while the other weighs 100 kg. Both are in good shape, and they plan to run at the same pace for the same amount of time. Who will burn more energy during the run?

The heavier person has to do considerably more work (moving the extra 50 kg) and thus burns considerably more energy. Actually, the relationship between weight and energy expended is straightforward; the 100-kg runner spends about twice as much energy running as the 50-kg runner.

To use the Energy Expenditure Table, you need to know your weight in kilograms. To convert pounds to kilograms, divide the number of pounds by 2.2 (because 1 kg = 2.2 lb).

1 kg/2.2 lb

5. The whole equation and calculations.

Now we can express energy used as kilocalories spent per unit of weight per unit of time. To convert your data into this form, look up each activity in the table. Refer to your data to see how long you spent on that activity. Multiply the time spent in hours or parts of hours by the kcal value in the table by your weight in kilograms. Do this for all activities, then add the numbers for your total energy expenditure.

OPTIONAL EXAMPLE

In case you want it, here is a worked-through example for Giselle, who weighs 143 pounds and who performed activities including the following yesterday.

ACTIVITY	TIME SPENT
Sleeping	8 hours
Walking to and from school (3 miles per hour)	1 hour
Sitting in class	6 hours
Bicycling outdoors	45 minutes

To calculate her energy usage, Giselle needs to do the following:

1. Convert her weight from pounds to kilograms.

143 lb × (1 kg/2.2 lb) = 65 kg

2. Calculate the energy she expended while sleeping (see the Energy Expenditure Table for the rate of energy use).

1.0 kcal/kg/hr × 65 kg × 8 hr = 520 kcal

3. Calculate the energy she expended while walking.

3.0 kcal/kg/hr × 65 kg × 1 hr = 195 kcal

4. Calculate the energy she expended while sitting in class (see "Classwork, lecture" in the Energy Expenditure Table).

1.5 kcal/kg/hr × 65 kg × 6 hrs = 585 kcal

5. Calculate the energy she expended while bicycling outdoors.

Since Giselle bicycled only moderately hard, she chose a value near the lower end of the range. Also, because she did not bicycle for a full hour, she has to convert the number of minutes for this activity into hours.

6.0 kcal/kg/hr × 65 kg × 0.75 hr = 292.5 kcal

Thus, for the 15.75 hr included in her activity log, Giselle used 1,592.5 kcal.

READING 1
WHEN IS AN ACTIVITY NOT AN ACTIVITY?

Now that you have analyzed your activity data, did you find any time during the 24 hours when you were <u>not</u> active? That is, was there any time during the 24 hours that you were not using any energy?

So we are making a distinction here between performing an action or an activity (walking, sitting, eating) and being <u>metabolically</u> active, that is, just being alive. Were you spending the least amount of energy when you were sleeping?

All study of energy use includes this idea of minimum metabolic activity, or the energy necessary to stay alive. Not surprisingly, it is called resting state or basal (baseline) metabolic rate (BMR).

Actually, it gets more precise than that. Suppose you had been cold during the night of your data collection. You likely would have been shivering and restless, trying to increase your temperature. Both of those use energy. Technically, the basal metabolic energy of an animal is the amount of energy it needs to stay alive while it is resting and not using energy to change its body temperature, or digest, or do anything but be alive.

Knowing the basal metabolic rate of an organism is very useful. It gives us a starting point, energetically speaking, in understanding that organism. Suppose you ran a zoo and your lions are in a small enclosure, not out in the wild. In addition to the food (calories) they need for staying alive (for maintaining their BMR), who needs more calories, your zoo lions or wild lions? Why? What will happen to your zoo lions if they get too many calories? What will happen to the wild lions if they get only the amount of

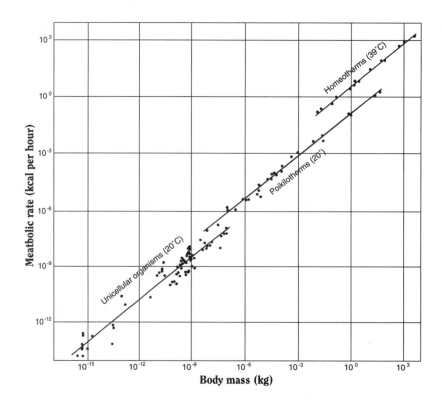

energy they need to keep up their BMR? (Bring all your answers from this reading to class.)

Basal metabolic rates vary for different kinds of animals, a point we will see from different angles in the next few chapters. From the preceding graph, what two things do you notice about who has what BMR?

To return to our question, When is an activity not an activity? When you are dead!

Exploration 2b
YOUR INTAKE LOG: DATA ANALYSIS

You still have lots of data—amounts of food and drink, calories, and kilocalories. Here we boil down these data into one number representing your total energy intake during the 24-hour sample period.

Materials
- Your **Intake Log**
- **Reference materials on caloric values** of foods and drinks
- **Food labels**, if you saved any

Procedure

1. **Adding up amounts of foods and drinks.**
Using your Data Log, add up the amounts of each type of food and drink. Once you have your totals, you are ready to convert them into energy consumed.

2. **Converting amount of food eaten into kilocalories.**
You can find the kilocalorie "values" of foods you ate in reference materials in class or on the food labels you saved. The energy content of foods is expressed in two formats. One way is the amount of energy in a typical serving of food, such as a bowl of cereal or a sandwich, which is the format we use here. Alternatively, you can compare equal quantities of food. In that case, weight is the best measure, not serving size. Some calorie tables are arranged for such comparisons, say, a half kilogram of beans compared to a half kilogram of steak.

No matter what type of table you use, remember that food energy is measured in kilocalories, abbreviated as kcal. (Kilocalories are also known as Calories, with a capital C.) Each kilocalorie is equal to 1,000 calories, and 1 calorie is the amount of energy needed to raise a cubic centimeter of water from 14.5°C to 15.5°C. Warning to consumers of Calories! When you read on a box of cookies that "each cookie contains 73 calories," you should know that those "calories" are actually <u>kilocalories</u> (or <u>Calories</u>).

3. **"Balancing" your energy budget.**
In small groups, consider the following. Each of you has two numbers, one representing the approximate energy taken in and the second representing the energy spent on activities. Are your two numbers the same? Why might that be?

4. **Small groups or class discussion.**

Consider the following questions:

Why are the numbers the same (or not)?

How typical or accurate a sample of your activity and food consumption was this day? If you wanted to build a more realistic picture, how many days might you sample and combine? Why?

How much of your activity was related to getting food (that is, getting energy)?

Was there time when you were not using any energy? If not, what was the lowest energy state you were in? How long did you spend in that state?

What surprised you about your energy budget?

READING 2

ENERGY IN FOODS: HOW IT IS STORED AND HOW YOU GET AT IT

In this Unit we are studying energy, energy flow, and foods. You have just been considering energy intake and use from the perspective of a whole organism, in this case, yourself—a human being. But what does it mean that energy is "contained" in food? How does an animal "get" energy from food? What exactly is energy? And while we are at it, what is food? Food for humans is not the same as food for wolves or deer or termites. Why, and how, do different organisms use different types of food for their energy needs?

We will consider the flow of energy in ecosystems and the entire planet, as well as how plants acquire and use energy. It helps to grasp those concepts if we start with a solid understanding of the types of energy that live organisms use and what organisms do with the energy they acquire.

WE ALWAYS NEED ENERGY

All living organisms require energy for everything they do. It costs energy to move, to keep warm, to repair damaged tissues. Even sitting still and sleeping require some expenditure of energy, since the body's organs are always performing some kind of task, such as pumping blood or breathing. This is such a basic, overwhelming factor for living things that it bears repeating: **To live is to expend energy.** Living things change dramatically when they stop expending energy; that change is known as death.

To help understand the flow of energy among living organisms and within ecosystems, it may be useful to think of energy as a currency, as a form of money. You—and all living creatures—are always "spending" energy. True, you spend less when you sleep and more when you run, but as long as you are alive, you are always spending some amount. This continual drain on your energy budget means you need a way to "earn" enough energy to spend on your needs. How do you earn the energy your body is always spending?

To continue with the currency analogy, ecologists often talk of how animals "make a living." That phrase includes many aspects of an animal's life such as the types of food it eats and how it finds and captures its food, as well as other aspects of how and where it lives. In this Unit, we focus mostly on the energy features of "making a living."

HUMANS AS MODEL ORGANISMS

Periodically in this Module we will consider humans animals as well as others. Why? Because we are typical mammals (in some ways), and because humans can be relatively easy to study.

ENERGY: A FEW BASICS

Energy is found in many different forms. We make use of several of those forms every day. Take a moment now and write down in your notebook all the different kinds of energy with which you are familiar.

What Is Energy?

Technically speaking, energy is the capacity to do work. What does the word "work" mean to you in this context? The term "work" has a very specific meaning to a physicist. Work is defined as force times distance. Fine, but what does "force" mean to a physicist? Force is defined as mass times acceleration. What does this thicket of technical terms and definitions mean? An example should help.

Imagine that you have to raise a heavy box a certain distance, from the floor to a high shelf. Technically speaking, you have to do work on the box, applying a force over a certain distance, that is, you accelerate the mass of the box as you lift it. Without a source of energy, you would be unable to do this work. However, if you had access to electrical energy that could turn an electric motor and if you also had some rope and pulleys, you could make use of the electrical energy's capacity to do work to raise the box (with the help of the machinery). How could you make use of the chemical energy in food to do this work?

Measures of Energy

Just as there are various measures of distance, such as feet and meters, there are multiple measures of energy. The measure that we have chosen to use in this course is the **calorie**. The calorie is defined as the amount of energy it takes to raise the temperature of 1 cubic centimeter or gram of water from 14.5°C to 15.5°C. The energy content of foods is typically discussed in terms of kilocalories (or Calories), each of which is equal to 1,000 of the "small-c" calories. How many kilocalories were in the last sundae you ate? There was probably enough energy in that sundae to raise the temperature of several liters of water 100°C, or from freezing to boiling! Can you calculate how many kilocalories were in the sundae?

Energy Transformations

Energy can neither be created nor destroyed. Energy can, however, change (or be changed) from one form to another. Most of the machines that we use every day function only because energy can change form. Such changes are usually inefficient, that is, some of the energy always ends up as heat, a rather unusable form of energy. For example, consider the ways in which energy gets transformed in your car and the various ways in which energy gets "wasted" as heat.

When you start your car, the car's battery changes stored **chemical energy** into **electrical energy**. Some of the electrical energy becomes **heat**, as the ignition wires warm slightly. The electrical energy becomes **mechanical, or kinetic, energy** when the car's starter motor turns (and some of the energy becomes heat because of friction in the starter motor). To keep the engine running, gasoline (which contains a great deal of chemical energy) is combined with air and a spark (electrical energy) to release heat. The heat causes the mixture of gases in the engine's cylinders to expand and push the pistons, thus changing the energy into mechanical or kinetic energy. The motion of the piston is transferred to the wheels via the crankshaft and drive train, thereby propelling the car forward. As the car moves, there is some friction between the tires and road, and some of the mechanical energy becomes heat (that's why your tires get hot). Throughout this chain of events, energy is changed from one form to another. At each step, though, only a portion of the energy is transformed into the desired form; some of it becomes heat, which is not useful in moving the car forward.

A CAVEAT

It is true, as we have seen, that energy changes form, but cannot be created or destroyed. Under exceptional circumstances, however, energy can change state. That is, energy can be converted to or from matter, as Einstein's famous equation, $E = mc^2$, tells us. Such conversion of matter to energy is the source of energy for nuclear power plants. But because nuclear power is not in the realm of ordinary ecological processes, we will not be studying it.

Exploration 3 (Class)
PATTERNS IN INTAKE AND ACTIVITY DATA

How do you think your energy budget might differ from that of a classmate? A five-year-old's? An eighty-year-old's? From your biggest friend's? From your smallest friend's? From a squirrel's? From a snake's? From an ant's? Why? Let's compare data to look for patterns in who uses how much energy and in what ways.

Materials
- Your **energy data**, in kilocalories, for intake and activity
- Your **data on growth** (your current and past height, weight, shoe size)
- **Graph paper**

Procedure

1. **Group patterns of energy use.**
   Working in groups of three to five, graph all your data. Discuss what comparisons make sense. If you graph height or weight on the Y axis by energy intake on the X axis, what do you think the graph will look like?

   If you prefer, represent the data in some other way—frequency histograms, pie charts, whatever you think will work.

2. **Data from nonclass members.**
   If one of you used another person as your subject, perhaps an infant or an older person, how might that affect energy use patterns? The graph?

3. **Classwide patterns.**
   Put all the class data on one big graph. For example, everyone's height or weight by energy intake, and height or weight by energy use. What patterns do you see? What do you think those patterns mean?

4. **Balanced energy budget.**
   What happens if you plot all the data on energy intake against energy use? If the pairs of numbers are equal for each person, how will the line connecting the points look? You know the numbers are <u>not</u> equal. How does the graph look? Which number tends to be higher? What does that mean?

DUNG BEETLES AND YOU
BUILDING A COMPLETE ENERGY BUDGET

In this Chapter, we consider the food habits of dung beetles and how those habits help replace the > in intake > energy use (previous Chapter) with =.

CASE STUDY
WHAT IS IT DOING?

A rock sits and cannot move. Water from rain or dew collects in its crevices. If temperatures go below freezing, the water freezes and expands (water in frozen form takes up more space than the same weight of water in liquid form). This expansion might cause cracking, flaking, peeling, and even large cracks in the rock. Dust might blow into the cracks; seeds might fall into that dust and germinate. The roots might deepen the cracks. The rock sits. It might get moved by someone or something. Mostly it sits. Maybe for thousands, even millions of years.

A plant also sits—that is, it is rooted. It can bend toward the sun. It takes up water through its roots, takes in carbon dioxide through its leaves, and loses water through its leaves. It produces flowers. They likely bear fruit. The plant might sit for days, months, even a thousand years. But not longer.

A sea cucumber sits—that is, it is affixed to a spot on the sea floor. It can move with the current and against it. It keeps out both water and salt from the water. It produces baby sea cucumbers. It might sit for days, months, perhaps a dozen years. But not longer.

A branch that has fallen off a tree "sits" and cannot move. Water might collect in its nooks. Fungi and other things might grow on it. The branch sits. It might get moved by something or someone. After some months or a few years, it has been cracked apart into tiny pieces.

An aardvark does not sit. It moves from termite nest to termite nest. It might have young. It will rest but it will move again. It will keep doing all those things for maybe a dozen or more years.

What does a rock, a sea cucumber, a plant, a pet do in a minute, a day, a month, a year, its lifetime?

	ROCK	SEA CUCUMBER	PLANT	YOUR PET (SPECIFY)
A minute?				
A day?				
A month?				
A year?				
Its lifetime?				

Fill in your ideas in your notebook.

How would you group these entities according to energy use? What is the profound difference between them?

Exploration 1
THE THREE "D'S": DUNG BEETLES, DETRITIVORES, DECOMPOSERS

By comparing your energy intake and use with those of a dung beetle (in the short, medium, and long term), you can develop your unbalanced equation (intake ≠ energy use) into a complete and balanced equation.

Materials
- Personal **intake and energy use data**, in kilocalories (from **Chapter 2**)
- **Case Study** data (from this Chapter)

Procedure

1. **No dung beetles.**

   The Australian continent and New York City have one thing in common: not enough dung beetles. Seriously. When you last visited New York City or any other large city, did you see any dung beetles?

   So what? you may say. Good question. What do dung beetles eat? Yes, really. Actually, the adults eat leaves and things. But they make wonderful nests in hollow balls of dung, in which they lay their eggs, to develop and grow relatively protected and surrounded by their food, the dung.

2. **What does it mean?**

   The key words here are <u>food</u> and <u>eat</u>. What does it tell us about dung if dung beetle larvae eat it? What does it tell us about pizza if you eat it? You can get energy from pizza. The dung beetle can get energy from dung.

3. **Your energy use data.**

   Now look back at your intake and energy use data from **Chapter 2**. Intake ≠ energy use, right? The equation is "unbalanced," that is, the two sides are not equal. Given what we know about energy in dung, what did we leave out that helps explain why your intake is greater than your energy use?

4. **What is missing?**

   Working in small groups, look at your charts from the Case Study. Substitute yourself—or "Human"—as a label for the last column. Fill in your activities for that column in your notebook. What else is missing from the list of energy uses for a 24-hour period? Remember your original data. What time span do the data now cover? Remember the "renaming" tool from **Unit 1, Chapter 1?** Use it here. For example, when you started calculating your energy uses, you had a long list of activities. You collapsed them all into something like daily energy expenditure. Use a time scale to help you sort energy uses: what happens every day (respiration) versus some years (growth) versus a few times over your whole lifetime (reproduction).

5. **Class list and the energy use equation.**
   Make a list of each group's suggested uses on the board. Put as many things as possible into as few categories as possible. Have you included all types of energy use from your Case Study data? How does your equation look now? Intake = ?

READING
WHO BALANCED THE ENERGY USE EQUATION?

Energy is neither created nor destroyed but merely changes form (unless it is converted to or from matter, which is what $E = mc^2$ means). Thus, as the first law of thermodynamics tells us, **all** the energy an animal ingests can be accounted for, since energy cannot be destroyed. The energy balance equation tells us that this energy is divided up, as excretion, respiration, or new tissue.

Now let's change perspective, from that of the organism whose diet and energy uses we have been discussing to the perspective of other organisms or the ecosystem as a whole. What do they get out of the energy that is respired, converted into new tissues, or excreted?

Respired energy is unavailable to the ecosystem, since it takes the form of heat and cannot be used by other organisms (no one can "eat" heat). Respired energy heats up the environment and eventually radiates into space. Consider what happens when a person runs 3 miles, fast. Chemical energy that the person has stored gets used to power the body's muscles, thus turning the chemical energy into kinetic (mechanical) energy. But, just as in the example of the transformations of energy in a car (**Chapter 2,** Reading 2), the chemical energy that is used ends up as heat (think about how hot you get when you exercise vigorously). This heat radiates away from your body and is not available as an energy source for any other animals. If you did not run and instead used that energy to produce new tissues, there would be something for another animal to eat (a chunk of your body!).

Energy present in newly produced tissues is "available" to other organisms in the ecosystem. Predators, parasites, and microorganisms can make a living off those tissues. (This energy can also be used by the organism itself. When people diet, they break down their own tissues and use the energy in those tissues for respiration.)

Dung typically contains significant amounts of energy that can be used by other organisms in the ecosystem: detritivores and decomposers.

In fact, in every ecosystem, most of the energy that passes through nonplant organisms goes through the three D's. Although we think of ourselves (and mammals in general) as pretty important, in terms of energy flow we are just a blip on the screen. (We will explore this further in **Chapter 10**.)

So what does this have to do with Australia or Manhattan? Australia has huge sheep stations (ranches) with tens of millions of sheep, each producing a few pounds of dung every day—and very few dung beetles. Manhattan has fourteen-plus million humans and several million dogs, cats, and other pets, all producing dung—and <u>no</u> dung beetles. Of course, Manhattan has a sewage treatment system for human dung. But in both Australia and Manhattan, a great deal of energy—maybe 50% of the total produced by vertebrates—is tied up in dung and not getting recycled into the ecosystem.

Some ecologists suggest that such an imbalance actually shows that these are not real ecosystems. Sheep are not native to Australia; they were introduced by human settlers over the past few hundred years and in numbers far greater than can survive on their own in the desert and semidesert environment. Similarly, large cities have concentrations of humans far greater than can be supported by the environment. Cities must bring in food and other energy and send waste (trash, dung, etc.) out. We will continue to explore effects of such unbalanced "systems" as we proceed.

Now let's consider energy budgets of some nonhuman organisms.

DUNG BEETLES, CHEETAHS, AND OTHERS

CHAPTER FOUR

CONTENTS

Do different animals use energy in the same or different ways? How? Why?

READING 1
TWO ECOSYSTEMS

THE NORTHERN HARDWOODS ECOSYSTEM

The Northern Hardwoods is a layered, patchy world of trees, shrubs, and herbs in the north temperate United States that is shaped in major ways by the rhythms of the seasons. Winter, a time of cold and drought, puts a stop to most plant growth and places great energy demands on the animals of the area. Some respond by migrating, some by sleeping through the worst of it, some eat what they can find, changing their territorial behavior as required.

Fall is thus a time of preparation for the coming winter. Changes in light or temperature can act as signals that trigger changes in behavior. Trees retract nutrients and liquid from their leaves, and their sap and circulatory system change to limit damage by the cold. Many insects die or prepare to persist over the winter in a dormant state, such as larvae or chrysalides. Birds and mammals, whose intensive parenting is over for the season, change their foraging habits, consuming as much high-calorie food as they can and storing it as fat in advance of their winter habits.

Northern Hardwood Forest

Spring and summer open with the green flush of plant growth, the sudden mobilization of water and nutrients in the soil, and the beginning of the flowering season. Animals hatch or emerge from winter stasis or return from their winter ranges. They enter their reproductive phase, which places primary energetic demands on them for the whole growing season.

By midsummer, the ecosystem's productivity reaches its peak, along with the peak time of solar input and the peak demands for moisture, as plants and the sun throw tons of water into the air daily.

The organisms' life stages, energetic needs, and behavioral patterns fit within these great seasonal patterns, and the patterns created within the seasons by species' responses to them.

THE SERENGETI ECOSYSTEM

The Serengeti Plain in East Africa is a wide grassy plain, shaped by both the rhythms of the seasons and the behavior of the great herds of grazing beasts that move across it. The Serengeti is near the equator, so the temperature does not vary as much as in the Northern Hardwoods; seasons are defined more by the coming and going of the rains. As the rains come and the grasses begin to grow, the wildebeest, the zebras, and the antelopes move in waves to take advantage of the new growth. Each wave of animals takes its nourishment from what the last wave left, consuming much of the plant tissue created during the season. The grasses, however, rebound, stimulated by the grazing and by the droppings from millions of grazers. Around and among the big animals, hares, hyraxes, locusts, and dozens of other herbivore species harvest an unknown amount of the primary reduction. As the rains taper off and the land dries, the herds mostly move off, concentrating in more promising areas until the next cycle begins.

The herbivores gather in huge numbers to harvest the grasses; the carnivores gather in amazing concentrations to harvest the grazers. Wild dogs, three species of big cats and several small ones, mongooses and their kin, hyenas, and birds of prey hunt here in greater concentrations than in any other terrestrial system. Humans, too, have been part of the harvest over the years, and their domesticated animals have moved with the grazing herds.

The leftovers and excretions from two or three million grazing animals support enormous communities of specialists in various kinds of

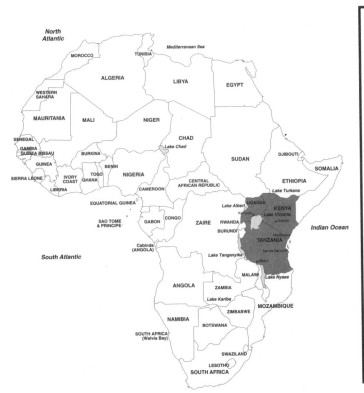

clean-up foraging. For the small creatures that cannot follow the herds, there is an urgency to take advantage of a bonanza that will soon cease. Vultures, jackals, and other scavengers, on the other hand, can range farther to seek their nourishment.

The organisms' life stages, energetic needs, and behavioral patterns fit within these great seasonal patterns, and the patterns created with the seasons by species' responses to them.

Exploration 1
COMPARING ABSOLUTE ENERGY EXPENDITURE

For the Integration in **Chapter 3**, each of you "became" an animal from either the Serengeti ecosystem of East Africa or the Northern Hardwoods ecosystem in the north temperate United States. In this Exploration, consider your total energy use as that animal.

Materials
- **Graph paper**
- **Colored pencils/markers**
- **Your Integration data** from **Chapter 3**
- **Your energy use data**

- **Data for millipedes and dung beetles** (There are many species of both these animals, which vary widely in size and weight.):

Millipede: weight, 2.5 g; intake, 5.2×10^3 kcal/kg/year; R = 11.5%, P = 3.8%, E = 85%

Dung beetle: weight, 0.03g; intake, 3.5×10^4 kcal/kg/year; R = 21%, P = 14%, E = 65%

Procedure

1. **Your organism in its habitat: The animal cards.**

   Your animal lives in one of the two habitats described in <u>Reading 1</u>. Read about "yourself" and your habitat, so you know where you live and how you make a living.

   NOTE: Not all data are available for all animals. <u>Reading 2</u> briefly considers data sources and credibility; please think about those points as you work with the data.

2. **Absolute or total energy use of your group's animals.**

   Each of you has an energy budget with the same terms but different numbers. Working in groups, decide how best to represent those data to allow for direct, easy comparisons among your animals. Use the data from your Integration work. Include the size of each animal in grams plus its absolute or total energy expenditure (i.e., the amount of energy in kilocalories that the animal takes in and the number of kilocalories that go toward respiration, production, and excretion.)

   The data table.

   Start by writing the values for each animal in a data table. How might that table look? Set it up in your notebook and fill in the data. Include data for the millipede if your group is from the Northern Hardwood Forest or for the dung beetle if your group is from the Serengeti.

3. **Patterns in group data.**

   Examine the data table. What patterns do you see about size and intake or any other data? Rearrange the data if that makes patterns clearer.

4. **Comparing the data: Class discussion.**

   List each group's data on the board in some way that helps show the patterns in the data. Do the trends your group noticed hold? Are they clearer, or have they become part of some other patterns?

READING 2
DATA SOURCES

As we discuss elsewhere in the curriculum, it is always important to examine the sources of your data rather than simply to accept all statements as "facts" carrying equal weight.

The data in the animal cards have been assembled from several different sources, and it is important for you to understand the differences among those sources. For instance, there are many different types of animals in the two ecosystems we feature here, and there are many different ecosystems beyond those two. Not all these animals (or ecosystems) have been studied directly. That is, most of them have not been the subject of intense investigation (or study). Therefore, some of the data that we include have not actually been collected for those animals. For example, there are many animals for which energy balance equation data have not been gathered.

In those cases, however, we can use data that come from a model. Data that have been collected from some animals <u>directly</u> are used to build a model. And this model allows us to make predictions about data for other animals that have not yet been studied. These predictions are a reasonable approximation of data for the unstudied animals. But data drawn from a model are not the same as carefully performed measurements on real organisms. Are we saying that data from a model are not useful? Not at all. In fact, data drawn from models can be very useful for giving us a sense of differences among different types of animals. However, because they are not direct measurements from the animal itself, we cannot be as certain about predicted data as we are about measured data.

VARIATION, ESPECIALLY IN POPULATION DENSITIES

There is also often a great deal of variation in data from actual measurements, because animals are different, places are different, and researchers are different. Think, for instance, of all the students in this class. Although they are all members of the same species, they differ a lot in height, weight, temperament, and so on. The same is true of other animals. For example, we present data from various studies on population densities of animals in natural habitats. Frankly, those data are hard to interpret, since there can be tremendous variation in the density of animals from one study site to another. Even a single local population can vary in size by more than a factor of 10 (i.e., more than an order of magnitude) over a period of years. In fact, populations of some animals appear to increase and decrease in numbers regularly. For example, lynx and hare populations appear to rise and fall in about a 10-year cycle. (See the lynx/hare Explorations in **Chapter 11**.) Thus, population density data should be treated as a rough guide, not as absolute truth.

OTHER DATA YOU HAVE COLLECTED

Remember your own energy use and intake data? Remember that those data were just a "slice in time"—one 24-hour period? And remember the issues you raised discussing averages during the seed-cracking work in **Module 1**? These are also among the issues you should keep in mind when assessing a data set and what it can really tell you.

Exploration 2

ALL ENERGY BUDGETS ARE NOT EQUAL: RELATIVE ENERGY USE

What do a millipede and a dung beetle have in common? A weasel and a mongoose? A deer and a topi? A rabbit and a cheetah? Compare their energy use data and see.

The energy use data you have just represented can help you answer those questions by showing patterns—similarities and differences among the animals—in their relative energy use. Represent these data graphically on posters to compare the patterns of relative energy expenditures among all the animals. What are the patterns? Are they correlated with anything else?

Materials

- **Colored paper** (several colors)
- **Graph paper**
- **Colored pencils or markers**
- **Scissors**
- **Glue or tape**
- **Energy use data** from Exploration 1
- **Animal cards**
- **Millipede and dung beetle data**

Procedure

1. **Calculating relative energy use: Percents.**
   Relative energy expenditure is the proportion of an animal's total energy spent on respiration, production, and excretion. Working with the same students, animals, and data as you did in Exploration 1, calculate the percent of energy intake in kilocalories per year your animal "spends" on each of the processes represented by the terms of the equation (**I**, **R**, **P**, and **E**). Be sure to include either the millipede or the dung beetle also.

   Rounding off and percents.
   Notice that some numbers include parts of a percent, such as 39.4. It is okay to round down if the number you are considering is less than 5; and to round up if it is 5 or larger. Why are we using percents?

2. **Representing the data.**
   Consider how best to represent those data to allow for direct, easy comparisons among your animals. What are important issues to consider in visual—or any—representation of data? How does your method of representation help with data interpretation? How does it help you present and explain your results to other people?

3. **Patterns in energy use.**
   What patterns do you find? Which of your group's animals are like or unlike which others? Discuss your findings with another group.

   Present your data to the rest of the class and post your representation. Be clear about why you chose that method and how it shows similarities and differences among your animals. Leave your data up so everyone can compare different animals.

Exploration 3
RELATIVE ENERGY USE: MORE PATTERNS

1. **Classwide patterns and their meanings.**
    Compare within and between different animal sets, types, and so on. For example, consider carnivores versus herbivores, small versus large, bird versus mammal, endotherm versus ectotherm.

    Make graphs, tables, or lists—whatever is easiest for you to use in your comparisons. Discuss with your groupmates reasons for the similarities and differences.

    What other comparisons interest you? What do you expect (predict) to find?

2. **Correlations and group discussions.**
    Using your animal cards, and remembering all that you have been discovering (about skulls, diet, etc.), discuss what might explain or match some of the patterns above. What do you think this match might mean? Note your thoughts for your Integration writing.

THE ANIMAL CARDS

Please note that animals from the Serengeti are presented first (sixteen animals); those living in the Northern Hardwood Forest follow.

THOMSON'S GAZELLE *(Gazella thomsoni)*

The Thomson's gazelle is a medium-size antelope that can sprint faster than any of its predators except the cheetah. These gazelles can reach speeds of up to 80 km per hour (50 mph), but they start to tire after running only 1 or 2 km. After a few kilometers of running, the gazelle's body temperature rises 5–6°C (remember, energy spent on respiration is transformed into heat), and the animal becomes exhausted. Hyenas and wild dogs have much better endurance than the gazelle (they pant while running to keep cool) and often catch up after the gazelle's initial sprint and bring down their prey.

Since they eat only green vegetation during the dry season, Thomson's gazelles typically move to areas of higher rainfall or near water in search of green plants. They also need to drink water, so when in dry areas, they travel up to 16 km every other day to get it.

Although these gazelles, with dark stripes along their flanks, are featured in nearly all nature films about the African savannahs, they are actually quite restricted in their distribution. They inhabit only the area around the Serengeti and two other regions in East Africa and only above 600 m in elevation. (How might this higher altitude affect their sunning and their heat production?)

Average adult weight: 20 kg

Size: 58–70 cm shoulder height

Common foods: grass (only when it is green); green herbs and leaves of bushes (when grass is dry and tough)

Food intake: 6.0×10^5 kcal/individual/year

Energy use: $I = R + P + E$; $I = 6.00 \times 10^5$, $R = 2.90 \times 10^5$, $P = 1.02 \times 10^4$, $E = 3.00 \times 10^5$

Offspring: typically 1 calf at a time. (However, because pregnancy lasts only about six months and females can mate two weeks after giving birth, two calves can be born in just over a year.)

Is eaten by: wild dogs, cheetahs, spotted hyenas, lions, leopards

Population density: approximately 25–30/km²

WILDEBEEST (BRINDLED GNU) (*Connochaetes taurinus*)

Wildebeest are large, powerful, and fast antelopes, with short curved horns and a beardlike tuft on their chins. An outstanding feature of wildebeest is their migratory behavior—virtually all of the 1.3 million wildebeest in the Serengeti migrate on a seasonal basis in search of green grass and water (they need to drink daily). Think of it: hundreds of millions of kilograms of wildebeest flesh moving en masse about the Serengeti. Over 1 million mouths—hungry mouths—all moving together. Over 4 million hooves bearing on the ground. What are the implications for grasses growing in the areas wildebeest migrate into? What are the implications for other herbivores? What are the implications for carnivores that prey on these animals? And for dung beetle populations?

The wildebeest, along with the other herbivores of the Serengeti, are the last great assemblage of large land mammals. In other comparable grassland areas (the North American grasslands, the South American pampas, and the Russian steppes), humans have taken over much of the habitat for cattle and feed production and/or have killed the native herbivores. Even the Serengeti is under severe pressure by humans for agricultural uses.

Average adult weight: 250 kg

Size: 115–138 cm shoulder height

Common foods: short grass

Food intake: 4.0×10^6 kcal/individual/year

Energy use: $I = R + P + E$; $I = 4.00 \times 10^6$, $R = 1.96 \times 10^6$, $P = 4.00 \times 10^4$, $E = 2.00 \times 10^6$

Offspring: typically 1 calf per year, with most calves being born during a 2- to 3-week period early in the rainy season

Is eaten by: lions, hyenas; wildebeest calves are eaten by wild dogs, cheetahs, and leopards

Population density: approximately 60/km²; however, typically found at much higher densities since they form very dense groups

TOPI *(Damaliscus lunatus)*

The social behavior of the topi is remarkably variable. In some areas, mature males hold fairly permanent territories extending over 100–400 hectares. Each such territorial male maintains a group of several female topis and their young; intruding males are driven away by the resident male. In other regions, males maintain only small, temporary territories during the breeding season; such territories are about 1–3 hectares in extent. In still other regions, males form large breeding groups of up to 100 individuals. Females visit these groups (which are known as leks) to mate. The leks are located at the same places year after year, even though the topi herd moves around the plains almost constantly. Topi females and their young can either form small herds within a single male's territory or be part of a larger aggregation milling about the plains. (What might be advantages or drawbacks of the different types of territories?)

Average adult weight: 115 kg

Size: 104–126 cm shoulder height

Common foods: grasses

Food intake: 2.3×10^6 kcal/individual/year

Energy use: $I = R + P + E$; $I = 2.30 \times 10^6$, $R = 1.13 \times 10^6$, $P = 2.30 \times 10^4$, $E = 1.15 \times 10^6$

Offspring: 1 per year

Is eaten by: young eaten by several different predators; adults sometimes preyed on by lions, although not where wildebeest or zebras (preferred prey species) are plentiful

Population density: 2/km²

HARTEBEEST *(Alcelaphus buselaphus)*

Formerly very numerous, hartebeest populations have declined due to loss of habitat, hunting by humans, and competition with domestic cattle. Hartebeest typically live in herds containing up to 300 females and young; occasionally multiple herds join together in loose groups of up to 10,000. Adult males typically are not members of herds and can be either territorial or nonterritorial, while younger males often form large bachelor herds. Once young males mature, they set off to challenge for ownership of a good territory. Such territories contain a variety of plant types, good access to

water, and several other features attractive to hartebeest. Competition for good territories is fierce, and males are usually able to defend and keep a good territory for only a few months. What might be advantages and disadvantages to belonging to each of the different social groups?

Average adult weight: 135 kg
Size: 107–140 cm shoulder height
Common foods: grasses
Food intake: 2.6×10^6 kcal/individual/year
Energy use: $I = R + P + E$; $I = 2.60 \times 10^6$, $R = 1.27 \times 10^6$, $P = 2.60 \times 10^4$, $E = 1.30 \times 10^6$
Offspring: 1 per year
Is eaten by: may be preyed on by lions, although not where wildebeest or zebras (preferred prey species) are plentiful
Population density: approximately 0.7/km²

IMPALA (*Aepyceros melampus*)

Impala herds typically contain 6 to 100 females and young. Multiple herds are loosely grouped into "clans." Clans are quite stable in their membership and quite faithful to their home ranges—they do not move very far.

Adult males typically are not members of herds; they can be either territorial or nonterritorial, with younger males often forming "bachelor herds" of 5–35 animals. Once these young males mature, they challenge mature males for ownership of territories. (What advantages or disadvantages might there be for a male to being territorial or nonterritorial?)

Average adult weight: 52 kg
Size: 40–90 cm shoulder height
Common foods: grasses when they are green; herbs and foliage at other times
Food intake: 1.0×10^6 kcal/individual/year
Energy use: $I = R + P + E$; $I = 1.00 \times 10^6$, $R = 4.90 \times 10^5$, $P = 1.00 \times 10^4$, $E = 5.00 \times 10^5$
Offspring: 1 per year
Is eaten by: leopards, wild dogs, cheetahs
Population density: 5/km²

PLAINS ZEBRA (Equus burchelli)

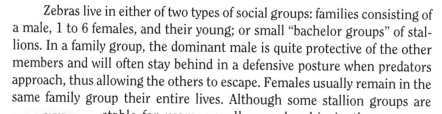

Zebras live in either of two types of social groups: families consisting of a male, 1 to 6 females, and their young; or small "bachelor groups" of stallions. In a family group, the dominant male is quite protective of the other members and will often stay behind in a defensive posture when predators approach, thus allowing the others to escape. Females usually remain in the same family group their entire lives. Although some stallion groups are stable for years, usually membership in those groups changes fairly frequently. (What advantages might there be for a female to stay in her family group throughout her lifetime? What disadvantages?)

Average adult weight: 235 kg
Size: 127–140 cm shoulder height
Common foods: grasses
Food intake: 3.8×10^6 kcal/individual/year
Energy use: $I = R + P + E$; $I = 3.80 \times 10^6$, $R = 1.86 \times 10^6$, $P = 3.80 \times 10^4$, $E = 1.90 \times 10^6$
Offspring: 1 every 1–3 years
Is eaten by: hyenas, wild dogs
Population density: $8/km^2$

ROCK HYRAX (Procavia johnstoni)

Although they are mammals, hyraxes are notable for their poor ability to regulate their body temperatures metabolically. They are quite gregarious and live in colonies of up to 26 animals. These two aspects of rock hyraxes explain a great deal of their behavior.

These plump, short-legged animals live on and in rocky outcrops that emerge from the plains. There, they live in groups deep among the rocks, using entrance holes too small for their predators to pass through. The temperature deep in their rock homes fluctuates far less than the outside temperature, which is a real advantage for them. They often sunbathe early on sunny mornings, presumably to raise their body temperature after the cool nights. Conversely, they avoid the midday sun, since they overheat under such conditions. These animals are able to feed unusually rapidly for herbivores. They take large mouthfuls of grass and eat their fill in less than an hour a day. Such rapid feeding enables them to choose the times of day when they feed, rather than having to feed for long hours during both hot and cold times. It also means they spend less time in the open, where they are more vulnerable to many predators.

Not only do rock hyraxes form colonies with members of their own species, they often share home territories, sleeping holes, and huddle in the sun with bush hyraxes. Such close association between two mammal species is also highly unusual for mammals. The only possibly similar examples may be some monkeys that live in multispecies groups. (What advantages and disadvantages can you think of for two species to share resources so closely?)

Average adult weight: 3 kg
Size: 40–60 cm length
Common foods: grasses
Food intake: 1.8×10^5 kcal/individual/year
Energy use: $I = R + P + E$; $I = 1.80 \times 10^5$, $R = 8.82 \times 10^4$, $P = 1.80 \times 10^3$, $E = 9.00 \times 10^4$
Offspring: 1–3 per litter and 1 litter per year
Is eaten by: snakes, eagles, owls, jackals, several different cats (including leopards and lions), foxes, weasels, and mongooses
Population density: 500–4,000/km²

BUSH HYRAX *(Heterohyrax brucei)*

Although they are mammals, hyraxes are notable for their poor ability to regulate their body temperatures metabolically. They are quite gregarious and live in colonies of 5 to 34 animals. These two aspects of bush hyraxes explain a great deal of their behavior.

Smaller than the closely related rock hyrax, bush hyraxes live on and in rocky outcrops that emerge from the plains. There, they live in groups deep among the rocks, using entrance holes too small for their predators to pass through. The temperature deep in their rock homes fluctuates far less than the outside temperature, which is a real advantage for them. They often sunbathe early on sunny mornings, presumably to raise their body temperature after the cool nights. Conversely, they avoid the midday sun, since they overheat under such conditions. Bush hyraxes feed mainly on the foliage of trees and bushes, especially acacia leaves, and are excellent climbers.

Not only do bush hyraxes form colonies with members of their own species, they often share home territories, sleeping holes, and huddle in the sun with rock hyraxes. Such close association between two mammal species is also highly unusual for mammals. The only possibly similar examples may be some monkeys that live in multispecies groups. (What advantages and disadvantages can you think of for two species to share resources so closely?)

Average adult weight: 1.8 kg
Size: 30–47 cm length
Common foods: leaves of trees and bushes
Food intake: 1.2×10^5 kcal/individual/year
Energy use: $I = R + P + E$; $I = 1.20 \times 10^5$, $R = 5.38 \times 10^4$, $P = 1.20 \times 10^3$, $E = 6.0 \times 10^4$
Offspring: 1–4 per litter and 1 litter per year
Is eaten by: snakes, eagles, owls, jackals, and several different cats (including leopards and lions)
Population density: 2,000–5,000/km²

ELEPHANT *(Loxodonta africana)*

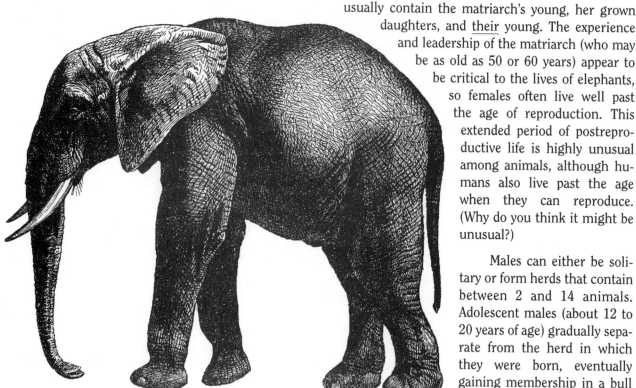

Elephants have remarkable social lives. Herds of females and their young typically contain 9–11 individuals (range 2–24). These herds are distinctly matriarchal—they are led by the oldest female of the group and usually contain the matriarch's young, her grown daughters, and their young. The experience and leadership of the matriarch (who may be as old as 50 or 60 years) appear to be critical to the lives of elephants, so females often live well past the age of reproduction. This extended period of postreproductive life is highly unusual among animals, although humans also live past the age when they can reproduce. (Why do you think it might be unusual?)

Males can either be solitary or form herds that contain between 2 and 14 animals. Adolescent males (about 12 to 20 years of age) gradually separate from the herd in which they were born, eventually gaining membership in a bull herd.

Because an elephant eats about 4–6% of its own body weight each day, a moderate-size herd can have a major impact on an area's vegetation. In Kenya's confined Tsavo National Park, the population density of elephants rose high enough during the 1960s and 1970s that a woodland was changed into a grassland by the elephants tearing up young trees and knocking over mature trees to get at leaves. These changes altered the food supply available for other herbivores, for example, other ungulates, insects, and monkeys, and elephant populations then dropped by a quarter to a third during a severe drought.

These extraordinary animals can alter their surroundings tremendously if they cannot migrate away from areas such as some national parks where their food supplies have been reduced. On the other hand, in many areas elephant populations have been in serious decline lately; the animals were heavily hunted over the past 15 or 20 years as the price of ivory increased astronomically (several orders of magnitude per kilogram). Only with the recent ban on the international sale of ivory has this hunting been somewhat checked. Humans must learn how to deal with elephant populations somehow; to ignore the elephant is a choice that has major implications for entire ecosystems, as well as for the elephants themselves.

Average adult weight: 3,500 kg (males much larger than females)

Size: 2.5–3 m shoulder height

Common foods: grasses, herbs, and leaves of bushes and trees

Food intake: 2.0×10^7 kcal/individual/year

Energy use: $I = R + P + E$; $I = 2.00 \times 10^7$, $R = 9.80 \times 10^6$, $P = 2.00 \times 10^5$, $E = 1.00 \times 10^7$

Offspring: 1 every 4–9 years

Is eaten by: young elephants may be eaten by lions and hyenas; habitat loss and human killing account for most deaths

Population density: approximately 6/100 km² but varies greatly among regions

LION *(Panthera leo)*

Lions are the largest of the African carnivores. They are considered to be the only social cats—they typically live in close-knit groups of about 15 lions (the groups range in size from 4 to 37 animals). Living in groups enables lions to hunt in groups, and the success rate of group hunts is roughly 60% higher than that of solitary hunts. (About half of the hunts performed by lions involve two or more lions working in concert.) Of course, there is a trade-off here—group hunting means that more food can be brought in, but group living also means that there are more mouths to be fed. On average, however, group hunting is overall more efficient. (What other advantages and disadvantages might there be to living in a group?)

Although lions are able to reach maximum speeds of 48–59 km per hour, they rarely can sustain this speed for more than 100 m. Thus, lions must carefully stalk their prey and usually do not charge unless they are within 30 m of the animal they are hunting. (How might group hunting fit in with this need to stalk prey?)

Lions were once the most widespread wild land mammal. Ten thousand years ago, lions were found in most of Africa, Europe, Asia, North America, and northern South America. Their decline appears to have been due primarily to habitat destruction. Also important are competition from humans hunting the same prey species and humans hunting lions in defense of livestock or for sport. Because they reproduce readily and are relatively flexible about where they can live, African lions are not endangered in some parts of Africa. (The Indian lion is near extinction.)

Average adult weight: 170 kg

Size: 110–120 cm shoulder height

Common foods: wildebeest, zebras, Thomson's gazelles; they also scavenge a great deal

Food intake: 3.3×10^6 kcal/individual/year
Energy use: $I = R + P + E$; $I = 3.30 \times 10^6$, $R = 2.57 \times 10^6$, $P = 6.60 \times 10^4$, $E = 6.60 \times 10^5$
Offspring: usually 3–4 cubs per litter and 1 litter every 18–26 months
Is eaten by: cubs that have been left alone temporarily may be eaten by lions from other prides and by spotted hyenas; old and diseased lions may suffer the same fate. The primary killers of lions, however, are humans.
Population density: about 12/100 km²

SPOTTED HYENA *(Crocuta crocuta)*

Spotted hyenas are typically the most abundant large carnivores in the undisturbed savannas of East Africa. Moreover, they are probably the most efficient carnivores when it comes to eating vertebrate prey: they eat everything, including bones, horns, hair, and skin. The only parts of their prey that they typically do not eat are the contents of the rumen (the first "stomach" of ruminants such as antelopes) and the heavy horn bases of large animals such as wildebeest. They also scavenge, eating dead prey of other carnivores or animals that have died of wounds, age, or illness. They will even take over a kill made by lions or other carnivores, chasing away the animals that actually made the kill.

Like most members of the dog family, hyenas live in family groups, packs of related animals. They also hunt in groups, which further increases their efficiency at getting food. (What do you think might make the spotted hyena less vulnerable to extinction than, say, the wild dog?)

Average adult weight: 58 kg
Size: 79–90 cm shoulder height
Common foods: wildebeest, Thomson's gazelles, zebras
Food intake: 1.4×10^6 kcal/individual/year
Energy use: $I = R + P + E$; $I = 1.40 \times 10^6$, $R = 1.09 \times 10^6$, $P = 2.80 \times 10^4$, $E = 2.80 \times 10^5$
Offspring: 2 per litter (range 1–4) and 1 litter every 12–18 months
Is eaten by: essentially no one
Population density: about 12/100 km²

WILD DOG *(Lycaon pictus)*

Wild dogs are social animals. They live in packs that typically contain 10 individuals (6 adults and 4 young), although they can form packs of over 40 animals. Because they have specialized to feed on prey animals that are too large for a single dog to hunt efficiently, they must hunt in packs. By hunting in groups, wild dogs are remarkably effective: up to two kills per day, with success rates of up to 70–85% in their chases—a remarkable record.

Although wild dogs are slower than gazelles, they have much greater endurance than their prey animals. If the dogs can keep their prey in sight, working as a pack they can often run an animal to ground in a couple of kilometers. Although not sprinters, wild dogs can maintain a pace of 56 km per hour (35 mph) for a few kilometers without overheating (they pant while running to stay cooler). In addition, the hunting ranges of these animals can be very large; a single pack in the Serengeti may have a range of 1,500–2,000 km².

Despite this hunting efficiency, however, wild dogs are in severe decline and may be suffering from some disease, perhaps a domestic dog disease. Mostly, the survival rate of pups in the Serengeti is very low, due to predation by lions and hyenas. Unfortunately, these creatures are in grave danger of extinction. (Why do you think the hyena might not be similarly endangered?)

Average adult weight: 23 kg
Size: 60–75 cm shoulder height
Common foods: Thomson's gazelles, impalas, hares, wildebeest calves, zebras
Food intake: 7.5×10^5 kcal/individual/year
Energy use: $I = R + P + E$; $I = 1.50 \times 10^5$, $R = 5.85 \times 10^5$, $P = 1.50 \times 10^4$, $E = 1.50 \times 10^5$
Offspring: about 10 pups per litter and 1 litter every 12–14 months
Is eaten by: young eaten by hyenas and lions
Population density: 1 adult/200 km²

LEOPARD *(Panthera pardus)*

These large, solitary cats are widespread, ranging from Africa to Korea and Java. Although they are capable of running at speeds of up to 60 km per hour, their hunting method is to stalk prey to a very short distance, less than 5 m if possible. From that point, they pounce. If they miss, they rarely chase their prey. If they do chase, they do not run more than 50 m.

A single leopard on the ground is no match for the social carnivores (lions, hyenas, and wild dogs), which readily take over a leopard's kill. To prevent losing their prey, leopards often carry their kills up into trees, where they can eat unmolested.

Leopards are listed as threatened or endangered throughout all of their range. (What do you think might make leopards more vulnerable to extinction than, say, lions?)

Average adult weight: 45 kg
Size: 55–70 cm shoulder height
Common foods: impalas, Thomson's gazelles, young wildebeest and zebras, hares, birds, even beetles; they also scavenge

169

Food intake: 1.2×10^6 kcal/individual/year

Energy use: $I = R + P + E$; $I = 1.20 \times 10^6$, $R = 9.36 \times 10^5$, $P = 2.40 \times 10^4$, $E = 2.40 \times 10^5$

Offspring: 1–3 cubs per litter and 1 litter about every 2 years

Is eaten by: Leopards have been heavily hunted by humans throughout much of their range for their pelts. Cubs are easy prey for other carnivores, and habitat destruction contributes to their decline.

Population density: about 4/100 km²

CHEETAH (*Acinonyx jubatus*)

Known as the fastest land animal alive, the cheetah can reach speeds of up to 90–112 km per hour (60–70 mph). However, the cheetah pays a price for this sprinting speed—it cannot run very far at high speed without overheating (remember that energy spent on metabolism ends up as heat). Cheetahs try to get to within 50 m of their prey before they begin their sprint. After a mere 300-m run, a cheetah's breathing rate may get as high as 150 breaths per minute, its body temperature goes way up, and it needs half an hour to cool down before its next chase. Although cheetahs are faster than Thomson's gazelles (their preferred prey on the Serengeti), gazelles make sharp turns that cheetahs often cannot match; after a few turns the cheetah may be so tired that it must give up. All in all, though, cheetahs are quite successful hunters, observed in one study as catching their prey in over 40% of hunts.

Being built for speed has one additional cost: their light build does not equip cheetahs to defend their kills against other large predators. Cheetahs lose at least 10% of the prey they catch to lions, hyenas, and other carnivores. They often also lose their cubs to the same predators and may well soon be extinct, at least in the Serengeti. (What might happen to the balance among mammals in the Serengeti if cheetahs become extinct?)

Average adult weight: 50 kg

Size: 70–90 cm shoulder height

Common foods: Thomson's gazelles, hares, young wildebeest, impalas

Food intake: 2.4×10^6 kcal/individual/year

Energy use: $I = R + P + E$; $I = 2.40 \times 10^6$, $R = 1.80 \times 10^6$, $P = 1.20 \times 10^5$, $E = 4.80 \times 10^5$

Offspring: 3–4 young per litter (range 1–8) and about 1 litter every 2 years

Is eaten by: cubs eaten by many large predators, including other cats and large eagles

Population density: 1–2/100 km²

BANDED MONGOOSE *(Mungos mungo)*

Banded mongooses are highly social animals, typically living in packs of about 15 individuals (although packs may be twice that size). Breeding within a pack is synchronized, so that multiple females bear young within a few days of each other. The young suckle from any of the lactating (milk-producing) females in the pack, not just their own mothers. Both male and female adults in the pack "babysit" for the young while their mothers are out hunting; they also play with the young. In the process of such play, the young learn to socialize within the group and how to forage.

A mongoose that discovers an especially good food item, such as an ant nest, resists sharing the food with other members of the pack, squealing and growling at them. However, a mongoose that makes such a find generally cannot keep from making excited twittering and churring sounds, which immediately draw its fellow pack members to the food. As is usually the case, social life has both costs and benefits. (Consider also the lion or any of the dog family members: what are the costs and the benefits of their being social?)

A striking aspect of banded mongoose social behavior is their mobbing attacks. Fairly large predators, including large dogs, jackals, eagles, and vultures, can be repelled by one of these attacks. The mongooses cluster in a writhing, growling, spitting, snapping mass (with the young in the center) and advance toward their foes. Moreover, an individual mongoose will risk its own safety to free a fellow pack member from a predator. One male was seen climbing a tree to threaten an eagle that was about to eat a mongoose; the eagle dropped the captured mongoose, which survived.

Average adult weight: 1.5 kg
Size: head and body length, 30–40 cm; tail, 15–29 cm
Common foods: invertebrates, including beetles, millipedes, earwigs, ants, crickets, termites, plus some birds, eggs, and small vertebrates
Food intake: 1.0×10^5 kcal/individual/year
Energy use: $I = R + P + E$; $I = 1.00 \times 10^5$, $R = 7.80 \times 10^4$, $P = 2.00 \times 10^3$, $E = 2.00 \times 10^4$
Offspring: 2–3 per litter (up to 6) and about 1–3 litters per year
Is eaten by: few species, although a number of medium-size mammalian carnivores and birds of prey sometimes try to hunt the mongoose
Population density: up to 18/km²

SLENDER MONGOOSE *(Herpestes sanguineus)*

Unlike the banded mongoose, the slender mongoose is solitary in its behavior. Both sexes maintain territories; female territories seem not to overlap with one another, while male territories do. In addition, a male's territory is larger and typically includes the territories of two females. Being solitary, the slender mongoose does not have the option of threatening predators in a group, as the banded mongoose does. Instead, it becomes motionless or hides at the sight of predators such as eagles. Interestingly, these creatures show little fear of snakes and are willing to attack even poisonous snakes that threaten them. (Have you ever seen how fast a snake can

strike—that it is almost too fast to see? What sorts of movements would a mongoose or any animal need to be successful in a "boxing match" with a snake?)

Average adult weight: 0.5 kg

Size: head and body length, 28–32 cm; tail, 28 cm

Common foods: rodents, lizards, snakes, birds, hyraxes, squirrels

Food intake: 5.4×10^4 kcal/individual/year

Energy use: I = R + P + E; I = 5.40×10^4, R = 4.21×10^4, P = 1.08×10^3, E = 1.08×10^4

Offspring: 2–4 per litter and about 2 litters per year

Is eaten by: eagles, snakes

Population density: no data available

BEAVER *(Castor canadensis)*

Beavers are large rodents that are well known for their remarkable feats of engineering. Beavers can drastically alter their physical environment, creating new types of habitat in the process. When beavers build a dam across a small stream, they create a pond that can be many hectares in area (a hectare is slightly larger than two football fields). The pond floods and kills vegetation (often trees) that previously existed at the site, thus affecting both plant and animal life in the area.

Over time, the beaver pond fills with silt deposited by the stream and is then abandoned by the beavers (much the same process happens in reservoirs behind human-built dams). The filled pond becomes a meadow, creating an area of vegetation that is good browse for many species. As time goes by, bushes and then different tree species fill in the meadow, until after decades or centuries the meadow has become a forest. (Where do you think beavers go when their pond gets too big and they have used the available food trees? What risks might they run?)

Average adult weight: 18 kg

Size: head and body length, 62–76 cm; tail, 23–25 cm

Common foods: During summer: seeds, stems, roots of sedges and water grasses, and other aquatic plants. During winter: inner bark of tree branches stored during the summer; preferred species include aspen, poplar, birch, maple, willow, and alder.

Food intake: 6.2×10^5 kcal/individual/year

Energy use: I = R + P + E; I = 6.20×10^5, R = 3.04×10^5, P = 6.20×10^3, E = 3.10×10^5

Offspring: usually 2–4 per litter and 1 litter per year

Is eaten by: wolves; also hunted heavily by humans for their pelts

Population density: approximately 4/km² (increasing in the northeastern United States, where reforestation creates good beaver habitats but there are no wolves to help control the numbers of beavers)

EASTERN COTTONTAIL *(Sylvilagus floridanus)*

The diet of the cottontail, a small North American rabbit, contains a wider variety of plant food than that of any other mammal in North America. They do not hibernate during winter but get through the cold months eating twigs and bark from woody plants.

Widely hunted by humans for sport, food, or to prevent damage to crops, the cottontail has been transplanted to a number of areas outside its natural range to improve hunting. Among the consequences of this human activity is the decline of populations of the New England cottontail (a related species), which is suffering a double disaster: loss of its habitat and out-competition by the Eastern cottontail. (What does it actually mean if one species "out-competes" another? Is that also what is happening between the African wild dog and some of its carnivore competitors, like lions and hyenas? How might humans help keep that from happening?)

Average adult weight: 1.5 kg
Size: head and body length, 35–43 cm
Common foods: large variety of herbaceous vegetation in summer, bark and twigs in winter
Food intake: 1×10^5 kcal/individual/year
Energy use: $I = R + P + E$; $I = 1.00 \times 10^5$, $R = 4.90 \times 10^4$, $P = 1.00 \times 10^3$, $E = 5.00 \times 10^4$
Offspring: 3–6 per litter (range 1–12) and 3–7 litters per year
Is eaten by: wolves, foxes, weasels, owls; killed by humans
Population density: approximately 1,000/km² in two studies

SHORTTAIL WEASEL (ERMINE) *(Mustela erminea)*

This small, lithe animal undergoes two complete color changes every year. In winter, its fur is completely white, except for the tip of the tail, which is black. During that time, the shorttail weasel is typically called an "ermine" and is often trapped by humans for its fur. In summer, its back and sides become a chocolate brown (the underside remains white, and the tip of the tail stays black); in this color phase, it is often called a "stoat" and its fur has little or no economic value. (What advantage might such color changes offer? Think about where weasels live and the seasons there. Why might the summer coat have no value to human fur dealers?)

Females become sexually mature at the age of 2 or 3 months and sometimes mate during their first summer. As with many other weasels, the shorttailed weasel exhibits a remarkable phenomenon: the delayed implantation of fertilized eggs into the uterus wall. Fertilized eggs may go for as long as 9 months before implantation in the uterus and development of the embryos. Once development begins in the early spring, it is only about a month before the tiny young are born, weighing only 1.5–3 g at birth, or less than an 8½ × 11 inch piece of paper. (Why might it be advantageous to bear young only during the springtime rather than later in the summer?)

Average adult weight: approximately 0.2 kg
Size: head and body length, 13–25 cm; tail, 0.5–1.2 cm

Common foods: mice and other small rodents, birds, eggs, insects, frogs, and occasional larger animals such as hares

Food intake: 2.6×10^4 kcal/individual/year

Energy use: $I = R + P + E$; $I = 2.60 \times 10^4$, $R = 2.03 \times 10^4$, $P = 5.20 \times 10^2$, $E = 5.20 \times 10^3$

Offspring: approximately 6 per litter (range 3–18) and 1 litter per year

Is eaten by: owls

Population density: up to 10/km² where prey animals are abundant

RED SQUIRREL *(Tamiasciurus hudsonicus)*

Like the common gray tree squirrel, the red squirrel does not hibernate. (This is in contrast with many ground squirrels, which do hibernate.) Thus, red squirrels must either find food during winter (often a difficult task) or put aside stores of food to be eaten during the cold months. Red squirrels cache large amounts of food, especially entire conifer cones and mushrooms, for winter use. (A related species of red squirrel, *T. douglasii*, carries unopened cones to streams or damp spots under rotting logs, where it stores them. The wet conditions keep the cones from opening until the squirrel retrieves them later in the winter.)

The red squirrel's habit of burying seeds in the ground appears to have helped reforestation in areas that have been heavily deforested by humans. Although the squirrels are able to retrieve many of the seeds that they bury, some seeds germinate before the squirrels get to them. Thus, the squirrels can have a marked effect on their entire ecosystem.

Red squirrels live in forests rather than in the more urban areas favored by the gray squirrel, which was brought to this country by European settlers. (Could red squirrels live in more urban areas if larger gray squirrels were not there? How might you find out?)

Average adult weight: 0.25 kg

Size: head and body length, 17–20 cm; tail, 10–15 cm

Common foods: primarily pine and spruce seeds; nuts, buds, fruits, bark, mushrooms, sap, bird eggs and young; also mice and young rabbits

Food intake: 3.0×10^4 kcal/individual/year

Energy use: $I = R + P + E$; $I = 3.00 \times 10^4$, $R = 1.47 \times 10^4$, $P = 3.00 \times 10^2$, $E = 1.50 \times 10^4$

Offspring: typically 4–6 per litter (range 1–8) and 2 litters per year (spring and summer)

Is eaten by: hawks, owls, foxes

Population density: up to 700/km² in good habitat

EASTERN CHIPMUNK *(Tamias striatus)*

Chipmunks do not hibernate but survive the winter by eating food they have stored in underground burrows. Another help in getting through the winter is the ability of chipmunks to become torpid for 1 to 8 days. During such periods of torpor, their metabolism slows down considerably and their body temperature drops, so they consume far fewer calories.

As you may know, chipmunks have special enclosed cheek pouches that open into their mouths. A chipmunk can transport surprisingly large quantities of food in these pouches—one biologist counted 31 kernels of corn in a chipmunk's cheek pouches. When full, each pouch can be nearly the size of the chipmunk's head.

Average adult weight: approximately 0.1 kg
Size: head and body length, 12.7–15 cm; tail 7–10 cm
Common foods: acorns, nuts, seeds, mushrooms, fruits, berries, and occasional insects, bird eggs, and small vertebrates
Food intake: 1.7×10^4 kcal/individual/year
Energy use: $I = R + P + E$; $I = 1.70 \times 10^4$, $R = 8.33 \times 10^3$, $P = 1.70 \times 10^2$, $E = 8.50 \times 10^3$
Offspring: 4–5 per litter (range 1–9) and 1–2 litters per year
Is eaten by: snakes, birds of prey, coyotes, foxes
Population density: approximately 500–1,000/km²

RED-BACKED SALAMANDER *(Plethodon cinereus)*

Which single vertebrate species contains the most biomass at the Hubbard Brook Forest in New Hampshire? Red-backed salamanders. Not only that, but red-backed salamanders make up more biomass there than all birds during their peak breeding season. Researchers have calculated that there are about 2,600 red-backed salamanders per hectare. Since a hectare is a bit larger than two football fields, that works out to over 1,000 salamanders in an area the size of a football field—a lot of salamanders!

The number of salamanders found in different areas of Northern Hardwood Forest probably varies, but these creatures are clearly important in the forests. (Remember Dr. Wyman's salamander-density data and hypothesis from the Reading on approximations in **Unit 1, Chapter 1**.) Salamanders appear to play a key role in nutrient cycling by eating many of the small invertebrates that mechanically break down leaf litter. By eating vast numbers of tiny detritivores, salamanders might markedly decrease the rate of nutrient cycling in these forests. In turn, salamanders form a high-protein food source for garter snakes, small mammals, and some birds. Thus, as both predators and as prey, these small, hard-to-see creatures play a major role in the energy picture of the Northern Hardwood Forest.

The single vertebrate species that contains the most biomass in the other habitat, the Serengeti, is probably the wildebeest or the two hyrax species. Compare the numbers to determine which habitat seems to have more biomass per square kilometer (km²) of its top species. For salamanders, 0.7 g each × 260,000 animals per km² = 182 kg of salamander. What about the biomass per square kilometer of the wildebeest or the two hyrax species combined? Use 60 wildebeest/km², 2,800 rock hyrax/km², and 3,500 bush hyrax/km². Which habitat has more biomass in its top biomass species?

Average weight: 0.7 g
Size: 5.9–10 cm length

Common foods: large variety of invertebrates, especially mites and insects; also earthworms, snails, slugs, spiders, sow bugs, and millipedes

Food intake: approximately 4.0×10^0 kcal/individual/year

Energy use: $I = R + P + E$; $I = 4.00 \times 10^0$, $R = 1.70 \times 10^0$, $P = 1.60 \times 10^1$, $E = 7.0 \times 10^{-1}$

Offspring: 7–10 eggs deposited during summer

Is eaten by: garter snakes, shrews, ground-feeding birds

Population density: 260,000/km^2 at the Hubbard Brook Forest in New Hampshire

GRAY WOLF (TIMBER WOLF) *(Canis lupus)*

Timber wolves are very social animals, typically living in packs of 5–8 (packs may contain as many as 36 wolves). It appears that success in hunting their large prey, such as deer and moose, depends on their ability to work as a group. In fact, pack size increases where the most common prey species is very large and where more wolves are needed to take part in the hunt. For example, on Isle Royale in Michigan, where moose are their main food, packs contain 15–20 wolves. Packs consist of a mated pair and their offspring of several different years. Large packs may split and eventually create separate territories. Alternatively, individual wolves may leave the pack and join another single wolf to begin forming a new pack.

Before being hunted heavily, the timber wolf had one of the largest ranges of any living land mammal; it was found throughout most of the Northern Hemisphere, including much of North America, Europe, and Asia, and even occurred in North Africa (although it did not live in dry deserts or tropical forests). Now, however, the wolf's range is much more restricted, and populations are greatly reduced. In the United States, for example, where wolves previously lived throughout most of the country, they are now found only in Alaska and small portions of Minnesota and Wisconsin, on Isle Royale in Lake Superior, and in a few remote areas in the Rocky Mountains. An experiment currently underway is reintroducing them to their native habitat in Yellowstone National Park.

Average adult weight: 45 kg

Size: 66–71 cm shoulder height

Common foods: deer, caribou, moose, and elk

Food intake: 2.0×10^6 kcal/individual/year

Energy use: $I = R + P + E$; $I = 2.00 \times 10^6$, $R = 1.56 \times 10^6$, $P = 4.00 \times 10^4$, $E = 4.00 \times 10^5$

Offspring: 5–7 per dominant pair in a pack

Is eaten by: heavily hunted by humans

Population density: 0.2–4/100 km^2

GRAY FOX *(Urocyon cinereoargenteus)*

Gray foxes live in family groups of two parents and their offspring. Young foxes stay with their parents for several months, then forage on their own within their parents' home range for a few more months after that. Finally, they go off to find mates and establish their own territories. Females typically breed during their first year.

The gray fox is a remarkably good tree climber and is sometimes called the "tree fox." Their homes (dens) may be in piles of brush or rocks, burrows in the ground, or a hollow tree. One such tree den was found 9 m above ground level. When pursued by human hunters, gray foxes sometimes climb trees to escape.

(This species is in competition with the red fox, which was introduced a few hundred years ago by European settlers. What effects might this competition have had on the gray fox?)

Average adult weight: 5 kg
Size: head and body length, 53–74 cm; tail, 28–41 cm
Common foods: small vertebrates, insects, fruits, grains, and other plant materials (these foxes eat more plant matter than do other foxes)
Food intake: 2.0×10^5 kcal/individual/year
Energy use: $I = R + P + E$; $I = 2.00 \times 10^5$, $R = 1.56 \times 10^5$, $P = 4.00 \times 10^3$, $E = 4.00 \times 10^4$
Offspring: approximately 4 per litter (range 1–10) and 1 litter per year
Is eaten by: young occasionally eaten by birds of prey; adults and young killed by humans
Population density: 0.4–10/km²

SHORTTAIL SHREW *(Blarina brevicauda)*

If shorttail shrews were to have a motto, it would probably be "Live fast, die young." Few individuals survive past the age of a year, but they reproduce at an early age: females can mate 6 weeks after birth and males 12 weeks after birth. These animals are active throughout the year, spending much of their time scurrying along runways in leaf litter, snow, or underground. They can consume huge quantities of insect larvae underground. Since many of these larvae develop into plant-eating insects, shrews can help protect gardens and crops. They are, however, often killed by the pesticides people apply to the ground to kill the very larvae the shrews eat. (If you were a farmer, how might you figure out if you would be better off with more shrews and no larva-killing pesticide? What data might you need, and for how long?)

These tiny, quick animals (they weigh less than five nickels) are fierce predators. When they bite their prey, they inject a paralyzing nerve poison from special glands in their jaws. Shrew bites are reportedly painful for humans for several days.

Average adult weight: 23 g
Size: head and body length, 7–10 cm; tail, 1.9–3 cm
Common foods: insects, worms, snails, other invertebrates, salamanders, mice, and plant material
Food intake: 4.86×10^3 kcal/individual/year
Energy use: $I = R + P + E$; $I = 4.86 \times 10^3$, $R = 3.79 \times 10^3$, $P = 9.72 \times 10^1$, $E = 9.72 \times 10^2$
Offspring: about 5–7 per litter (range 3–10) and up to 3 litters per year
Is eaten by: extremely distasteful, so hardly ever eaten by anything; however, often killed by humans
Population density: 300–3,000/km²

DEER MOUSE (*Peromyscus maniculatus*)

Deer mice, which may be the most abundant mammal in their habitats, remain active throughout the year. They typically set aside a store of food for the winter, up to 3 liters in volume. Males often stay with the females and help raise the young. In fact, these mice are generally quite tolerant of others of the same species, and they may huddle in groups in winter. Such sociality is not always the case among rodents; some are quite aggressive toward individuals of their own species. (What might be advantages and disadvantages of such sociality within a species?)

Average adult weight: 27 g
Size: head and body length, 7–10 cm; tail, 5–12 cm
Common foods: seeds, nuts, acorns, insects
Food intake: 5.49×10^3 kcal/individual/year
Energy use: $I = R + P + E$; $I = 5.49 \times 10^3$, $R = 2.67 \times 10^3$, $P = 5.49 \times 10^1$, $E = 2.74 \times 10^3$
Offspring: 3–4 per litter (range 1–9) and 3–4 litters per year (in the laboratory, up to 14 litters per year)
Is eaten by: owls, weasels, foxes, domestic cats
Population density: 100–2,500/km²

WHITETAIL DEER (*Odocoileus virginianus*)

These large herbivores are well known for their hides, their meat, and their movie role, and as garden pests. The history of these widespread animals is quite interesting, and illustrates several of the different effects that humans can have on ecosystems.

Before Europeans settled in North America, whitetail deer populations were probably in the range of 23–40 million individuals. Native Americans hunted deer and actually managed many of the eastern forests by frequent controlled burning to improve habitat for deer and other game animals (deer like to eat many of the plants that colonize areas after fires). With the arrival of Europeans, several conditions changed. First, commercial markets developed for both venison (deer meat) and deer hides. These markets meant that hunters (now using firearms) were not simply supplying their families with food but might be fulfilling the needs of dozens or hundreds of people. In addition, with the spread of agriculture, the deer began to lose their preferred habitats—forest edges and regenerating forests. On the other hand, settlers were also eliminating wolves from much of the deer's range, thus freeing them from their primary animal predators. Overall, though, deer populations took a real beating. By 1900, deer were totally absent from most of their range; there were probably only 300,000 or 500,000 individuals left alive.

Around the turn of the century, regulations were enacted protecting deer, and states began management programs to increase deer populations (largely for hunting). In addition, with the abandonment of many agricultural areas in the east and the subsequent regeneration of forest in these areas, tremendous amounts of prime deer habitat were created. Finally, with wolves exterminated throughout most of the United States, the stage was set for deer populations to rise rapidly. The whitetail deer population is currently estimated to be 14 million, a far cry from where they were in 1900. In just a few centuries, humans nearly wiped this creature out by overhunting and habitat destruction and then enabled its remarkable comeback through creation of habitat and overhunting of its predators.

Average adult weight: 70 kg

Size: 91–107 cm shoulder height

Common foods: many types of leaves, including yew, hemlock, white cedar, and yellow birch, plus fungi, acorns, grass and herbs when available

Food intake: 1.5×10^6 kcal/individual/year

Energy use: $I = R + P + E$; $I = 1.50 \times 10^6$, $R = 7.31 \times 10^5$, $P = 1.95 \times 10^4$, $E = 7.50 \times 10^5$

Offspring: typically 1 fawn at a time (range 1–4) once a year

Is eaten by: wolves; fawns may be eaten by coyotes; adults hunted by humans

Population density: up to 25–50/km^2

GARTER SNAKE (*Thamnophis sirtalis*)

Like most reptiles, garter snakes do not maintain a high body temperature by metabolic means. They do increase body temperature by changing their behavior, such as by moving into the sunlight to warm up. In winter, when temperatures are so low that these snakes cannot move about, they hibernate, typically underground and often in groups. The snakes migrate to special hibernation sites in about October and return to their home ranges in March or April. Members of each hibernating population tend to be genetically related to one another, a loose family group. They do not, how-

ever, seem to show the same sort of social behavior as, say, a lion, elephant, or hyrax family group. (What advantages and disadvantages might there be for garter snakes to hibernate in such groups?)

Average adult weight: approximately 200–300 g

Size: 46–66 cm length

Common foods: earthworms (80% of food items eaten) plus many other types of small vertebrates and invertebrates

Food intake: 1.5×10^2 kcal/individual/year

Energy use: $I = R + P + E$; $R = 1.08 \times 10^2$, $P = 1.2 \times 10^1$, $E = 3.0 \times 10^1$

Offspring: typically 14–40 per litter (range 3–85) and 1 litter per year. Garter snakes bear live young.

Is eaten by: owls, weasels, blue jays, to name a few

Population density: data unavailable

GREAT HORNED OWL *(Bubo virginianus)*

Great horned owls are impressive predators, capturing a wide variety of prey, some of which outweigh the owls by a large margin. These birds appear to dislike other predatory birds nesting nearby; one owl was observed killing a red-tailed hawk that nested too close to its nest. In the far north, population densities of these owls are heavily influenced by the wide fluctuations in the populations of hares, which are key components of their diet.

Average adult weight: approximately 1.3 kg

Size: 46–63 cm

Common foods: wide variety of small and medium invertebrates, including skunks, minks, weasels, rabbits and hares, birds, mice, amphibians, reptiles, and scorpions

Food intake: 7.0×10^4 kcal/individual/year

Energy use: $I = R + P + E$; $I = 7.00 \times 10^4$, $R = 5.39 \times 10^4$, $P = 2.10 \times 10^3$, $E = 1.40 \times 10^4$

Offspring: 2–3 per year

Is eaten by: hunted only by humans

Population density: one well-studied pair had a 15.5-km² territory

BLUE JAY *(Cyanocitta cristata)*

These familiar birds have remarkably broad diets. They are among the most intelligent of birds and have excellent memories—they store large numbers of seeds and are able to find many of them. They also show good memory in laboratory situations. Feed them something red and bad-tasting once, and they avoid all red foods for a long time.

One of their springtime feeding methods makes use of their ability to mimic the scream of the red-shouldered hawk. When small birds hear this sound, they often flee for dense underbrush, thinking the predatory hawk is nearby. The jays then raid the birds' abandoned nests, sucking out the contents of eggs or eating the young.

Jays also mob other predatory birds, including hawks, crows, and owls. Several adults together repeatedly circle and attack a predator in the air, finally driving it away from the area. (Why do you think jays might carry out such so-called "mobbing" behavior?)

Average adult weight: approximately 77 g

Size: 28–31 cm

Common foods: feeds from ground to treetops on fruit, seeds, acorns, nuts, insects, spiders, snails, tree frogs, small fish, eggs, and young birds

Food intake: 1.5×10^4 kcal/individual/year

Energy use: $I = R + P + E$; $I = 1.50 \times 10^4$, $R = 1.10 \times 10^4$, $P = 3.00 \times 10^2$, $E = 3.75 \times 10^3$

Offspring: 4–6 per year

Is eaten by: owls

Population density: data not available

BLACK-CAPPED CHICKADEE *(Parus atricapillus)*

These lively little year-round residents of the Northern Hardwood Forest have a difficult time trying to eat enough to keep warm in winter. They have such relatively large surface areas that they lose heat very rapidly. On normally cold winter days, chickadees must spend most of the daylight hours looking for food to get them through the night. And, according to one study, at –40°C (which is the same as –40°F) chickadees must spend <u>20</u> times as much time feeding as they would during normal springtime weather.

Average adult weight: 10 g

Size: 12–14 cm

Common foods: insects, seeds, and fruit

Food intake: 3.5×10^3 kcal/individual/year

Energy use: $I = R + P + E$; $I = 3.50 \times 10^3$, $R = 2.56 \times 10^3$, $P = 7.00 \times 10^1$, $E = 8.75 \times 10^2$

Offspring: 6–8 per year

Is eaten by: owls

Population density: data not available

INTEGRATION

By now you are getting a picture of how an animal "functions," that is, pieces of its lifestyle and how they fit together. Describe the pieces you can identify and consider how they fit together.

Use what you have discovered so far about how animals in general "work" and about your animal in particular. Include some library work and perhaps build on the research you did on "your" skull and animal at the end of **Chapter 1**. Write no more than a page.

MOOSE ARE NOT MICE— SIZE MATTERS

CHAPTER FIVE

CONTENTS

OVERVIEW

"Sideways data"—that is, let's take the data from Exploration 2 in **Chapter 4** and turn our findings "sideways." We found that animals with similar diets have similar energy use patterns (even as we saw in **Chapter 1** that they have similar teeth). Did size matter? Do small and large carnivores differ in that respect? So our "slice" was by diet type. Let's slice by size, now, and see why size matters.

Exploration 1
RELATIVE INTAKE AND BODY SIZE

Why are there no ants the size of ponies, no wasps the size of vultures, no caterpillars the size of cobras, and almost no small animals in really cold regions? (The Arctics have few reptiles, amphibians, and small mammals; small birds migrate away for the cold season; and insects die.)

The data below are a first step in addressing those questions. The value listed for each organism represents the amount of energy, in kilocalories per gram of body weight that the organism needs just to exist. (Remember that an organism's **R** energy term includes two components, basal metabolic rate and energy activities. Basal metabolic rate is the energy necessary to keep a typical nonpregnant adult of the species alive when it is resting, that is, inactive, awake, not digesting food, and not gaining or losing heat. So the energetic costs of any activities such as movement, pregnancy, growth, youth, illness, cold, and excitement are not included in these values.)

What pattern do you see? On a page in your notebook, rearrange the data to reflect that pattern.

Organism	Size by Weight (kg)	Relative Energy Intake kcal/kg/day
Cheetah	39.0	14.9
Wolf	45.0	17.7
Whitetail deer	70.0	18.7
Thomson's gazelle	20.0	15.1
Snowshoe hare	1.6	37.9
Meadow vole (mouse)	0.04	79.7
Wildebeest	140.0	8.2
Uganda kob	100.0	11.3
Shorttail weasel	0.2	79.2
Wild dog	8.8	27.8
Mink	0.7	31.1
Muskrat	0.8	34.5
Moose	500.0	7.1

Can you suggest why that pattern might hold? Make a guess if you do not know. Write it below your rearranged data.

Although they may seem dissimilar, the questions at the beginning of this worksheet are about different aspects of body size and the physical properties that apply to all three-dimensional objects. In the next session, we will step back from the animals listed here to think about the relationships between some physical properties and body size.

Exploration 2
SIZE, SHAPE, AND ENERGY NEEDS

We were thinking about reasons for the differences among organisms in their relative intakes. You have already considered patterns in data on animal size and relative intakes. Now we look for patterns in data and about (body) size.

Animals are three-dimensional objects and are alive, to boot. However, they are subject to the same physical properties as nonliving three-dimensional objects. To consider some of those basic properties, we will simplify animals by ignoring their legs and different shapes and treating them all as cubes.

Materials
• **Paper and directions for making cubes** (if your teacher suggests this)
• **Sugar cubes** or other cubes
• **Reference set** of cubes
• **Tape measure or ruler**
• **Graph paper**

Procedure

1. **Cube surface area.**

   If you are using blocks or sugar cubes, make various cube-shaped models of animals. (Each sugar cube is about 1 cm by 1 cm by 1 cm.) What is a cube, actually? How do you know if your animal is cubic? (Note this and other answers in your notebook.)

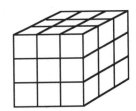

   What is the surface area of any side of the cube? How did you calculate that? What is the relationship between the length, L, of a cube edge and the surface area of that side or face of the cube? ("Edge length" is the length along an edge of the cube, the intersection between any two faces or sides of the cube.)

   If SA stands for surface area and L for edge length, what is the equation for the calculation you just performed? (This is all renaming work.)

   $$SA = L \times W$$

   What are the actual measurements of L and W? Note them on a data sheet, which should begin as follows:

L	SA = $6L^2$	V = L^3
"Small cube"		
"Large cube"		

   Since the figure is a cube, what can you see about L and W? Now, using only the measurement L, rewrite the equation for SA:

   $$SA =$$

   (How many sides does the cube have? What is the surface area of each?) How do you modify this equation to include all the sides of the cube, that is, so that it represents the total cube surface area?

2. **Cube volume.**

   What is the volume of the cube? Write that equation, using V for volume and L for the length of the cube edge.

   $$V = L \times L \times L$$

   Summarize your data in the table you started. Add data for cubes that are much bigger and much smaller than those you have measured. Make up side lengths if you do not have real cubes of the size you want, up to L = 1,000. Add all your calculations to your data table.

3. **Patterns in the data.**
    Graph your data and consider these questions:

    How will you label the X and Y axes?

    If L is the same, which is larger, that is, increases faster, surface area or volume?

    How does the relationship between surface area and volume look for a small value of L? For a large value of L?

    Remember the renaming or substitution tool? Relabel the columns in your data table, using names based on edge length, L. Now you can see more clearly the relationships between L and the other properties, surface area and volume.

4. **What does it mean? Cubes as model animals.**
    Now, what does that have to do with rates of intake? Well, any bodies, including animal bodies, are governed by the same properties. Small bodies—those with small "edge lengths"—have relatively larger surface areas than volumes. For larger bodies, the reverse is true. And that has lots of implications for living things.

BODIES ARE PERMEABLE

In previous work in this curriculum, we have seen that a living being is not inert—"stuff" moves in, out, and through. An organism interacts with its environment in many ways, taking in things (such as food or sun energy, oxygen or carbon dioxide) and putting out or producing things (such as heat energy, gases, waste products, or offspring). When we considered energy use by an organism, where did most of the energy go? Did it go to metabolism, that is, respiration, or to tissue production? Remember that the animal-cube is solid, its volume full of cells packed side by side. Those cells are respiring (metabolically active), using oxygen, generating heat. Where does heat energy go? How does it do so?

HOW IS HEAT LOST?

Imagine two plastic cubes of water. One has an L of about 8 ft, the other, an L of 2.5 in. You put both into a large walk-in freezer. Which one will freeze first? Why?

Now imagine that these two cubes are animals. If they start at the same body temperature, which one will lose heat faster? Why?

Discuss this with your group members or as a class, then turn to Exploration 3: Moose-Mouse Comparisons.

Exploration 3
MOOSE-MOUSE COMPARISONS

Now we have several kinds of data: some on relative energy use, animal size, and the surface area for several cube sizes. We are also considering which of two cubes of water would freeze first and why; a large cube (L = 8 ft) or a small one (L = 2.5 in.). How can we unify these data?

Materials
- **Data on relative intake** for moose and mouse (meadow vole) from the list in Exploration 1, in kcal/kg/day
- **Calculator**

Procedure

1. **Ice cubes as model animals.**

    Suppose that the first cube, with L = 8 ft, is a moose. While it is certainly true that a moose is not a cube, it is also true that a moose is about 8 feet long. Because we are simplifying, let's also say that the moose is solid all the way to the ground instead of having legs. Similarly, let's rename the mouse as a cube, with an L of about 2.5 in. (Actually, if you feel up to it, a realistic assumption is that each animal is a three-dimensional rectangle. The moose is about 8 by 3 by 3 ft; the mouse, 2.5 by 1 by 1 in. Now perform the following calculations, but instead of working with cubes, substitute these figures instead.)

    What is the surface area (SA) of each? Record it in your notebook.

	L	SA = $6L^2$	V = L^3
Moose			
Mouse			

2. **Weight-for-weight comparison.**

    "So what?" you may be thinking. "A moose is bigger than a mouse, and it has larger surface area (and volume). What does that have to do with relative intake or anything else?"

    Good question! Let's make the comparison direct. A moose weighs about 500 kg, a mouse about 0.03 kg. Let's consider an equal weight of each:

    500 kg = 1 moose
    500 kg of mice = how many mice?

    How much energy does that amount of moose and mouse use for metabolic respiration in one year?

    From your notebook (and Exploration 1), we can make these calculations: A moose uses, per day, 7 kcal/kg, or $500 \times 7 = 3,500$ kcal for a 500-kg moose. An equal weight of mouse uses, per day, 79.7 kcal/kg, or $500 \times 79.7 = 39,900$ kcal for 500 kg of mouse.

3. **Surface area for weight.**

    What is the surface area of 500 kg of mouse? Of one moose? Which is greater?

4. **What does it mean?**

    Step back for a moment and consider the types of data we listed at the start of this Exploration. Would the moose cube or the mouse cube freeze faster?

    To freeze means heat leaves the item being frozen; metabolic respiration releases heat. Heat is a form of what?

    All endothermic animals at rest lose the same amount of heat per unit area of skin. Thus, food (energy) intake is proportional to animal surface area, not to weight. Which has a greater surface area, 500 kg of mouse or 500 kg of moose? Which must eat relatively more to compensate? Is that what the data show?

READING
THE MICROWORLD AND THE MACROWORLD

As we have discovered in the Explorations, animals, like other bodies, are subject to physical effects or laws, such as gravity and drag and lift. How an animal is affected, however, depends on its size and weight and whether it is terrestrial or aquatic, flat or round, flies or walks. Living things span eight or nine orders of magnitude in their linear dimension, L, ranging from about 102 m to 10–7 m long.

L (m)	EXAMPLES
10^2	Giant tree (redwood)
	Large whale
10^1	Basking shark
	Elephant, ostrich, human
10^0 (1 m)	Cat, eagle, pig
10^{-1}	Large insect (sphinx moth, dragonfly)
	Small bird (hummingbird)
	Small mammal (shrew)
10^{-2} (1 cm)	Medium insect (housefly, beetle)
	Very small fish
10^{-3} (1 mm)	Small insect (flea, small ant)
10^{-4}	Protozoa
	Pollen grain
10^{-5}	Large bacterium
	Human red blood cell
10^{-6} (1 µm)	Minute bacterium
10^{-7}	Virus

Sphinx moth

Hummingbird

For comparison:

10^{-8}	Large molecule (starch)
10^{-9} (1 nm)	Water molecule
10^{-10} (1 Å)	Radius of an atom

If those organisms were built to the same scale, their surface area would vary as L^2 (as you demonstrated), and their volumes or weights would vary as L^3, thus spanning a staggering twenty-four to twenty-seven orders of magnitude of difference. Even across size differences of eight orders of magnitude (in length), organisms clearly face different physical realities; differences at twenty-four orders of magnitude seem as from another planet.

These differences have been crudely divided into two categories. They are the macroworld, in which gravity and its forces rule how creatures are designed and move, and the microworld or molecular world, ruled by molecular forces such as adhesion, cohesion, and drag. That is why it is easier for a beetle turned over on its back to right itself than it is for a land tortoise to do the same. Similarly, a flying gnat is helpless to convection but free from gravity, while a sparrow's flight is the opposite—not influenced by micro-drafts and governed primarily by gravitational forces.

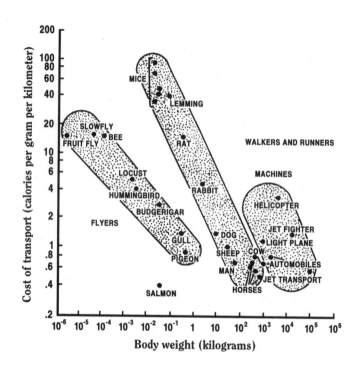

Following are a few other examples of the effects of body size. Note that each case represents a physical law or constraint (such as gravity or effects of body size on surface area and volume) and a biological response to that constraint (e.g., small mammals eat relatively more to compensate for greater heat loss). Some examples involve more than one constraint.

SUPPORTING BODY MASS: INTERNAL VERSUS EXTERNAL SKELETONS

Insects and other invertebrates have exoskeletons, that is, external skeletons unlike the internal skeletons of humans and other vertebrates. What does a skeleton do? It provides protection, stiffens a body so that an animal can move about, and helps the body hold together against the micro- or macroforces that the body meets. Internal and external skeletons each have advantages and drawbacks.

Let's consider the exoskeleton of invertebrates. It is a hardened outside "shell" of some sort—think about an insect, a lobster, a clam, or any other animal that has no bones but a hardened outside skeleton. Consider also how big any of these creatures gets. Have you ever seen a caterpillar the size of a dog, a lobster the size of a calf, or a wasp like a vulture? You are correct—having an exoskeleton sets an upper limit to the possible size of a creature. Let's consider why.

Because an exoskeleton is on the outside of the body, the animal is effectively a series of hollow tubes: the main body, head, and legs. Although hollow cylinders like exoskeletons are extremely strong, that is true only if they are below a certain size. Above that size, they would start to buckle from any pressure exerted on them, or they would have to develop such thick walls that the tubes would no longer be hollow but all filled in. And if they became filled in, there no longer would be any room inside the tube for the body parts of the animal.

One thing that applies pressure to the exoskeleton is moving about, especially the force of wings in winged invertebrates. The muscles that move the wings or legs (and thus the animal) need to contract and push against something, something strong and stiff enough to withstand that pressure. So there is a balance between the size of the animal and its ability to fly or walk. It is not surprising that the largest invertebrates are all aquatic—that is, they live in the water—where the water helps buoy up some of their weight and removes some pressure from their exoskeletons. Many of them do not walk at all, and certainly none of them fly.

Now, exoskeletons must be stiff. Earlier we said that a major function of a skeleton is to provide stiffening to an organism. But if you-as-an-organism are in a stiff and inflexible box-like body, like that of a lobster, beetle, or clam, what happens when the soft body parts inside that box grow? Where can they "go"? The organism must shed its box-like exoskeleton, or "molt," in order to grow. First, it sheds its old exoskeleton and then it secretes, from its body tissues, chemicals that form around the soft body and harden into place as a new, larger-size box to accommodate the new, larger-size soft body. During the molting process, the soft bodies of small animals that have shed their exoskeletons hold together by cohesion of molecules and by hydrostatic pressure—remember, these small animals are virtually independent of gravity. But the unsupported bodies of larger animals would collapse under the force of gravity. Then, when the newly secreted exoskeleton hardened into place around that collapsed body, it would, in the words of one author, "harden to produce an animal like a great tough pancake"—not a functional shape for an animal that was designed to be some other shape!

Because they are hollow and brittle, exoskeletons are also very sensitive to impact. Sensitivity also increases with animal size, since the stress of impact is proportional to length (L). And exoskeletons are sensitive to dings and scratches, even those produced by the animal itself. Since larger animals are stronger and exert more force on their own skeletons when moving, larger animals would tend to damage their own skeletons more than do smaller animals.

SURFACE AREA AND VOLUME

We have explored one consequence of differing ratios of surface area to volume, namely that small animals lose heat faster because they have relatively more surface area. Another loss associated with surface area is water loss: small animals are in greater danger of dehydration through their body surface. But an exoskeleton, unlike an endoskeleton, is also waterproof. In fact, most small terrestrial invertebrates have some waterproof, hardened covering: insects, snails (Mollusca), isopods, millipedes, centipedes, and arachnids (Arthropoda). (We explore this further in **Module 3**, **Water**.)

Yet another aspect of the different ratios of surface area to volume at different body sizes has to do with getting things (in addition to heat) from inside the body to outside and vice versa. We know that a living thing is not inert—things move in, out, and through it. An organism interacts with its environment in various ways, taking in things (such as food, sun energy, oxygen, and carbon dioxide) and putting out or producing things (such as heat energy, gases, waste products, and offspring). At larger body sizes, volume is very much greater than at smaller sizes, so for those "things" to move into or out of the body becomes more difficult, or at least takes longer. Diffusion, the passive movement of dissolved materials, is not an efficient way to move something. Rather than rely on diffusion, larger animals tend to have "systems" and move things around actively. For example, a respiratory system gets gases in and out, and a circulatory system gets those gases around.

Insects do not have either system like that of vertebrates. Instead, they have specialized openings into the body tissue called tracheae, into which air and oxygen pass directly. In fact, one reason that insects can be so active compared to other same-size organisms is that they are getting vastly more oxygen per unit time through their tracheae than other organisms do through their tissues. Oxygen diffuses through air (as in the tracheae) 800,000 times faster than it diffuses through tissue (as in a respiratory system or through muscle tissue)!

SUMMARY

Thus, we can see that size is neither good or bad—being any size has advantages and drawbacks. One especially interesting thing about size is that, although we have some idea about how small something can get and why, we still have only hazy ideas about the limits at the other end of the spectrum, at least for vertebrates. The smallest known endotherms weigh about 2 g, and there are only a few, such as hummingbird and shrew species. Below that limit, apparently it is not possible to eat enough to survive as an endotherm. By contrast, we do not know the possible upper limits to body size in endotherms: How large can a vertebrate be? How large were the largest dinosaurs? Were they the largest beings that ever lived on the planet? These are hot topics of research and debate right now. Everyone has theories and ideas, but no one has definite answers.

THERMOREGULATION
A LARGE PART OF R

CHAPTER SIX

C O N T E N T S

CASE STUDY
HOT AND COLD: THERMOREGULATION IN ANIMALS

Have you ever heard the expression "hot-blooded"? Although it can refer to temperament, it also has a more literal meaning, referring to whether animals keep their bodies warm metabolically.

The chicken *(Gallus gallus)* and the iguana *(Iguana iguana)* are roughly the same size. Chickens, like most birds and mammals, regulate their body temperatures and keep warm by producing heat metabolically, that is, by metabolizing or combining oxygen and carbon compounds from food or stored body fat. Iguanas, which can grow to 2 m long, also regulate their body temperatures. But they do not use food primarily as fuel to keep warm. Instead, these tropical reptiles combine an external energy source and their own behavior to provide warmth—they bask in the sun. Like many lizards, when they are cooler than they want to be, they move to a sunny spot and turn sideways to the sun's rays, to expose as much surface area as possible and to absorb the maximum amount of warmth. When they are too hot, they can turn parallel to the sun's rays (exposing less surface area) or move out of the sun altogether. With this combination of sun and behavior, iguanas are able to regulate their body temperatures surprisingly well without spending much energy.

STAYING WARM

Once the sun sets, the iguana loses its heat source. What does it do to stay warm? It cannot act like the chicken and keep its body temperature high by metabolizing food at a high rate. The iguana might not do much at all—just let its body temperature fall as the air temperature falls. In fact, nearly all reptiles and amphibians take this last course of action; they do not do much of anything about their body temperatures at night, letting body temperature change with air temperature. (Do you think many amphibians and reptiles live in Antarctica? Why?)

TWO ISSUES

Notice that there are two separate issues to thermoregulating. First is the mechanism by which an animal gets warm. Endothermic animals —mammals and birds—warm themselves from the inside (endo- means internal, -thermic means pertaining to heat). In contrast, reptiles and amphibians are described as being ectothermic because they warm themselves from external sources such as the sun and warm rocks (ecto- means external).

Second is temperature control. Endotherms have a biological version of a thermostat. When they are cold, they metabolize more energy to create more heat—shivering is an extreme example of this. When too hot, they cool off by panting, sweating, or moving to a cooler spot. Endotherms can thermoregulate metabolically.

Ectotherms do not have such elaborate gear. Although they can sense when they are too warm or too cold, there is little they can do to alter the situation metabolically. Instead, ectotherms thermoregulate behaviorally. If an ectotherm is cold, it moves to a warmer place, such as a patch of sunlight or a warm rock. Too hot, and it moves to a shady spot or to a cool burrow.

WHAT IS THE DIFFERENCE?

Do endotherms or ectotherms tend to be covered by fur or feathers? Why? How does that relate to regulating body temperature? Actually, why does it matter whether an animal is warm? And does it really matter how an animal goes about regulating its body temperature? In fact, these issues matter tremendously.

Muscles function much better when they are relatively warm than when they are cold or overly hot. A cold reptile is a sluggish reptile; it cannot run fast to catch prey or to escape a predator. (Too hot, however, and the animal dies.) Chickens, along with most birds and mammals, keep themselves warm 24 hours a day by metabolic means, so their muscles function well regardless of the air temperature.

Digestion is more efficient and much more rapid at warm temperatures than at cold ones for most organisms. Endothermic animals (birds and mammals) can digest efficiently 24 hours a day. In contrast, ectothermic animals (e.g., reptiles and amphibians) digest their food slowly at times when their body temperatures are low. (That is why snakes eat so infrequently—some species feed only once every few months.)

Not only does an animal's own digestive gear function better when warm, so do the gut bacteria that help animals such as iguanas, cows, and termites digest plant matter. (In case you are wondering how much more effective bacteria are when they are warmer, consider how quickly milk

spoils due to bacterial action when it is left at room temperature than when it is in the refrigerator.)

In sum, there are good reasons to stay warm. Getting and staying warm can be accomplished in two ways: by internal metabolic means (i.e., "burning" calories) or by behavior (such as basking in the sun).

THE TELL-TALE HEART

We are just skimming the surface of differences between endotherms and ectotherms. Nearly all endotherms have a four-chambered heart and efficient blood circulation. Most reptiles also have a four-chambered heart, but with incomplete separation of two chambers, so oxygenated and deoxygenated blood mixes. Amphibians have a three-chambered heart, with incomplete separation. Invertebrates have various types of pumps, and we have already considered their absence of a circulatory system. That, too, contributes to ectothermy. Most insects do not live at cool temperatures, but there are a few exceptions. (Those exceptions have a chemical, glycerol, in their haemolymph [insect blood] that is similar to and acts just like antifreeze—literally. So these "hot-blooded" insects can be active even in the winter.)

ANOTHER COST/BENEFIT

There is yet another crucial difference between the chicken and the iguana that is related to their methods of staying warm. From what you know about their different methods of staying warm, what might you predict about the relative amounts of food that a same-size chicken and iguana eat in a day?

Exploration 1

DESIGN A TEMPERATURE-REGULATING ANIMAL

Why does it matter how much energy an animal spends on staying warm? Remember the **R** term? Energy that an animal spends has to come from food that the animal eats. Animals that need less energy do not have to spend as much time looking for or eating food. On the other hand, since warm muscles function more effectively, warm animals can find food or escape from predators when cold animals cannot.

So let's design and build a model endotherm or ectotherm—your choice—and explore the costs and benefits of each strategy.

Safety

> **WARNING**
>
> The heater apparatus is simple to assemble and fairly safe. Be careful when there is current flowing through the power resistor—it can get quite warm to the touch. To assemble a heater, place a D-cell battery in a holder and connect one of the wires from the holder to one of the resistor leads. We recommend that you connect the other leads from the battery holder and resistor to a switch, so it is easy to turn the system on and off. (Alternatively, you can simply twist the leads from the battery holder and resistor together when you want power flowing to the resistor.) Place the resistor inside the film canister, then close the cover over the resistor leads; the cover should keep the resistor in place.

Materials

- As provided

Procedure

1. **Rationale.**

   Just as real animals spend energy building (growing) their tissues, you will "spend" energy building your "animal." Your animal can also save calories (by not moving or by external heat sources) or eat more calories than it spends.

   Remember that both endotherms and ectotherms maintain a relatively constant temperature over a period of time. But as you saw in the Case Study, the two groups of organisms use markedly different methods to thermoregulate. These differences affect your animal's design and lifestyle. What <u>major</u> differences do you expect in net energy balance between endotherms and ectotherms?

2. **Groups prepare to design and build an "animal."**

   Keep in mind that to survive, a model ectotherm must break even between "building" costs and "living" costs, while an endotherm must gain more energy than you spent building it.

   The first major decision your group must make is whether to design an endotherm (include a warmer in your animal, on the mammal/bird design) or an ectotherm, without a warmer (the reptile/amphibian style). This is not a light decision! Internal warmers (Figure 1) are expensive to build and

196

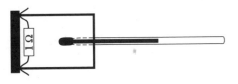

Figure 1. Film canister with 1-ohm power resistor inside and leads going to a switch and D-cell battery.

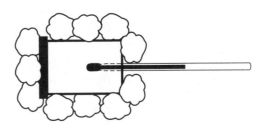

Figure 2. Film canister covered with cotton balls for insulation.

expensive to run. You will be able to forage longer with your internal heater, but you will also <u>need</u> to forage more, to support your energy-expensive lifestyle.

3. **Materials.**

Use a film canister as the animal's core, so all the animal models are comparable. Build your animal around this core.

Use various materials to insulate your animal (Figure 2). Make legs, wheels, whatever, if you want it to get off the ground. But remember that more material costs more energy at the start (it costs a wolf energy to grow its thick fur and an elephant energy to have thick sturdy legs).

An ectothermic animal model will not have the heat-generating apparatus (it will get warmed under a lamp), whereas an endothermic animal model will have such equipment.

4. **Experiment.**

Experiment with your design. Try out various versions of your animal, using different materials. See how well different designs and materials heat up and retain heat. Such experimentation will take time. Keep notes of your results as you test different designs.

5. **Your beast.**

Once you have built your final design, record all the "energy costs" of the materials you used to build your model animal, according to Table 1.

Table 1 | **Energy Costs**

MATERIAL	COST
Film canister	30 kcal
Cotton	5 kcal/cotton ball
Construction paper	10 kcal/sheet
Woolen sock	100 kcal
Heat-generating apparatus (battery, resistor, associated hardware)	100 kcal
Toothpicks	1 kcal each
Popsicle sticks	2 kcal each
Tape	1 kcal/10 cm
Glue	Free

CONTINUED

MATERIAL	COST
OPERATING COSTS	
Running heat-generating apparatus	5 kcal/minute
FORAGING BENEFITS	
Energy gained while foraging	10 kcal/minute

Exploration 2

FORAGING: YOUR ANIMAL MEETS REALITY

Now your animals will "forage," so you can compare building costs with foraging efficiency and see whether your model is actually endothermic or ectothermic.

Materials
- Your **animal model**
- **Data on the energy costs** of building and operating your animal (from Exploration 1)
- **Thermometer**
- **Clock or watch**
- **Centimeter ruler or tape**

Procedure

1. **The foraging periods.**
   After your group has built its model animal, test its energy efficiency during an official "foraging period." During that time, alternate periods of "daylight" (turn on the lamps) and "night" (the lamps are off). We will assume that your model animals can forage only during daylight hours. (This is a reasonable limit, because no real individual, endothermic or ectothermic, can forage 24 hours a day. In nature, animals typically are active either at night or during the day, but rarely during both.)

2. **Time and temperature.**
   During nighttimes endothermic animals must maintain their body temperatures above 27°C, much as most mammals and birds do. Ectothermic animals can let their body temperatures drop to room temperature.

3. **Foraging and data collection.**
   At the start of the "day" or foraging period, place the tip of a thermometer 2 cm deep inside your animal's body cavity (Figure 3). When the foraging

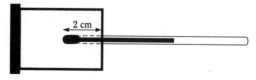

Figure 3. Film canister with thermometer inserted through hole in base.

period begins, record the time and temperature in your notebook. Next, either move your animal to a position 5 cm under a lamp (as an iguana moves into the sunlight) or turn on its heat-generating mechanism (as a mammal warms up metabolically from its nighttime sleep before foraging).

When the animal's temperature reaches 28°C, record the time—your animal can now begin to forage. Credit for foraging can be given only if your animal keeps its temperature energy between 28°C and 32°C. All foraging is to take place at least 0.5 m from lamps. (When your animal is foraging, it does not really have to move around, it just has to be some distance from the heat source.) Continue monitoring the animal's temperature as it forages.

If your animal's temperature drops below 28°C or rises above 32°C, record the time and stop foraging. Cold animals must warm up before they can forage again ("ectothermic" animals can move back under a lamp; "endothermic" animals must pause while they warm up). Overheated animals must cool off before they resume foraging.

NOTE: You might increase your foraging time by letting your animal's temperature rise well above 28°C, close to 32°C, and then have it forage as it cools down. You also can turn off "endothermic" animals' heaters for a while (thus saving energy). Be sure, however, to keep your animal's temperature above the minimum foraging temperature (28°C). And keep track of the amount of time that the heaters are on, so you can calculate how much energy they are using.

4.   **Data analysis: Did you make it?**
     You have numbers in two sets of units: energy costs and gains in kilocalories (building, heating, foraging) and time spent foraging or at different temperatures. Group these sets of numbers so you can calculate whether your animal survived. Were you a successful endotherm or ectotherm? What might you do differently to be more successful?

5.   **Class discussion.**
     In class, discuss the costs and benefits of both forms of thermoregulation.

READING

STARS AND ODDBALLS IN BODY-TEMPERATURE REGULATION

Many people talk about animals as being "warm-blooded" or "cold-blooded," but by now you may have begun to see that these terms are vague. The phrase "warm-blooded" typically is used to describe birds and mammals that warm themselves metabolically and that maintain relatively high core-body temperatures. As you will read in a moment, however, many birds and mammals frequently stop maintaining high temperatures and let their body temperatures fall close to the air temperature. Are these species "warm-blooded"? On the other hand, many so-called "cold-blooded" animals, such as reptiles, are actually able to regulate their body temperatures quite well during daylight hours by moving in and out of sunny spots and altering their positions relative to the sun's rays.

Clearly there are two separate issues: whether an animal can regulate its body temperature and if the animal raises its body temperature by metabolic means. Let's take a look at several remarkable animals, creatures that do unusual things with their body temperatures. As you read about these animals, think about the animals that you and others in your class designed. How do the "designs" of these real-life animals compare with your model "animals"?

STAYING WARM: SOMETIMES JUST TOO EXPENSIVE

Think back to your model animals. It was great to generate heat internally so you could always forage, but it was very costly—especially at night, when you were using up energy to stay warm but unable to forage to get any new energy. What if you could warm yourself metabolically some of the time and let your temperature drop at other times? Well, many organisms, especially small birds and mammals, have evolved to exactly that pattern. Small animals that warm themselves metabolically require a tremendous amount of energy to stay warm, since they lose a lot of heat through their relatively large amounts of surface area. (Remember the moose and the mouse from **Chapter 5**?)

Hummingbirds, for example, use extraordinarily large amounts of energy per gram when they are awake and active. They fly from flower to flower at high speed, hovering in place while they drink small amounts of nectar, then darting off to the next flower. When they are sitting still and saving energy by not flying, they still have to spend a lot of energy to keep warm, because they are so small. Despite these heavy energetic costs, daytime is the easier time of day; at least they can get something to eat. Nighttime is tougher, since the birds cannot get food. For many species of hummingbird, if the birds were to try to maintain high body temperatures metabolically throughout the night, they would starve to death. As an alternative, the birds allow their body temperature to fall to the point where it is not much above the air temperature. By not attempting to stay warm the entire night, the birds save enough energy to stay alive!

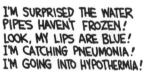

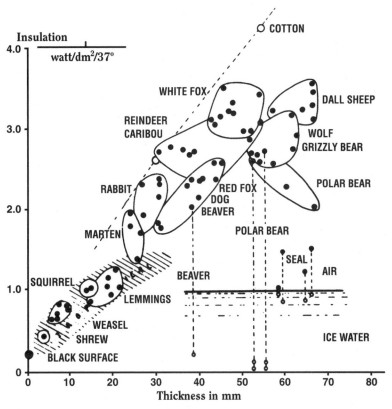

Figure 4. Maximum insulation of fur of arctic and tropical animals as a function of thickness. Values for aquatic animals are given in air (●) and in ice water (O). Insulating value of medium weight cotton is given by broken line.

When birds or mammals allow their body temperatures to drop, they go into a state known as <u>torpor</u>. Although this state saves energy, it has costs as well. The animal is not fully alert and thus may be caught by a predator. It is only when the animal warms itself up (again an energetically expensive process) that it can respond well to stimuli such as the approach of a predator.

Many animals undergo periods of torpor on a daily basis. Most hummingbirds go into torpor at night, and many bats become torpid during the day. Still other animals go into extended periods of torpor, especially when there is not much food available or when environmental conditions are stressful. Such extended periods include hibernation (during the winter) and estivation (during the summer). (Can you name animals that do either? What is estivation? Hibernation? Look up these terms in a dictionary or other reference work.) Check out the relationship between the insulation value of fur and its thickness (Figure 4). Some of your Serengeti and Northern Hardwoods animals are included. Do the results surprise you?

PRODUCTION
GROWTH, FAT, AND REPRODUCTION

CHAPTER SEVEN

OVERVIEW

What does it mean to "grow"? Getting taller, adding fat, and having babies are all included in the **P**roduction term of the energy equation. Can we put numbers or energy values on growth? Do the data match our work on energy budgets? How many babies is "enough," evolutionarily speaking? Let's explore these issues.

CASE STUDY
SOME GROWTH RATES

All multicellular organisms grow—anyone who has raised a pet or watched him- or herself over a period of years knows that. What is striking is how important growth and development are and yet how little energy is actually put into tissue production. Here, we look at a few different growth rates.

VOLES

The meadow vole *(Microtus pennsylvanicus)*, a small mammal of North America, grows so quickly that females are sexually mature by the age of 25 days. And, on average, a vole can live up to a year (although some live longer). In contrast, many insects, although they are smaller, take nearly a full year to reach maturity and then live several years beyond.

In your notebook, make a graph of what we know about the weight increase (growth rate) of a vole. Our data are limited: adult weight is about

202

3 g, which is reached by about 25 days; birth weight (at day 0) is about 6% of that. How would you label the X axis and the Y axis? Let's say that 1 g of vole tissue (average vertebrate tissue) has an energetic value of about 1.5 kcal. How can we translate the growth data into energy values? Please bring your work to class for further discussion.

AN INSECT AS OLD AS YOU ARE

In the eastern United States lives the seventeen-year cicada, whose name is not a folk name, exaggerated and given for effect. It accurately describes the seventeen-year life-cycle of several species of cicadas in the genus *Magicicada*. The female lays her eggs inside live twigs (which often die as a result of the number of eggs inserted). About a month after an egg is laid, a cicada nymph hatches out, falls to the earth, and burrows underground, where it spends the next seventeen years.

The nymph stays underground, sucking sap from plant roots and growing toward adulthood. When it is finally mature, it digs its way out of the ground, climbs a tree, and pupates, emerging from its exoskeleton. In addition to each individual cicada taking seventeen years to develop, the entire population is synchronized. So when one nymph emerges, it emerges with millions of others, all of which have been developing underground since they hatched seventeen years previously. In the period between hatching and emergence aboveground, not a single individual of the species has emerged and matured.

Antipredatory Strategy

Ecologists believe that the exceptional life-cycle of these cicadas may have evolved as a response to predation. Cicadas are quite tasty to birds and other predators and do not have any obvious defenses against predation (except perhaps their piercingly loud sound). Instead, seventeen-year cicadas (and a related group, the thirteen-year cicadas) probably were selected for and evolved a dig-and-hide sort of lifestyle. By disappearing for seventeen years, they avoid supplying predator populations with large quantities of nutritious insect flesh. If they emerged every year, predators would "expect" them and would certainly eat more of them. Predator populations likely would increase, while the survival rate of cicadas likely would be much lower. When the cicadas do emerge, they do so in such huge numbers at a time (many thousands) that even if predators eat nothing but cicadas during the emergence period, the probability that any single individual cicada will be eaten is much lower. After all, if you are one cicada out of only a thousand, you are much more obvious and much more likely to be caught than if you are surrounded by tens and tens of thousands of fellow cicadas.

Think about it—17 is a prime number as well as a long time, which makes it hard to "predict" if you are a cicada predator. How many biological, ecological, or abiotic things have a seventeen-year cycle? One-year cycles, sure. Two-year cycles, yes. After that, cycles become rarer and more varied. What can you think of that has a three-, or five-, or eight-year cycle? And is it a true cycle, highly synchronized among the entire population and highly predictable? (There are some among plants, but not at seventeen years.)

So, presumably as a response to predation, seventeen-year cicadas evolved an extremely slow growth and development rate instead of spines, bad-tasting chemicals, or a stinger or biting mouth. It takes them seventeen years to reach a length of 2–3 cm. Their lifestyle allows them to remain safe underground, hooked directly to a good food source and away from dangerous predators and many bothersome influences, for nearly two decades.

PLANT CYCLES

Interestingly, some plant species seem to have evolved a defense similar to that of the seventeen-year cicada. They protect their fruit from predators by fruiting only once every so many years, often with whole populations in sync. The apparent plant champion in this realm is a bamboo species that flowers and fruits only once—after 120 years of growth—and then dies. No one has experimentally tested the antipredator hypothesis on this species—think how long it would take to collect data on several generations.

THE BLUE WHALE: A KILOGRAM EVERY 16 MINUTES

At the other end of the growth rate scale is the blue whale *(Balaenoptera musculus)*, the largest animal alive. Whalers have found individual whales 33 m long and weighing 190,000 kg. (Take a moment to compare that weight to the weight of the entire student body of your school. Do all the students together outweigh the whale? This is a good subject for a Fermi calculation.) This magnificent species was hunted almost to extinction earlier this century, and their populations are still quite low, with perhaps fewer than 3,000 left worldwide.

Despite a relatively short gestation period (pregnancy) of only ten to twelve months (shorter than that of an elephant), the whale mother delivers a calf 7 m long and weighing about 2,000 kg. Baby blue whales are estimated to grow up to 90 kg per day, before they are weaned at the age of eight months. (How many kilograms is that in total?)

Exploration 1
GROWTH: OUR NEW TISSUE

We will explore the small and the large of it—weights from birth to adulthood—and use those data to test our ideas about the energy that goes into getting from one size to the other.

Materials
- **Chalk- or white-board or poster board**
- Your **animal cards (Chapter 4)**
- **Calculators**
- **Graph paper**

Procedure

1. **Prepare the data.**

   Each animal card includes an average adult weight. Note it. Calculate the average weight at birth of your organism as 6% of that adult weight and note it.

2. **Graphing the data.**

   In groups first, or as a whole class, plot your own birth weight and your current "adult" weight. Make "weight" the X axis and "age" the Y axis. We are not using actual years on the Y axis, so there are just two points: birth and adult. For our purposes, that will be adequate, but in other cases it is not. (Can you think when it might not be?)

   (How might you label each data point? Lowercase "j" for jackal birth weight and uppercase "J" for jackal adult weight? Some other way?)

3. **As a class, consider the graph.**

   Discuss these questions and others as they come up. What pattern do the data show? Why are adult and birth weights so different? Since we have only two data points for each species, do we know anything about growth <u>rate</u>? Why or why not?

   Do you think growth rate is constant (i.e., the same per unit of time throughout the life of your organisms)? Why or why not?

4. **Testing some of our ideas.**

   We can answer some of the questions discussed by considering data from a sample animal, one we have used before—a human being *(Homo sapiens)*. Table 1 lists the raw data; Figure 1 presents those data graphically.

Table 1   Sample Growth Data of "Average" U.S. Children

| AGE (YEARS) | WEIGHT (KG) | |
	MALES	FEMALES
0	3.2	3.2
1	10	9.5
2	13	12
3	15	14
4	17	16
5	19	18
6	21	20
7	23	22
8	25	25
9	28	28
10	32	33
11	35	37
12	40	41
13	45	46
14	50	50
15	57	54
16	62	56
17	66	57
18	69	57

Is growth constant?

Consider Figure 1, which graphs the typical weights per age for U.S. girls and boys. Is the growth constant? How can we tell?

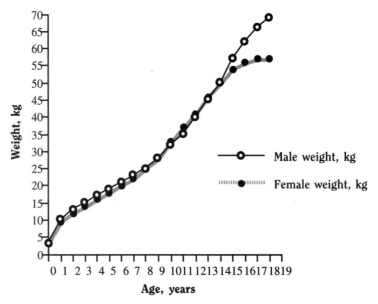

Figure 1. Average weights of U.S. boys and girls.

Is growth the same as adding fat?

Is it accumulated energy? Before answering, consider that the average height (or length, since they cannot stand) of U.S. newborns is 18 in., while the average height at maturity for women is 5 ft 4 in., for men, 5 ft 8 in. (Remember, these averages are across a population of many millions of people from many backgrounds. Very few individuals will be just those heights; many will be taller or shorter than the averages.)

5. **Converting weight into units of energy.**

   Convert the accumulated tissue weight values from Table 1 into units of energy, using the "vole conversion factor," that is, 1.5 kcal/g of wet tissue (or 1,500 kcal/kg wet tissue). Please note these converted numbers, so you can compare weight-as-energy with intake-as-energy. (Remember the tool of converting or renaming things, in **Unit 1**, **Chapter 1**, <u>Case Study</u>? This is another good example of applying that tool.)

6. **Graph the weight as energy data.**

   Using the converted data, graph them in a rough sketch in your notebook. Save it for graphing the cumulative energy intake data as well (step 7).

7. **Average energy intake per year.**

   Table 2 lists the average total caloric intake in kilocalories per year for the average kids graphed in Figure 1. Calculate the <u>cumulative</u> total, (i.e., how much energy an average individual uses by any age) by summing the yearly totals.

   Let each group plot the data on a rough-copy sketch of the weight-as-energy graph in Figure 1. What about the Y axis? First make a prediction:

will the lines be similar or different between the plots? Why and how? Write your prediction and thoughts in your notebook.

Table 2 **Average Intake per Year (kcal)**

AGE (YEARS)	MALES	FEMALES
1	370,000	351,500
2	481,000	444,000
3	555,000	518,000
4	561,000	528,000
5	627,000	594,000
6	693,000	660,000
7	598,000	572,000
8	650,000	650,000
9	728,000	728,000
10	832,000	858,000
11	700,000	629,000
12	800,000	697,000
13	900,000	782,000
14	1,000,000	750,000
15	912,000	810,000
16	992,000	840,000
17	1,056,000	855,000
18	1,104,000	855,000

8.   **Growth and energy intake.**
      Compare the two data sets. What happens to the Y axis? What does this work tell us about the difference between energy intake and tissue production? Roughly compare the proportion of kilocalories in tissue growth to those of intake. What is the order of magnitude difference? How does that relate to what we already know from our balanced energy budgets about the difference between intake and production?

READING 1
WHO ARE YOU CALLING FAT?

      Typically, organisms have very little body fat, or they have fat reserves for specific reasons. Such reasons include migration (caribou, salmon, birds, butterflies), hibernation or getting through cold periods (bears, raccoons, deer, and most other animals that live through and are active in cold seasons), insulation (walrus, seals, plus most sea mammals except sea otters), or for and at various stages of reproduction. (Lots of plants also put fat in their seeds or nuts.) In all these cases, having fat is not the same as being overweight. That is, the organisms gain and use energy reserves for particular reasons and usually on a cycle. (Which term of the energy use equation includes fat?)

FAT AS ENERGY STORAGE

Both endotherms and ectotherms use fat as energy-storage tissue. Fat is easy to make (given excess calories); it is light (fats and oils typically float); it is highly concentrated, energywise, with two times as many calories per unit weight as either protein or carbohydrates. (We explore how that is possible in **Chapters 8** and **9**.) Fat also can be converted to energy without harm to the body. An organism that uses its muscle tissue as an energy source will be handicapped by the loss of that muscle. But fat reserves can be drawn down quite low, to just a few percent of total body weight in animals that use fat as an energy reserve.

Real obesity is restricted to domestic and zoo animals, which get bored (because they may have too little to do) and which have no need to hunt or forage for food. In some species, there has been selection to gorge on food when it is available, because so often it is not. Such adaptations are not suited for captivity, where food may be too available and exercise hard to get.

TOO LITTLE FAT

Of course, very low fat reserves have negative effects on health and reproduction. In birds, mammals, and probably most organisms, if a female's percentage of body fat goes below some species-typical amount, she will cease to reproduce. Conversely, if her fat reserves are high, she will likely produce more and often healthier young. For both males and females, low fat reserves usually mean less margin for survival—less protection against fluctuations in food availability, less protection against cold, and possibly lowered resistance to illness and parasites.

So, in appropriate amounts, fat is an important and probably essential component of energy allocation. (Think back to the Integration in **Chapter 5**. Remember that high and low fat reserves were a clue for several animals. Does it make more sense now?)

AN EXAMPLE: THE LITTLE PENGUIN

The little penguin *(Eudyptula minor)* is found in New Zealand and the south coast of Australia. Average adult body weight varies by about 50%, between 1.0 and 1.4 kg, depending on the time of year and its annual cycle of activities. Table 3 shows how the little penguins' diet and weight change over the year. In the table, NA means data are not available (i.e., were not collected) for those months.

Note that molting, courtship, and incubation are periods of fasting, with low or relatively low intake. Note also that while intake increases during late chick rearing, expenditures are just about the same. Only after the chicks become independent feeders can the adults regain some weight to see them through the molt and upcoming winter, when their weight drops markedly again. Penguins lose so much weight after molting because their new feathers are not waterproof for about two weeks, during which time they cannot fish or enter the water at all. Penguins live 25–30 years.

Table 3 **Yearly Diet and Weight Changes of the Little Penguin**

	INTAKE (G/KG/DAY)	EXPENDITURE OF ENERGY (KCAL/KG/DAY)	AVERAGE ADULT WEIGHT (KG)
July: winter foraging	74	287	1.0
August–September: foraging	275	287	1.0
September: courtship, fasting	NA	137	1.0
October: foraging	NA	347	1.0
November: incubation, eggs hatch, fasting	300	157	1.0
November to mid-January: early: chick rearing, foraging	550	300	1.0
middle: foraging	600	425	1.05
late: foraging	664	603	1.05
Mid-January–February: premolt	660	NA	1.1
February–March: adult molt	183	NA	1.4
March–May: autumn fasting	NA	156	1.0

In Tasmania, little penguins breed in the summer (winter in the northern hemisphere), nesting within caves. The clutch size is two eggs, which are incubated for about 36 days. Chicks fledge at about 8 weeks of age. Both parents share equally in the incubation and care of chicks. Adults forage during the day near the shore.

How Their Diet Fits

The diet of little penguins contributes to their energy use picture in the following way. They have three major foods: fish, shrimp, and squid. Only the fish are high in fat, which has twice the calories (energy) per unit weight as proteins or carbohydrates. (You will discover why fat is so calorie rich and used for energy stores in **Chapter 8**.) Notice the correlation between high percentages of fish in the diet (Table 4) and intake and animal weight (Table 3). (Because the percentages are rounded off to the nearest 1%, not all the rows in Table 4 equal 100%.)

Table 4 **Little Penguin Diet**

	PERCENTAGE FISH	PERCENTAGE SQUID	PERCENTAGE SHRIMP
September	77	18	5
November	80	11	10
December	70	23	7
January	62	39	<1
March	25	74	<1
July	74	25	2

(Think about the amount in kilograms a penguin eats per day compared to its body weight. How does that compare with the percentage of your weight that you eat each day?)

So the penguin gains and loses a great deal of weight each year, but it is not "fat" the way people talk about being fat. It is not overweight. Rather, its body composition varies according to the stage of its yearly (and life) cycle. The same is true of the body-weight fluctuations and fat storage and loss in other organisms.

Exploration 2
HOW MANY GRANDCHILDREN?

Of the many interesting things about reproduction, two stand out. It is energetically very expensive, and it is the single criterion used by evolutionary scientists to indicate the success of an organism. Why? What do we mean by success? Actually the definition is straightforward: more successful individuals are those that leave more offspring because they better match their environment in some way(s). How does that work? We will carry out a numerical example here to illustrate just that.

Let's examine effects of the environment (through the process of natural selection) on a population of the seed-eating finch *(Geospiza fortis)*. This species lives on the Galapagos Islands and feeds exclusively on seeds (**Module 1**). Some individuals of the species happen to be better suited to the environment at the time of data collection; those individuals have more surviving and reproducing offspring, who in turn also have more surviving and reproducing offspring. So over even just a few generations, we can see that those individuals become more common in the population, that is, they are numerically more successful.

Materials

- **Calculators**
- **Graph paper**

Procedure

1. **Data for Year 1.**

   Let's start our example under normal conditions and see the selective effects of drought on the population. Suppose we start with 150 bird pairs that are of the same species but that vary in bill size. We class them into three groups by bill size: average, above average, and below average. Such individual differences mean that the birds have different capabilities in getting or cracking seeds (i.e., getting energy). And differences in their abilities to gather enough food (energy) will, if the environment changes (e.g., seed availability drops), also affect their ability to reproduce and even to survive.

	BILL SIZE AND STRENGTH		
	BELOW AVERAGE	AVERAGE	ABOVE AVERAGE
Year 1			
Number of pairs of adults	50	50	50
Number of chicks hatched	100	100	100
Number of chicks surviving	60	80	55

So, our population consists of three categories with 50 pairs in each category, for a total of 300 adults, plus all the surviving chicks.

End of Year 1

How many chicks survived? What is the current total population of chicks plus adults? What are the totals by bill-size class?

2. **Data for Year 2.**

Let's assume that 10% of the adults die every year (remember, these are imaginary numbers). Let's also assume that chicks become adults and breed the year after they are born. Thus, our second year's data look like this:

	BILL SIZE AND STRENGTH		
	BELOW AVERAGE	AVERAGE	ABOVE AVERAGE
Year 2			
Number of adult pairs surviving	40	40	40
Number of new adult pairs	30	40	22
Total pairs	70	80	62

So far, so good. But this year, the environment changes—there is a severe drought, and plants are producing fewer seeds. Less food is available, and far fewer birds reproduce than in the previous year.

	BILL SIZE AND STRENGTH		
	BELOW AVERAGE	AVERAGE	ABOVE AVERAGE
End of Year 2			
Number of chicks hatched	0	0	0
Number of adults surviving	2	3	27

3. **Data for Year 3.**

	BILL SIZE AND STRENGTH		
	BELOW AVERAGE	AVERAGE	ABOVE AVERAGE
Year 3			
Number of pairs	1	1	13
Number of chicks hatched	2	3	30
Number of chicks surviving	2	3	27

End of Year 3

Now what is the total number of birds in each bill-size class? Which class now dominates the population?

4. **Results.**

With graph paper, make frequency histograms to show the change in number of adults by the three bill-size classes across the three years. Please write down your conclusions. Who is surviving and reproducing? Who is not?

All the birds "needed" stronger, larger bills, but only those who already had them had a chance to survive the drought.

5. **Discussion.**

A common misperception about selection and evolution is that they are about <u>need</u>. Suppose conditions change (say there is a drought); to survive, creatures also need to change. People tend to think that because the creatures need to change, they can or will change. Although it may be true that creatures need to change to survive, that does not mean they are able to do so. Can a bird change its bill size just so? No. Thus, "need" is irrelevant to the mechanism of natural selection. Did the finches with less powerful bills try any less hard to survive the drought? Not likely. Did that make any difference? No. What made the difference? Hard physical realities about bill size and depth. In this case, birds with deeper, stronger bills were better equipped to survive under drought conditions and to reproduce.

Natural selection behaves the same way between as it does within species. That is, we would come up with the same sorts of results whether the three classes were based on different species or on different sizes within a species. In both cases, those individuals that successfully reproduce are those that will come to dominate the population. (For more on evolution by natural selection, see **Module 1**.)

READING 2
REPRODUCTION: THEIR NEW TISSUE

Evolutionary ecologists are obsessed with reproduction—not sex, but reproduction. (In fact, in most species sex—meaning meiosis and chromosome rearrangement—occurs independently of reproduction, so sex becomes even less important.) Evolutionists are obsessed with reproduction because it is the standard by which we measure effects of natural selection and, therefore, outcomes of evolution. (If you have already finished **Module 1**, this is not news to you.)

DIFFERENT STRATEGIES

Because all organisms reproduce, we are in a familiar position: all species have the same problem to solve, and they do so in different ways. There are many ways along a continuum of ways, but we will focus briefly on the two ends of the continuum. These are called "r" and "K" selection (after two terms from relevant mathematical equations), or the big bang versus repeat reproduction. The latter terms are more descriptive, so let's use those. Remember, these terms are relative, not absolute—we are being general here.

BIG BANG

This strategy might also be called putting all your eggs in one basket. Smaller, shorter-lived organisms tend to produce large, even huge, numbers of rapidly developing offspring. Those offspring, which need little or no care, develop rapidly. Many fail to reach adulthood, and the initially reproducing adults often reproduce just once in their lifetime. Many insects, other invertebrates, barnacles, fishes, and other water creatures fall into this group.

Because these organisms are smaller and shorter-lived, their world is often physically chaotic and unpredictable—the organisms are so small in the scale of things. The world is different for a mosquito and for a lion. (Remember the Reading on macroworlds and microworlds in **Chapter 5**?)

Some lovely exceptions, however, show how much we still have to learn about the natural world. Daddy longlegs (phalangids) and some spiders care for their young; some frogs and scorpions carry their young in their mouths or on their backs, respectively; and belastomatid beetles carry the young until they are almost mature, thereby protecting them from much of the chaos and dangers the world presents, especially to small creatures.

REPEAT REPRODUCTION

Obviously, the strategy of repeat reproduction is the opposite of the big bang. Organisms tend to be larger, to live longer, and to develop more slowly. They produce one or a few young at a time; the young may be dependent on their parents for years, during which time few or no other young are produced. They tend to have high individual survival rates. Here, too, however, there are exciting counterexamples. Female kangaroos (marsupials, remember) evict their young from the pouch if their own lives are threatened; the energetic cost of having new young is apparently offset by saving the mother's life.

COSTS OF REPRODUCTION

All variations on reproduction tend to have a few things in common. Energetically reproduction is very costly, especially to the female. She makes a disproportionate investment in eggs, which typically are much larger than sperm and which in many cases include food reserves (e.g., bird, reptile, and many fish eggs). When females also carry the young through pregnancy, investment costs skyrocket. Not only is she investing in the tissue of her offspring, her own respiration costs go up. In mammals, pregnancy takes more than double the calories that the female normally requires for her own living costs. Lactation is also expensive: it includes the energy in milk production, the cost of the milk itself, and the time invested in nursing. Repeat-reproduction mothers also tend to defend their young against, say, predators, and thus directly risk their own lives in ways that big-bang mothers do not.

Figure 2 shows the energy allocation by fertilized (column a) and unfertilized (column b) female guppies to three types of tissue. Notice that the energy in general body tissue is about the same for both. Although all females have eggs, those with unfertilized, nondeveloping eggs have more energy in body fat and less in their eggs; for females with fertilized eggs, the reverse is true. Cost of reproduction? Yes. And consider how much energy females might "save" if they had no eggs at all.

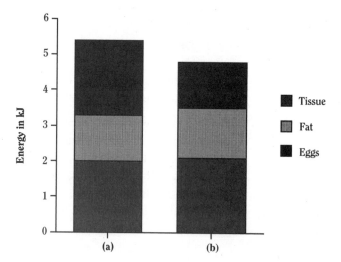

Figure 2. Reproductive (a) and nonreproductive (b) female guppies.

SO WHY DO EVOLUTIONISTS CARE?

Individual organisms that are well suited to their conditions will leave disproportionately more successful young than those less well suited. So we use reproductive success—specifically the number of grandchildren—as an indication of the match between an organism and its environment. If the match seems good (the species is doing well) or poor (it is not reproducing or surviving as well), we want to know why. Especially now, when human beings are altering the environment at rates and in ways wholly unprecedented, it is essential to keep track of which species are not surviving and why. How can we understand anything, let alone ourselves, if we cannot understand how or why some species are successful?

WHY IS THE WORLD NOT COVERED WITH ELEPHANTS?

Or fleas, for that matter? Fisher made the intelligent observation in the 1930s (more or less following on an intelligent remark by Malthus 200 years ago) that every organism need replace only itself for a species to continue to survive. As long as each organism replaces only itself, the number of organisms will remain the same. (Prove this to yourself with pencil and notebook, if you like.)

What also interests evolutionists is the makeup of a successful species. Why do some individuals reproduce more often and more successfully than others? In Exploration 2, we saw some individuals of a species spread in a population. Their physical characteristics gave them the opportunity, under those conditions, to raise more grandchildren and thus to be "more successful." Why do you think we might want to study differences among individuals or their reproductive success?

FOOD QUALITY
CARBON AND ENERGY CONTENT

CHAPTER EIGHT

OVERVIEW

If all animals need energy, why are they not all eating the same food? Why is grass calories for cows but roughage for cats? By now you have an inkling that animal diets vary tremendously and include stuff we likely would not put in our mouths.

Sometimes we have been talking about carbon, but often about energy (in kilocalories) instead. The two are linked, but how? When we get hungry, what are we really after? And what does that have to do with ecology, anyway?

Now let's explore the links between carbon content and energy content. We consider how or where energy is in food and how organisms get it out. (By energy we mean specifically the type of energy that organisms get from the foods they eat, or chemical energy.) We use two techniques to demonstrate how much energy and carbon are in any organic substance and consider animals' food habits and digestion and the chemistry behind chemical energy.

Exploration 1

CALORIMETRY: THE CONDENSED VERSION

Suppose we need to know how much energy is required to support a herd of 500 bison. Impossible, you say? Actually, it is quite possible. And here is a technique that helps us do just that.

This simple, accurate technique can determine the potential energy (calorie) content of almost anything that can be burned. This, of course, makes it exceptionally useful for studying energy storage and transfer in ecosystems, through plants, organisms, litter, dung, whatever.

So, throw some bison food (grass) into the apparatus, and let's go. (Once you know the caloric value of that grass, at any time of year, what else do you want to know in order to support your bison?) Here are some data categories you might include: sample, initial sample weight (mass), initial water temperature, burning time, final water temperature, final sample mass, and caloric content.

(Note that the process of oxidation by combustion is different from digestion as carried out by organisms, which occurs largely by enzymatic and chemical oxidation. We are using combustion merely as a way to measure energy content.)

In Advance

- Read the **Technique: Calorimetry**.

- Choose your samples. What items do you want to study and why? Maybe something eaten by your animal (**Chapter 4**), by you, or by your pet? Prepare your samples, if necessary, as described in the Technique.

Materials

- **Dried samples** (approximate size 0.5 to 1.0 g)
- **Calorimetry apparatus**

Procedure

1. **First steps.**
    After you have carefully read the **Technique: Calorimetry**, decide which items your group wants to analyze and why, perhaps some of your animals' foods (or reasonable stand-ins—gazelle meat may be hard to find). Or just compare general herbivore, carnivore, scavenger foods: meat versus plant matter, insect flesh versus vertebrate flesh, wood versus grass.

2. **Prepare your samples and data categories.**
    Dry your samples to a constant weight.

3. **Weigh the dried samples.**
    Weigh your samples to the nearest hundredth of a gram, and record the weights in your notebook.

4. **Water temperature.**
    Record the temperature of the 200 ml water in the soda can.

5. **Ignite a sample.**
    Put a sample into the calorimetry apparatus and ignite it. Note the length of time flames are visible. Adjust the distance between the sample and the bottom of the can so the flame covers the bottom of the can but does not reach beyond the bottom (about 2–3 cm). Stir the water in the can two or three times during heating.

6. **Time.**
    Keep track of the elapsed time between ignition and when the flames are no longer visible.

7. **Postburning water temperature.**
   Record the temperature of the water after the burning is finished.

8. **Weigh the burned sample.**
   Remove the burned sample from the calorimeter and weigh it again. Record the weight.

9. **Calculate the energy released.**
   Using the examples in the **Technique: Calorimetry**, calculate the energy released in the burning.

10. **Class data patterns.**
    Examine the data from each group. Do the results surprise you? Did some things have more than you expected? Less energy? Why do you think that is?

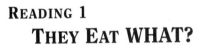

READING 1
THEY EAT WHAT?

TADPOLES OF DEATH

It is a spring day at a woodland pond in the Northern Hardwoods. Later in the season the pool will vanish, because the spring rains will fail to replenish the pool begun by the snowmelt. Now, though, in the cool shallows, the larvae of the tiger salamander swim and forage, shredding plant matter and filtering the water for algae and other edible chunks in the pond "soup." By midsummer they will have shed their gills and begun the land phase of their lives. Their survival depends, in part, on whether the short-lived pools last long enough that the nutrient-rich medium allows them to complete their metamorphosis. The little crowds of tadpoles browse energetically.

Not far away, in the same woods, other salamander young are facing more of a challenge. So many eggs have hatched in their pool that resources are under much greater pressure. Algae is scraped off the twigs and leaves as fast as it grows; as the water evaporates, the salamander larvae are packed tighter and tighter. The food and space resources available to those tadpoles are heavily overused.

Over the course of a few days, some tadpoles undergo a transformation: their heads broaden, their teeth lengthen, and their digestive abilities change. They solve the problem of an overexploited food supply by switching their prey. No longer do they eat algae and sludge. Instead, they eat what is available in abundance—other salamander tadpoles. The cannibals grow faster than the vegetarians and make the change to dry land sooner; the vegetarians must contend with the losing equation of less food to feed ever larger tadpoles. Starvation, as well as cannibalism, is occurring.

Not only have the cannibals changed in a way that allows them to exploit a plentiful food source, the food itself provides more, and more accessible, nourishment. The flesh of the salamander tadpoles has more calories and a higher percentage of protein, so the cannibals get more nitro-

217

gen and other nutrients per bite than do the vegetarians. Moreover, the calories in the protein and fat in the tadpoles are absorbed with less waste by the carnivorous cannibals.

The flesh of their fellow tadpoles is a higher-quality food than the algae. Such higher-quality food enables faster growth rates, so the carnivores can change their lifestyle and escape the deteriorating conditions of the pond.

By what steps might the ability to change eating habits have evolved? In many species, as young mature they change their food habits. Baby birds, for instance, switch from being fed insects by their parents to an adult diet that is often vegetarian or seed eating.

Where is the energy contained in the food that the salamander tadpoles are eating?

What really makes something a higher-quality food?

Why don't all animals prefer to eat the same things?

GRAZERS AND GRASS, PREDATORS AND PREY

Herbivores do not eat just anything plant-like. Some specialize on seeds, some on fruits, some on grass, some on twigs and leaves, and so on. Visit a horse pasture in the northern states, and you will see grass cropped close by the grazing beasts, and large tufts of goldenrod, which horses dislike, scattered all across the field. What makes a plant more or less attractive to a hungry herbivore?

We can be sure that, whatever the needs and preferences of herbivores may be, plants are not going to just sit there and accept whatever happens to them. But how can an immobile, nerveless, unconscious organism resist being consumed?

Several things affect a plant's appeal, digestibility, and nutritional value (how pleasant it might be to eat, how hard or easy it might be to digest, and how nutritious it might be). These aspects include the presence and amount of spines, fiber, silica, protective casing, and distasteful or toxic chemicals. From the perspective of herbivores, food plants can be high quality or low, and the quality depends on a balance between accessibility and digestibility and energy content. High-quality plant materials contain easily digestible soluble carbohydrates and protein. Typically, they are new growth, green, and soft, or they are storage organs, such as fruits, seeds, and tubers.

In contrast, low-quality plant materials typically are old, tough, woody or fibrous, and hard to digest. Actually, plant communities contain mostly low-quality food. That is especially true of perennial communities, such as forests. It is least true in communities of annuals and in early growth stages of communities during seasonal rains. Food resources become available in various quantities and various qualities over the course of a season; if animals survive in the area, it is because their behavior has adapted to take account of the seasonal changes in the food supply. (This is obviously true of animals anywhere!)

THE SERENGETI GRAZING SUCCESSION

The Serengeti supports millions of grazing animals of many species, each of which has its own requirements and tolerances. The Serengeti has a wet season (November to April) and a dry season (May to October). Usually, there is enough moisture from November into June for plant growth, especially the grasses and nonwoody herbs that are the Thomson's gazelle's foods. These plants show little or no growth during the dry season.

The Serengeti also has a river and wooded as well as fully open areas. During the dry season, the riverine and woody areas have more edible vegetation than do the open areas. This seasonal cycle of available food plants affects the Thomson's gazelle and other species that also eat those plants, drawing them into a seasonal, migratory cycle. Huge numbers of Thomson's gazelles, wildebeest, and zebras move slowly westward across the Serengeti as drought deepens; months later, they slowly return as the rains progress.

Despite the numbers of animals involved (over a million wildebeest, 200,000 zebras, and 500,000 Thomson's gazelles) and the distance involved (some 200 km east to west), this migration is not random. The three species do not move together, do not eat the same foods, and compete little. Rather, they move across the area in succession, one species tending to follow the other. And the effects of feeding on the plants by one species actually benefits the second species, which in turn improves the feeding for the last.

How is that possible? Each species is specialized in different ways with regard to digestion, metabolism, and chewing. Those differences determine which plants and parts of plants a species can eat, how quickly food can pass through its digestive tract, which nutrients it can easily obtain from what it eats, and how much energy it requires per unit food. Even the size and the shape of the muzzle (the projecting part of the face that includes the nose and the mouth) are important, since they affect how precisely an animal can select specific plants.

As high-quality young plants mature, the proportion of low-quality structural tissue increases. In the dry season, the grasses are tall and dry, and consist more of coarse stems than leaves. Zebras eat these coarse top stems. The zebra, a nonruminant, processes fibrous food faster and can afford to take in more roughage. Its intestines are not designed for the long, slow digestion that would break down much of the cellulose. Removal of the plant tops by the zebras stimulates the grass to grow and add leaves. The new growth is available, some days later, to wildebeest, the next animals passing through. The wildebeest, in turn, eat much of the new and some of the old growth. That stimulates further growth and crops the grasses short enough that small plants, which grow among the grasses, are exposed. This opens the way for the narrow-muzzled, highly selective Thomson's gazelle, which does not digest high-roughage food very well. The gazelles eat some new grass but especially take the herbs growing among the close-cropped grass stems.

Of the grass parts, the leaves are the least tough and most nutritious: that is, they have the lowest amount of indigestible cellulose (fiber) and the highest ratios of protein and soluble (meaning digestible) carbohydrates.

The stem is the opposite: it is the most fibrous and has the least protein and soluble carbohydrates. The sheath is intermediate between the stem and leaves. Other plant (e.g., dicotyleden) leaves contain more protein and soluble carbohydrates than do grass leaves, and their fruits are the most carbohydrate-rich of all five plant parts we are comparing. The fruits are not, however, correspondingly rich in protein. Wildebeest and zebras are pure grazers, that is, they eat only grasses. Up to 39% of Thomson's gazelle diets have been found to be herbaceous plant parts, mostly the fruits (73%) and leaves (27%).

READING 2

THE BIG THREE

There are three classes of biochemicals of major biological and ecological importance: proteins, carbohydrates, and lipids. Because they vary markedly in the quantity of energy they contain, the relative amounts of these biochemicals in food items has major implications for animals. By considering the number of weak and strong covalent bonds in different molecules, especially in these three classes of molecules, we can understand the energy they contain. One approach to the situation is to count the number of weak, or energy-rich, C–H and C–C bonds and compare them to the number of strong, or energy-poor, C–O and H–O bonds in the various molecules (Figure 1).

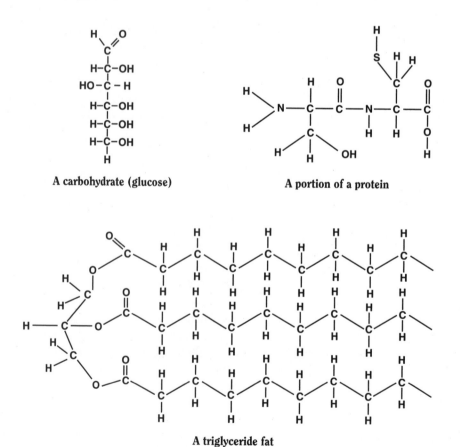

A carbohydrate (glucose)

A portion of a protein

A triglyceride fat

Figure 1. Bonds in three classes of molecules.

FATS

In lipids, only a small percentage of the carbon and hydrogen atoms are connected to oxygen atoms. That means that nearly every bond in a lipid can yield usable energy when an animal eats it.

CARBOHYDRATES

By comparison, each carbon atom has at least one bond with an oxygen atom, as do many of the hydrogen atoms (see Figure 1). Thus, fewer weak bonds are available to be broken, because many of the atoms are already involved in strong bonds.

What do all these bond energies mean in the real world, at the dinner table? Based on what you know of foods and their energy content, which contains more calories per unit of dry weight, sugar (a carbohydrate) or margarine (a lipid)? Why is that so?

PROTEINS

Proteins, which are far more complex in structure than either lipids or carbohydrates, contain numerous C–O bonds (see Figure 1), so they yield less energy than lipids when they are eaten. (In addition, proteins contain nitrogen and a few sulfur atoms.)

FATS: THE IDEAL CHOICE FOR MIGRATION

Storage and use of energy reserves by migrating organisms neatly illustrate how animals capitalize on differences in the energy content of the three major food biochemicals.

Many migrating birds and insects fly continuously for considerable periods of time—from several to many days—without eating. Because lipids are relatively lightweight and energy rich (9.0–9.5 kcal/g versus the 4.2–4.5 kcal/g of carbohydrates or proteins), they are the major source of energy during migration.

In insects, lipids are stored in the thorax and abdomen; birds preparing for migration store fats subcutaneously (under the skin) and in the abdomen.

The North American monarch butterfly is probably the best-known example of a long-range insect migrant. It travels distances of up to 3,200 km. For that purpose, it adds 125% of the lean weight of its thorax and abdomen in lipid reserves.

Size matters in the cost of migration, as it does for so many things. Costs are higher in small organisms: a mosquito weighing 8.2×10^{-3} g expends 35.0 kcal per kg-km, while a laughing gull weighing 310 g expends 1.5 kcal per kg-km.

Exploration 2

CARBONOMETRY: THE CONDENSED VERSION

This simple, accurate technique can determine the carbon content of almost anything that can be burned. That, of course, makes it exceptionally useful for studying carbon and, indirectly, energy storage and transfer in ecosystems, through plants, organisms, litter, dung, whatever.

In Advance

- Read the **Technique: Carbonometry**.

- Prepare your dried samples, if necessary, as described in the Technique.

Materials

- **Dried samples** (approximate size 0.5 to 1.0 g)

- **Carbonometry apparatus**

First, carefully read the Technique. Now you are ready to put carbonometry to work for you. This technique can answer one question: what carbon is available in a substance? Proceed as follows. Make sure you keep track of your data, so you can do the calculations at the end, and so your work is replicable.

Procedure

1. **Prepare your samples and data categories.**
    What materials do you want to investigate? Write them down in your notebook; make sure to indicate where you got each one. Here are some data categories you might include: sample, initial sample weight (mass), time burning, final sample mass, carbon content.

2. **Weigh the dried samples.**
    Weigh the samples to the nearest one-hundredth of a gram and record the weights in your notebook.

3. **Water temperature.**
    Record the temperature of the 200 ml water in the can.

4. **Ignite a sample.**
    Put a sample into the carbonometry apparatus and ignite it.

5. **Time.**
    Keep track of the elapsed time between ignition and when the flames are no longer visible.

6. **Insert the CO_2 tube.**
    When combustion is complete, quickly open the chamber and insert the CO_2 diffusion tube.

7. **Weigh the burned sample.**
    Remove the sample from the carbonometer and weigh it again. Record the weight.

8. **Calculate the carbon released.**
    Using the examples in the Technique, calculate the carbon content.

READING 3
WHO GETS ENERGY, HOW?

If all animals need energy, why are they not all eating the same food? Why is grass calories for cows but roughage for cats? By now, you have an inkling that animal diets vary tremendously and include stuff you likely would not put in your mouth. In fact, nearly everything organic is eaten by some organism. Even the crude petroleum oil that makes up the spills when ocean-traveling oil tankers leak is eaten by some microbes (which are being bred and refined for such clean-up work). Some animals eat only vegetable matter or only animal flesh; some are very broad in their diets or quite specific; some are very efficient and others quite inefficient in their ability to get energy from their food. Here is a thumbnail overview of who eats what and how they get the energy out of it.

ENERGY CAPTURE AND RELEASE

For an animal, energy capture and use consist of four phases: finding and capturing food the animal can digest; ingesting (eating) the food; digesting or biochemically breaking down the food in the digestive tract (so it is in a form that can be used by individual cells); and metabolic respiration (releasing energy in the chemical bonds of the now digested food, which takes place in the cells). We have already considered the first three phases in our study of the energy use equation.

Why Eat?

We already know one reason to eat—to get energy. In addition, animals eat to get ready-made molecules and elements they cannot themselves make biochemically, including amino acids, vitamins, minerals, and roughage. But where is the energy in food? How do organisms get it?

Where Is the Energy?

The digestion process mechanically and chemically breaks complex foods into simpler molecules that can be used by the body. Of special interest to us is the glucose molecule, a simple sugar that is a major end-product of digestion by most organisms. Following a long series of chemical reactions, much of the food ingested by an animal is passed to the animal's cells in the form of glucose. The processes of converting food components (lipids, proteins, and carbohydrates) into glucose and then liberating energy from glucose within cells are crucial, but we will simply point them out here. That is where the energy comes from. (Refer to a biochemistry or introductory biology book for the vivid details of digestion and the Krebs cycle.)

In respiration, cells perform a series of chemical reactions on glucose (or similar molecules) and oxygen, releasing energy in the process. Cells are able to use some of the energy released for growth and maintenance, while some of the energy is lost in the form of heat. The end products of the respiration process are the simple molecules carbon dioxide (CO_2) and water (H_2O).

TYPES OF DIET

Animals can be classed according to their diets. Carnivores eat only the flesh of other animals, herbivores eat only live plant matter, omnivores eat both flesh and plant material, and detritivores eat dead plants, dead animals, and feces. (Detritivores often are discussed along with decomposers, bacteria and fungi that break down the same materials that detritivores eat. The difference is that detritivores actually eat the materials in question.)

Specialists versus Generalists

Human diets are among the most varied in the animal kingdom: we eat many different types of plants, animals, and fungi. Most animals, however, are quite specialized in their diets. Many caterpillars, for example, eat only the leaves of a few specific types of plants. For them, other leaves, fruits and nuts, and meats are not food; either they cannot digest those materials or the items lack essential nutrients. Spiders, on the other hand, are strict carnivores; they can digest no plant materials at all. Even animals that eat a wide variety of things cannot necessarily digest everything. Milkweed leaves, for example, are the only food of monarch butterfly caterpillars, but they are poisonous or at least distasteful to most other feeders.

DIFFERENT DIGESTIONS: GETTING ENERGY OUT OF STUFF

In general, carnivores' digestive systems and enzymes are specialized to break animal flesh into chemical units for growth, maintenance, and energy. Carnivores typically are unable to digest bone, hair, feathers, and the hard external skeletons of insects, so the energy held in those materials is not available to them. (Do you remember one exception to this generalization, one of the Serengeti animals?) The indigestibility of these materials is a great help to ecologists who study carnivores. When they find the dung of a carnivore, they can examine the undigested bones, fur, and insect exoskeletons to discover what the carnivore eats. Owl pellets can be used the same way.

Digesting Plant Material

Plant tissue is largely constructed of carbohydrates of various kinds and would therefore appear to be a fine food source. Very few multicelled animals can make use of this energy directly, however, because much of it is stored in two difficult-to-digest carbon compounds, cellulose and lignin. (They form much of the support material of plants, such as wood.) How is it, then, that in any ecosystem so many animals eat just plant matter and apparently thrive?

Herbivores can get energy from ingesting plants in one of three ways, which might be described "Do it yourself," "Do it yourself inefficiently," and "Get help."

Do it yourself

A few highly unusual species of insects have evolved the physical and chemical systems for biochemically breaking down cellulose (found primarily in plant cell walls). Members of these species are able to digest directly most of the plant material they eat. Not much is known about these insects' rare abilities.

Do it yourself inefficiently

Some herbivores avoid cellulose altogether, simply breaking the hard cell walls (either mechanically by chewing or chemically in their guts) and digesting the <u>contents</u> of the plant cells. While this method avoids the problem of having to digest cellulose, a great deal of energy is left unused, since the cell contents contain only a small portion of the total energy contained in plant tissues. (Remember those large Excretion percentages and dung beetles diets?)

Get help

Finally, most herbivores depend on other organisms to help them release the energy stored in plant tissues. In fact, most of the animals we think of as "herbivores" do eat but cannot directly digest plant matter themselves. They need microorganisms to do the actual digesting of cellulose and lignin. So cows and deer have bacteria living in their guts to digest the cellulose in the grass they eat. Similarly, termites are unable to digest wood and require special bacteria or protozoa in their guts to digest cellulose and lignin. Without their gut bacteria, cows, deer, and termites would starve even if they ate large quantities of grass or wood.

Actually, most herbivores combine mechanical and chemical forces to break down plant tissues. Mammalian herbivores have highly specialized gastrointestinal tracts, which harbor the helpful microorganisms, allow for extended digestion times, and even have multiple compartments, each of which provides a different treatment for the greens. Many also eat their food twice, that is, they chew a cud or ingest their own dung.

(Remember the teeth of mammalian herbivores, which are specialized for crushing and grinding? Examine the mouth parts of herbivorous insects, such as beetles, grasshoppers, and millipedes, to see comparable specializations.)

DETRITUS, THE REAL TREASURE TROVE

Dead plant and animal tissues, along with animal feces, constitute a large and readily available energy source in all ecosystems. As you will see in **Chapter 10**, more energy moves through ecosystems via detritus and detritivores/decomposers than through birds and mammals. Detritivores can also be generalists, or they can specialize in eating dead animals, dung, or dead plant tissue. Some detritivores get a portion of their nutrition by grazing on bacteria and fungi that grow on detritus.

Intake Greater Than 100%

Decomposers have an exceptional energy use budget: it cannot be balanced. Because detritus is already biochemically broken down, that is, decaying, it has much easily available energy, even more than undecayed food after it is ingested and digested. Of course, it helps that decomposers are single-celled. Their energy budget is approximately $I = E (0) + P (40\%) + R (60\%)$. We have seen no other organisms that so efficiently use their intake. And we have seen no other food that can be completely assimilated, that is, where all the energy is available to and taken up by the ingesting organism. Compare this equation with that of your animal (**Chapter 4**). They also have a short lifespan (hours or days) but reproduce (by dividing) often. No wonder decomposers are so successful.

Making a Living and "History"

Although we considered <u>how</u> some species are specialized to eat different foods, we left out one important piece: history. <u>Why</u> are organisms herbivores, carnivores, microbes, or mammals? That has a great deal to do with their evolutionary history—their family tree and ancestors—and what kinds of natural selection they have encountered.

Considering "history" and natural selection also helps answer the question why at another level. Initially we wondered why all animals don't eat the same foods. What if they did? What if they had? What happens if everyone eats the same food type? And what about all those other types that no one is eating? Think back to the finches (**Module 1**).

Ah. Competition. Evolution by natural selection. Diversity. Darwin.

Exploration 3
CARBON AND ENERGY: CLASS DATA PATTERNS

Now we have two kinds of data about the "foods" of some organisms: energy value in kcal/g or kg and the amount of carbon. What is the relationship between the two? Graph the data and discuss the relationship. You may wish to reconsider these questions after you have completed **Chapter 9**.

BONDS
THE "GLUE" AND "SUPER GLUE" OF ENERGY

CONTENTS

OVERVIEW

Let's go submolecular—that is, move from (bio)chemicals to the component bonds in those molecules. How are high- and lower-energy bonds formed? How are carbon and energy functionally related? How does that relationship map onto the foods organisms eat and the energy they can get from those foods? Can we explain the final results of **Chapter 8** (the carbonometry and calorimetry data) by examining bonds and bond types? Having considered something about how much energy is in foods and how organisms get it out, now we are ready to take the discussion to another level—literally!

Exploration 1 (Homework)
POWERHOUSE BONDS

Although we cannot <u>see</u> bonds, we can tell quite a bit about them indirectly and use that information to deepen our understanding of our results from **Chapter 8**, as well as ecological energy availability, transfer, and feeding behavior.

Materials
- **Calculator**
- **Notebook**

Procedure

1. Different bond strengths.

Table 1 provides a list of bond strengths, measured as the amount of energy needed to break a specified number of identical chemical bonds. Are any of the atoms typically found in stronger bonds or weaker bonds?

Table 1   Covalent Bond Strengths or Energies

BOND	STRENGTH OR ENERGY
C–C	82.7 kcal/mole
C–O	83.9
O=O	96.1
C–H	98.7
O–H	110.7
C=C	147.0
C=O	170
C≡C	194

C stands for carbon; O, oxygen; H, hydrogen.
– indicates a single bond; = a double bond; ≡ a triple bond.
kcal/mole stands for kilocalories/mole, where a mole contains 6.02×10^{23} bonds.

Notice carbon. It has the rare and important property of each carbon atom being able to form chemical bonds with up to four other atoms, which allows carbon atoms to become part of very complex molecules. These molecules often take the shape of long chains, with carbon atoms forming the backbone of the chain. (The values listed are average values for each bond type; bond strengths vary somewhat, depending on the types of atoms that are near the bond in question.)

2. Calculations.

Figure 1 shows examples of three classes of biochemicals that vary markedly in the amount of energy they contain. How can we tell? One way is simply to count the number of weak, or energy-rich, bonds and compare that number to the number of strong, or energy-poor, bonds in the various molecules. Do so now and rank the three molecules in Figure 1 by amount of energy.

3. Summary and questions.

Which bonds do you class as energy rich (weak)? Which as energy poor (strong)? Why?

How does this relate to your carbonometry and calorimetry results from **Chapter 8**? Please bring your work to class, and let's find out.

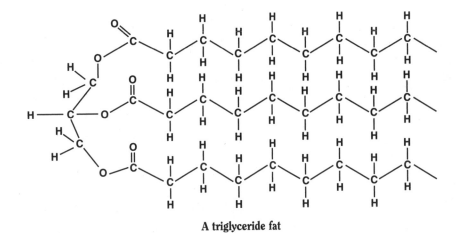

A carbohydrate (glucose)　　　　　A portion of a protein

A triglyceride fat

Figure 1. Bonds in three classes of molecules.

CASE STUDY
FOOD: WHERE IS THE ENERGY?

We have seen that there is energy in food, through the work in **Chapter 8**. But where or how is that energy stored in food? Let's try a thought experiment—the termite-apple diet thought experiment—and look for the energy in termites and apples.

Imagine being small enough to examine individual molecules in both termites and apples. At that level, we would be aware that molecules move, even in apparently solid items. Sometimes the molecules move rapidly (as when their temperature or metabolic rate increase); other times they move slowly. When the molecules are moving quickly, items are warmer (just like the water in the calorimetry soda can).

But such heat, although an important form of (kinetic) energy, is simply the motion of molecules. Unfortunately, neither we nor other animals can easily capture or use that form of energy. We need to find another type of energy in an apple or a termite.

CHEMICAL ENERGY

If we were small enough to see individual atoms within molecules, we would find a different kind of energy. Recall that molecules are made up of multiple atoms bound together. The (chemical) bonds between atoms can be manipulated so that they release chemical energy, the energy that animals use to make a living. (Remember the discussion of energy types in **Chapter 2**, Reading 2?)

Now we are at the level of energy that is biologically and ecologically useful. But how do we get, release, or make that energy available? Let's mess with the bonds and see what happens.

MANIPULATING CHEMICAL BONDS

First, let's break a chemical bond. **To break a bond, we must add energy.** So one of us will eat the termite, and someone else, a piece of apple. Digestion, remember, works more efficiently at warmer temperatures, in part because to break bonds we typically heat the molecule. That means we must use energy to break a chemical bond. By analogy with money, it "costs" energy to break a chemical bond.

In contrast, **energy is released when a chemical bond is formed**. So, as the former termite and apple atoms in our guts are being made into new molecules, energy is being released. When we form chemical bonds between atoms that are not already bonded together, we release energy. In other words, when we form a chemical bond, we receive an energy "payment."

The topic of energy in chemical bonds can seem counterintuitive: the following image may help you remember that it requires energy to break a bond. Imagine two large blocks of wood stuck together with a strong glue. To separate the blocks we probably need a crowbar and the input of a significant amount of energy. Similarly, on the molecular level, we must spend energy to separate atoms (i.e., to break a chemical bond).

Can you "make a living" by breaking and forming the same bond repeatedly? Sorry, but "No." If you were to break apart a chemical bond and then re-form the bond using the original atoms from the original bond, you would find that **the amount of energy required to break a bond is exactly the same as the amount of energy released when the bond is formed**. There is, however, a good way to get ahead in the energy game by breaking and forming bonds.

NOT ALL BONDS ARE CREATED EQUAL

Some chemical bonds are strong, that is, it takes a lot of energy to break them. Other bonds are weak and require less energy to be broken. Viewed from the perspective of bond formation—the other way around— when weak bonds are created, only small amounts of energy are released; when strong bonds are formed, they release large amounts of energy.

	WEAK BONDS	STRONG BONDS
In order to break—	Require less energy	Require more energy
Upon bond formation—	Release less energy	Release more energy

It is this difference in bond energies (or bond strengths) of chemical bonds that allows animals to make a living. Animals acquire the energy they need to survive by eating materials containing chemical bonds that require only a small amount of energy to break (weak bonds) and rearranging the atoms into bonds that yield a lot of energy when they are formed (strong bonds).

In other words, our goal as energy gatherers is to find and gather foods that contain weak chemical bonds; to break the weak bonds (this "costs" energy, but not too much since the bonds are weak); and to form strong bonds among the atoms that were in the weak bonds, which yields large amounts of energy.

The same kinds of atoms are in weak bonds and strong bonds. The molecules we eat are different from the molecules we give off after digesting our food; the atoms have been rearranged. The termites and the apples we ate are quite different, molecularly, from our heat, our tissue (if we are growing), and our dung.

READING 1
CHAPTER 8 REVISITED

Now that we know more about bond types and energies, how they are formed and energy is stored and released, and the role of lipids, carbohydrates, and proteins, perhaps we can better understand our data from **Chapter 8**, Exploration 3.

Now we know that lipids contain more energy per unit weight than carbohydrates or proteins (we showed that using calorimetry) and that lipids contain more carbon per unit weight than proteins, which have slightly more carbon per unit weight than carbohydrates (from our carbonometry studies.)

The punch line is that bond energies and the differences in molecular structure of lipids, carbohydrates, and proteins can help explain the differences in both energy content and carbon content. Lipids contain relatively few oxygen atoms (hence the higher proportion of carbon). That means that most of the carbon and hydrogen atoms in lipids are in weak bonds—specifically, they are not bonded to oxygen—so a great deal of chemical energy is available to be liberated from lipids. In contrast, many of the carbon and hydrogen atoms in carbohydrates and proteins already participate in strong bonds with oxygen atoms, so fewer weak bonds are available per unit weight to yield energy.

Exploration 2

COMBUSTION OF METHANE

Although we are not going to burn methane (sorry!), we will imagine we can and calculate the energies involved in the process.

To help in our understanding of energy transfer or loss during bond formation, let's work out a complete example: the combustion or burning of methane and the formation of water and carbon dioxide that result from that burning. First, we consider the bond energies of the organic (carbon-containing) molecules involved: methane, oxygen, water, and carbon dioxide. Then we see that energy is released when weak bonds in methane and oxygen dissolve, or are broken, and that energy is bound up when strong bonds in water and carbon dioxide are formed.

Materials

- Calculator
- Notebook

Procedure

1. **Breaking the bonds: Calculating the energies.**

   How much energy is released during the combustion (oxidation) of methane? First, calculate how much energy is needed to break the bonds in the methane and oxygen molecules (those to the left of the arrow in Figure 2).

Figure 2

The energy required to break each bond is listed in Table 2. Calculate the total energy required to break all the bonds. Is it a large or a small amount of energy?

Table 2

Covalent Bond Strengths or Energies

BOND	STRENGTH OR ENERGY
C–C	82.7 kcal/mole
C–O	83.9
O=O	96.1
C–H	98.7
O–H	110.7
C=C	147.0
C=O	170
C≡C	194

C stands for carbon; O, oxygen; H, hydrogen.
– indicates a single bond; = a double bond; ≡ a triple bond.
kcal/mole stands for kilocalories/mole, where a mole contains 6.02×10^{23} bonds.

2.   **Rearranging the atoms in those molecules.**
     Now, rearrange the molecules: link each hydrogen and carbon atom to an oxygen atom (i.e., model combustion, which is also called oxidation).

3.   **Making new bonds: Calculating the energies.**
     Calculate the amount of energy released. Compare it to the initial energy (step 1). It is more, right? (See Table 3.) So what has happened? Summarize your results in term of atoms, bonds, molecules, and energy change before, during, and after bond formation.

Table 3   **Energy Calculations in Combustion of Methane**

BONDS BROKEN		BONDS FORMED	
BOND	ENERGY/MOLE (KCAL)	BOND	ENERGY/MOLE (KCAL)
C–H	–98.7	O–H	110.7
C–H	–98.7	O–H	110.7
C–H	–98.7	O–H	110.7
C–H	–98.7	O–H	110.7
O=O	–96.1	C=O	170
O=O	–96.1	C=O	170
TOTAL	–587	TOTAL	783
GRAND TOTAL	–587 kcal + 783 kcal = 196 kcal		

Energy required to break bonds is listed as negative numbers; energy released by bond formation as positive numbers.

READING 2
BONDS AND BOND TYPES

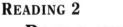

All matter consists of atoms. Atoms typically occur in more or less stable groups with other atoms; these groups are known as molecules. By describing molecules as stable, we mean they persist unless energy, such as heat, is added. Some molecules consist of just two atoms, while others contain thousands of atoms.

Atoms themselves contain a variety of subatomic particles. For our purposes, as the outermost parts of the atom, electrons play a critical role in interactions with other atoms.

The two most important characteristics of a chemical bond are the types of atoms that share the bond (for example, is the bond between an oxygen atom and a hydrogen atom or between two carbon atoms?) and the number of electrons shared by the two atoms. (Remember that electrons are the outermost parts of atoms and therefore the parts of atoms that touch each other in molecules.)

Electrons typically are shared in pairs, and a pair of shared electrons is called a single bond. Two pairs of shared electrons are called a double bond, and three pairs of shared electrons a triple bond. These bonds, in which atoms share one or more pairs of electrons, are called covalent bonds and are important biologically. If we could see a single covalent bond and determine what was happening with the atoms' electrons, we would find that the electrons are shared more or less equally among the atoms.

MOLECULES

Molecules may contain as few as two atoms or as many as thousands of atoms. It is useful to draw diagrams of molecules so we can easily understand the structure of the molecules. Chemists typically designate each atom in a molecule by the one- or two-letter symbol for the element and indicate bonds by drawing lines between the atoms.

The most important elements in organic molecules are carbon (C), oxygen (O), hydrogen (H), and nitrogen (N).

A single bond (a pair of electrons shared by two atoms) is drawn as a single line. For example, a diagram of a water molecule, the familiar H_2O, looks like this:

$$H-O-H$$

Note that the oxygen atom participates in two single bonds, one with each of the hydrogen atoms.

A double bond, that is, two shared pairs of electrons, is drawn as double lines. Molecular oxygen (the form in which we breathe oxygen) consists of two oxygen atoms with a double bond between them. The oxygen molecule diagram looks like this:

$$O=O$$

Finally, a triple bond is drawn as triple lines. Nitrogen gas consists of two nitrogen atoms that share a triple bond:

$$N\equiv N$$

Types of Chemical Bonds

So far, the chemical bonds we have discussed are covalent bonds, in which atoms share one or more pairs of electrons. If you were able to see a single covalent bond and determine what was happening with the atoms' electrons, you would find that the electrons are shared more or less equally between the atoms. (Unfortunately, we cannot study individual bonds in this manner, since to study them would necessarily involve disturbing the electrons.) The bonds in sucrose (table sugar) molecules are covalent.

Another type of chemical bond, which we will not discuss in detail here, is the ionic bond. Ionic bonds are formed between atoms that have acquired one or more extra electrons (known as negative ions) and atoms that are missing one or more electrons (positive ions). Because the two ions have different charges, they are attracted to each other. Common table salt is a good example of a compound that features ionic bonds; salt consists of positive sodium ions (Na^+) and negative chlorine ions (Cl^-). Although ionic bonds play major roles in the functioning of organisms, they are not crucial to a basic understanding of energy exchange, and we will not discuss them further.

What does all this mean? Recall our analogy between money and energy. Let's compare the expenditure of money in manufacturing with the expenditure of energy in gathering and processing food.

MANUFACTURING	GETTING ENERGY FROM FOOD
1. Buy raw materials (costs money).	1. Find and gather foods (costs energy).
2. Work the raw materials (costs money).	2. Break weak bonds in foods (costs a little energy).
3. Form finished products and sell them (earns money).	3. Form strong bonds with atoms that were in weak bonds (earns energy).
If you sell enough products, you make a profit over your costs.	If you form enough strong bonds, you make an energy profit over your costs.

Just as in manufacturing, there are costs involved in making a product. In neither situation can we go without making a profit for a long time. A company without profits eventually goes bankrupt, but if people do not get enough to eat, they eventually get sick or die.

By looking at the process of getting energy from food in this manner, we can see the costs involved in getting energy from foods. There are also energy "costs" in gathering foods. Both these costs must be offset by the energy in the foods eaten. Compare the energy "profits" for two teenagers: a 19th-century farmer and a 20th-century student.

19TH-CENTURY TEENAGE FARMER	20TH-CENTURY TEENAGE STUDENT
Walk to field several times a week	Get in car or bus
Plant potatoes	Drive to market
Weed and care for potato plants	Walk down store aisles
Harvest potatoes and haul to house	Pay for food
Wash, cut up, and cook potatoes	Drive home
Eat 1 lb of potato chips	Eat 1 lb of potato chips

Note that the food intake of the two teenagers is exactly the same. Is there a difference in their energy "profit," once we take their respective energy expenditures into account?

BREAKING AND FORMING CHEMICAL BONDS

Although combustion and the energy-releasing reactions of living organisms begin and end with similar products and both release energy, the processes themselves are remarkably different, as illustrated in Figure 3.

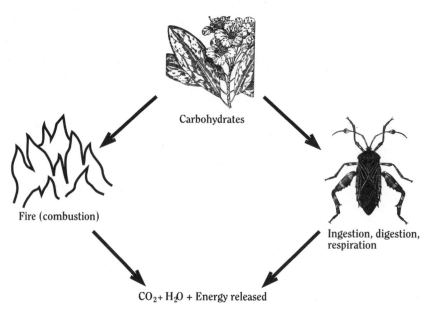

Figure 3. Releasing energy from a carbon compound: Fire and animals compared.

Exploration 3

BOND STRENGTHS: ANALOGY WITH MAGNETS

Chemical bonds, bond strengths, weak bonds, strong bonds—these are complex concepts. To help us better understand them, let's illustrate some of these ideas with magnets.

Granted, the principles governing magnetism are quite different from those governing chemical bonds. Several useful analogies can be made, however, that help explain some aspects of chemical bonds.

Materials
- Small **plastic sandwich bag**, the kind with the folded-over lip and a flap
- **Magnets**, at least 4 (2 each of 2 strengths) per group
- Many **small weights** or a few hundred pennies

Procedure

1. **When is energy released?**
Does the breaking of a chemical bond require **input** of energy, or is energy **released** when a bond is broken? Use two magnets, each of which will act as, or model, an atom. How does magnet behavior resemble that of atoms?

Set up the magnets so they are attracted to and touch one another. To break the bond, that is, separate the two magnets modeling as atoms, what do you do? Does it require energy?

2. **Pulling apart magnets or atoms.**
Yes, you need to apply some muscular force to pull the magnets apart. Not much force, perhaps, but force—and force is energy. So, too, chemical

energy must be applied to separate atoms that are bonded together in a molecule.

3. **Measuring magnet-atom bond energies.**
    To measure the strength of the bond between two magnets (atoms) that are attracted to each other, use a small plastic sandwich bag, weights, and magnets.

4. **The setup.**
    Place some weights in the bag. Put one of the magnets inside the folded-over lip and the other magnet opposite it, on the outside of the plastic.

5. **The bond.**
    Slowly lift the upper magnet, making sure you are not touching the plastic bag. The only support for the weight should be the magnetic attraction between the two magnets.

    Add weights to the bag until the magnets can no longer maintain their attraction (bond) and lift the bag and weights. Then reduce the number of weights slightly, until you have a maximum weight that can be lifted.

6. **Different bond strengths.**
    Repeat with other pairs of magnets, to collect data on a series of bond strengths. If you have two magnets of each of two types, you can obtain the following six measurements: A1 with A2, A1 with B1, A1 with B2, A2 with B1, A2 with B2, and B1 with B2.

7. **Class discussion and summary.**
    Summarize what you have discovered about bonds and energy from your calculations and by using magnets in the role of atoms to "form" and "dissolve " bonds.

COMMUNITIES ARE SOLAR POWERED

CHAPTER TEN

OVERVIEW

No organism exists in a vacuum—or does it? So far we have focused on individual organisms: how they get and allocate their energy. But we have yet to consider much about interactions among organisms. We have mentioned a few kinds of interactions—eating and being eaten, competition, parasitism—but we have yet to explore the flow of energy between organisms rather than just within one organism.

Using our two ecosystems and the animals from **Chapter 4**, we consider how energy cycles, or flows, and where it builds up, or pools, in ecosystems. How many deer does a wolf eat per year? How many wildebeest can the Serengeti grasses feed? Why? How do the lifestyles of salamanders and chickadees influence their effects on the energy flow of their whole ecosystems?

Exploration 1
FOOD WEBS: IS ANY SPECIES INDEPENDENT?

Up to now, we have studied several aspects of energy use by the species from two ecosystems, such as their caloric intake and how they use that energy. But what about relations between species? Can any nonplant species exist without others? Is any species actually independent of other species?

238

Materials
- **Animal cards (Chapter 4)**
- **List of organisms for each ecosystem** (near the beginning of Reading 1a and Reading 1b)

Procedure

1. **Making predictions.**
    From what you remember about your animal, do you think it is independent? Why or why not? Please jot your thoughts in your notebook.

2. **Checking with the data.**
    Reread the data on your animal. What does your organism eat? What eats your organism? How does that match—or not match—your thoughts? Why did you make your initial prediction? Please note that also.

3. **Diet.**
    Based on its diet, is your animal an herbivore, a carnivore, an omnivore, or a scavenger or detritivore?

4. **For plant eaters only.**
    If your animal eats plants, which part(s) does it eat? When ecologists consider plant matter as food, they often divide it into three rough categories: grass, other nonwoody plants (often called herbs), and fruits; woody tissue and leaves of woody plants; and nuts and seeds. Do many animals eat woody tissue? Why? How might that affect where your animal lives—in which ecosystem, say?

5. **Picturing the data.**
    Ecologists usually represent energy flow between organisms by arrows. Draw a picture in your notebook for your animal that represents all interactions between your animal and other organisms in the ecosystem (check the list of selected animals, if that helps, in Readings 1a and 1b).

    The arrows represent energy coming into or going out of your animal, based on your answer from step 2. Are there arrows in more than one direction from your animal? Why? Now do you think any organism is independent of other species? Why?

6. **Moving on.**
    In the next class, everyone puts his or her animal-and-arrows picture on poster board or the board, to get an integrated picture of how each animal fits in with and interacts with the other organisms in its ecosystem.

READING 1A

THE SERENGETI ECOSYSTEM

High plains, rimmed by rock escarpments, are dotted with spiny acacia trees. What catches your eye, though, are the animals: wildebeest, gazelles, other antelopes, giraffes, zebras—millions of hoofed animals moving across the land. Among the thousands of smaller grazers move Cape buffalo, elephants, and rhinoceroses; in permanent water, hippopotamuses congregate in noisy herds. There are hunters following the herds, of course: lions, cheetahs, leopards, wild dogs, hyenas, jackals. And scavengers abound—at least eight species of vultures, griffins, and scavenging storks. In the trees, on the ground, in the soil, dozens of other species are at work, but the eye is drawn first to the large animals, the big cats, the great herds, the circling birds. In fact, some researchers have defined the Serengeti Ecological Unit (SEU) not by physical boundaries, but by behavioral ones: it is the area included in the annual migratory cycle of the great wildebeest herd.

Here, as in earlier chapters, we are working with a (small) subset of Serengeti organisms so we can study them in more detail. They are already familiar to you from **Chapter 4**. We present the list here, because now we are considering them as an assemblage of interacting organisms, and it is helpful to have an overview of the players.

spotted hyena	rock hyrax
wild dog	bush hyrax
cheetah	Thomson's gazelle
lion	wildebeest
leopard	elephant
banded mongoose	topi
slender mongoose	hartebeest
impala	plains zebra

LOCATION AND ABIOTIC FACTORS (SUCH AS SEASONS)

The Serengeti Plain lies just below the equator, about 50 km southeast of Lake Victoria, in Tanzania. It is located between 34° and 36° east longitude and 1°15' to 3°30' south latitude. The ecological system covers about 25,000 km². It is limited on the north by the Loita plains of Kenya, which are dry and inhospitable at the time when migrants move north. The east is bounded by the wooded Loita hills, the south by the Lake Eyasi escarpment, and the west by the Isuria escarpment.

Around November, the short rains come, so that month can be called the beginning of the seasonal year. Rains may continue off and on into March, with perhaps a break in January and February. The long rains appear from March to May. The seasons are different in different areas: rains start in the north and move south. The drying sequence does the opposite, starting in May on the plains, and ending in July in the north. Differences in topography and geography also mean that some areas have a lot less rain than other places.

GRASSLANDS

The amazing array of animals in the Serengeti depends on the grass. Other such massive concentrations of large mammals once also existed on other grasslands over the past few millions of years. But the grassland systems of Asia, Europe, and North America are largely gone now, destroyed by the plough. In South America, the pampas remain, though diminished; in North America, remnants live on in reserves like Yellowstone National Park and other fragments of the old plains. A glimpse of former variety and abundance can be seen in the evidence from the La Brea Tar Pits, in Los Angeles, and other fossil sites.

Only on the Serengeti, though, does something like the original assemblage of species remain, with many kinds of grass eaters, many kinds of predators, many kinds of scavengers. In most other terrestrial ecosystems, the trees dominate the scene; on the Serengeti, the animals are on center stage, wading through a sea of grasses. Such a fantastic amount of animal life implies a vast, dependable source of food. Grasses are the conduit for tremendous amounts of energy, harvested by herbivores and, in turn, by predators, with plenty left over for the "clean-up" creatures that ultimately keep carbon flowing and make it possible for the system to continue.

THE GRASSES THEMSELVES

The Serengeti is a grassland or, more precisely, a savannah, which is a grassland with some trees and shrubs dotting the area. Grasslands now constitute 12% of the earth's terrestrial surface, although once they covered as much as 40%. Grasslands occur in many forms, depending on the moisture available and the species of grass present. They occur in tropical and temperate latitudes, where the rainfall averages between 200 and 800 mm per year. More rain than that, and continuous forest can grow; less than that, and the area is a desert, supporting sparse and often shrubby vegetation.

It is not the case, though, that grassland is produced by climatic conditions alone. Much of the American prairie has now become wooded or dominated by other types of vegetation. Grasslands in other parts of the world have changed to open woodlands or to deserts (as in the growing Sahara), depending on the types of disturbance they have undergone. Grasslands are maintained as such because of a balance of limited rainfall and two other important factors: wildfires and grazing. We will not address fires here, but turn to the grass-herbivore partnership.

The primary production that feeds the whole Serengeti system is concentrated in the grasses, which are the dominant features of the vegetation. Most of these are perennial grasses, called bunch grasses. They have extensive fibrous root systems, are tolerant of drought, and are well adapted to being grazed by herbivores.

The ways that grasses have evolved to deal with being grazed, especially with being cropped so close to their roots, help maintain the Serengeti grassland. How grasses grow, what is called their "growth habit," ensures that normal grazing will not harm them, despite the loss of so much biomass. Unlike most other flowering plants, the growing "tip" of a grass (called the meristem) is not actually at the outermost tip but at the base of the plant. Thus, when a gazelle bites off a grass blade, the grass can keep growing.

Moreover, once the grass is bitten off, the plant responds with a heightened photosynthetic rate, which fuels regrowth. Regrowth means that the plant grows new tissue. This new tissue differs from the grass blades it has replaced in two ways. Because it is newly grown, it has relatively more photosynthetic cells (which is good for the grass plant) and is more nutritious because it contains less fibrous structural material (which is good for the herbivores).

The extensive root systems of grass also are important for plant regrowth after grass blades have been munched off by herbivores. The roots store energy that the plant can use for growing photosynthetic tissue. Then the photosynthetic tissue "captures" the sun's energy, some of which is stored back in the roots, as reserves for the next time the grass blades get eaten, and so on.

In addition to growth habits that help grasses survive being grazed, grasses also have some ways of keeping themselves from being eaten in the first place. Many have silica in their leaves, especially the older leaves. Silica is a mineral that makes the plant tissue harder both to chew and to digest. Thus, some herbivores avoid older grass blades or dried grass, both of which have relatively higher amounts of silica.

THE BENEFITS OF BEING GRAZED

While grasses are equipped to resist or to recover from damage from grazing, grazing also benefits the grass plants in several ways. When grasses are not grazed, dead leaves, grass stems, and other plant parts accumulate over the course of the seasons. This "thatch" can shade grass leaves and thus reduce the plant's productivity. Thatch also shades the soil. Shade can help protect the ground from drying, but it also prevents the germination of seeds and the establishment of new plants. Finally, thatch, being dead, dry plant matter, burns easily, so the more thatch there is, the greater the chance of fire. Once a fire has started, it burns hotter the more thatch is present (thatch is a good fuel). The hotter the fire, the more likely it is to kill seeds and damage or kill plants. In the Serengeti, the huge numbers of herbivores tend to keep thatch from forming.

Grazers also recycle the nutrients immobilized in plant tissues, making them available for new growth. That includes materials that otherwise would form the thatch of dead leaves, which would act as a reservoir of nutrients, which would be inaccessible for long periods. As noted elsewhere, herbivores often absorb (make metabolic use of) only about 50% of what they eat; the rest is waste in various forms.

Grazing also can benefit grasses by removing plants that are palatable to the grazers but not as well adapted to grazing. That reduces competition from herbs and the seedlings of trees and shrubs, which would shade the grass (i.e., outcompete the grass for sunlight) or outcompete the grass for water or other nutrients. It even has been suggested that the saliva of grazing herbivores can stimulate grass growth, and some experiments support that hypothesis.

The grasses of the Serengeti (and other grasslands) are thus adapted to grow vigorously under conditions imposed by climate and by the animals that eat the grasses. "Vigorous growth" means that a system has a high primary productivity over the course of the year. Savannahs (such as the Serengeti) have an average net primary production (above ground) of 900 g/m^2/year of dry-weight biomass; under good conditions, the productivity may be as high as 2,000 g/m^2/year.

Note that the below-ground production, in the roots, may be equal in size, or even larger. This is in sharp contrast to the situation in forests. There, the dominant vegetation has much woody tissue, which is unavailable except to specialists. In the Northern Hardwood Forest, perhaps 20–30% of annual primary production is in woody tissue. In grasslands, essentially all the above-ground primary production is edible, which enables a much greater harvest. Thus, while less than 1% of primary production in a forest may be consumed by herbivores, it is estimated that up to 18% of primary production in grasslands like the Serengeti is consumed by herbivores. That means there is a much larger flow of energy through the herbivores in a grassland system than in the forests. You can perhaps imagine some consequences from that fact.

SERENGETI ORGANISMS

The Serengeti supports a tremendous variety of herbivores of all sizes and specialties. The unique feature of this ecosystem is the large number of species of large-bodied herbivores and the size of their populations. Elephants, rhinoceroses, giraffes, and Cape buffalo share the stage, but the vast majority of the herbivores are antelopes. R. D. Estes calls Africa "the land of antelopes." These members of the Bovidae occur in just about every ecosystem in Africa (and extend into Asia as well), from rain forest to desert. On the plains of the Serengeti, there are seventeen species of antelope, from the cow-size eland to the little dik-dik. Some species remain in more or less the same region throughout the year; most make some seasonal movement. Perhaps the most prominent migrants are wildebeest, Thomson's gazelles, and the non-bovid zebras.

WHAT DO YOU MEAN BY AN AVERAGE ANTELOPE?

In this Module and in other publications, you will see numbers that characterize some feature of an organism or system. For example, you might read that 62% of a Thomson's gazelle's intake consists of grass. Data like that on food intake are averages. The data were obtained by identifying and counting food particles from the rumens (part of the stomachs) of wild animals. To ensure that the animals had about the same food plants available to them, several animals from the same place were shot at the same time, and their rumen contents analyzed. Thus, the data include observations on more than one animal, combined as an average.

Ecological data can be collected at more than one season of the year. (Thomson's gazelle data used in this Unit are for the dry season in the

Serengeti. For other species, data were obtained during both the wet and the dry seasons.) And data can be taken for more than one year, on animals from more than one area, or on animals of both sexes or different ages.

It is important to know just what is in a set of data, and careful researchers always label their data. That way, a reader knows what the data definitely include versus what they might be assumed to include. For instance, the Thomson's gazelle data do specify season, area, and when the data were collected. The data imply animal age as adult, although they do not specify that. And they apparently include both sexes. The researchers involved must have reasoned that for their purposes, the sex of the animals was not important. They may have combined data from equal numbers of both males and females, from only one sex, or from any combination of males and females. But if, for instance, we were testing hypotheses of possible sex differences in diet, we would not combine data from males and females.

THE UNGULATES

The largest group of herbivores on the Serengeti is the ungulates. The term "ungulate" means "hoofed animal" and refers to two different orders of diverse and successful animals. The even-toed ungulates (Artiodactyla) include major groups such as the cow family (Bovidae), which comprises cattle, sheep, goats, and gazelles (along with a few smaller groups); the deer family (Cervidae); the giraffes (Giraffidae) and the camels (Camelidae); and the pigs (Suidae) and the hippopotamuses (Hippopotamidae). The odd-toed ungulates (Perissodactyla) is a smaller group that includes the horses (Equidae), the tapirs (Tapiridae), and the rhinoceroses (Rhinocerotidae). In addition, there are several orders sometimes called primitive ungulates, which include the elephants (Probiscidea), the hyraxes (Hyracoidea), and the aardvark (Tubulidentea), the last representative of a once-widespread family. (A slightly more distant group of relatives is Sirenia, which comprises sea cows and manatees.)

What besides hooves makes an animal an ungulate? And why is all this anatomical detail important to an ecologist interested in carbon and energy?

Ungulate Digestion Systems

The ungulates as a group exploit a wide range of plant material that is high in fiber. The carbohydrate construction materials, such as cellulose, that make up fiber are hard to digest, which means the energy (and nutrients) contained in them is harder to extract. As you may remember, few organisms have the ability to break down those carbon compounds to extract the energy they contain. Thus, multicellular organisms that eat such foods generally must have developed a partnership with bacteria that can begin the digestion process. Gut-dwelling anaerobic bacteria ferment the vegetable matter and turn the complex carbohydrates into simpler sugars, which the host organism can then metabolize.

Ungulates have two strategies for this digestion process; both strategies have the effect of giving the bacteria time to do their work by retaining the food matter in the gut long enough for the fermentation process to happen. Foregut fermenters, such as wildebeest and gazelles (and cows), have elaborate chambered stomachs, which allow fermentation to take place in a series of stages, each operating on the output of the previous stage. Such animals chew their food twice, first on eating it, and second as "chewing the cud." The bacteria have begun to work during the first chewing, but cud chewing shreds the fibers more finely, creating more surface area for the bacteria to work on. This multistage process allows the animal to extract a higher percentage of the calories from the food.

Hindgut fermenters, such as elephants (and horses), harbor their bacterial symbionts in the latter part of the digestive tract, after the stomach. They do not chew the cud and do not retain the ingested matter for as long, so their digestion is less complete than that of foregut fermenters. They must, therefore, ingest larger amounts of food for their body size or specialize in new plant growth, which is less fibrous and also higher in protein and other nutrients (per unit weight).

Ecologically speaking, these details matter because ungulates are well equipped to eat a diet high in fiber, such as grass, and to do so they must eat in high volume. It also means that the variation in size and digestive strategy among the ungulates means that different parts of the plant resources will be exploited by different species. This is most clearly seen in the Serengeti in the grazing succession: the seasonal parade of animal species that follow the grasses' annual cycles and each other, partitioning the primary productivity in such a way that the Serengeti fauna exploits the energy resources to a unique degree.

THE PREDATORS

The vast herbivore population provides rich resources for a wide variety of predators, including hyenas and the aardwolf, several members of the dog family (the bat-eared fox, the jackal, and the wild dog), and several cats, including three big cats (the lion, the leopard, and the cheetah). The leopard is the most versatile of the big cats, eating protein in almost any form, from insects to middle-size antelopes. The lion, which works in groups, is adapted for the hunting of larger herbivores, especially larger antelope such as the wildebeest. The cheetah is the most specialized of the three, taking the medium to small antelopes, especially the Thomson's gazelle.

The cheetah, like the leopard and the lion, had until recent times a very wide range, covering much of Africa, Arabia, and parts of Asia as far as India (where it became extinct in the 1950s). Now it is widely but thinly distributed south of the Sahara. It is between the lion and the leopard in size: average height is around 78 cm and average weight around 50 kg, though males tend to be ±10 kg larger than females. It preys on the faster antelopes, such as Thomson's and other gazelles, the blackbuck, and the springbok. In some areas of the cheetah's range, it is possible for the animals to specialize on one or a few prey species; in the Serengeti, for example, many cheetahs specialize in Thomson's gazelles. The close linkage between these species in such areas makes them a good subject for the study of trophic relationships.

Cheetahs have large hunting ranges. For example, one authority claims that a typical range of female cheetahs that specialize on Thomson's gazelles is around 1,000 km², though some that followed gazelles that did not migrate as far had territories one-fifth that size. By contrast, the areas defended by males averaged 39–78 km². (This reverses the usual behavior of big cats, in which males have larger territories than females.) Young males wander great distances until they locate a suitable place to establish their own territories.

A famous thing about the cheetah is its great speed—its top speed is around 90–112 kph (60–70 mph), but it has to overtake prey within about 300 m. The cheetah's reliance on superior speed, expended in a burst, shapes its foraging habits: it outruns its prey by surprising it at short range. Thus, it needs to live in savannah and other areas that have bushes, termite mounds, and other features that can cover its approach to within sprinting distance. By contrast, a hunter such as the wild dog may be able to reach only about 50 kph (35 mph), but it can maintain that speed for as long as 5 km. That, plus hunting in packs, makes its hunting strategy very different from the cheetah's.

Cheetahs are not social in the same way that lions are, although coalitions form among siblings from the same litter. Cheetah litters separate from the mother as a group; the females slowly leave the sibling group over a few months before they reach reproductive maturity, at about two years old. Coalitions of juveniles sometimes cooperate to bring down larger prey.

We will return below to the Serengeti's cheetahs, because their heavy reliance on the Thomson's gazelle makes it relatively easy to understand the way they get and expend energy.

THE INDISPENSABLE CLEAN-UP CREW

Once I was an autotroph;
Earth, air, sun met all my needs.
I'd stand, and catch some rays, and loaf
Unless I felt like setting seeds.

But now I'm a detritivore;
My life of leisure's through.
I chew and chew and chew and chew
And chew and chew and chew.

Energy enters an ecosystem when it is captured by the primary producers—the plants. As you have read, organisms make use of energy in respiration, breaking carbon bonds and using the energy to power various processes, including maintenance and storage. The carbon (and other elements) are not used up, of course, but merely recombined over and over in

myriad forms. In every ecosystem, a high proportion of the energy-containing compounds remain unused—vegetable matter that falls directly to the ground or that passes through the gut of herbivores undigested and animal tissue, either directly (through death and decay) or indirectly (as food for a predator).

All this matter is not available to the rest of the ecosystem yet, because it is not in a form that many organisms can use. The detritivores and decomposers are the organisms that finally use the remaining energy and release the nutrients and carbon back into the cycle.

Although all these organisms are considered to be part of the decomposition cycle, it is useful to make a distinction between detritivores and decomposers. The distinction is based both on size and on trophic characteristics. By detritivores, we mean multicellular organisms—insects and other arthropods, worms, nematodes—that shred or otherwise break up the organic matter that is their food, increasing the surface area that is available to the decomposers and also making some material available after it has passed through their digestive tracts. The decomposers, including fungi and bacteria, absorb chemicals from organic matter, rather than ingesting complex pieces of organic matter using a mouth of some kind.

The herbivores of the Serengeti process a huge amount of vegetable matter of all kinds but (as mentioned before) assimilate only about 50% of it. There is, therefore, a lot of dung around (from a million wildebeest, half a million Thomson's gazelles, and perhaps another 1.5 million other ungulates). Dung, therefore, is a major potential source of nutrients, and there are organisms specialized to exploit it. The ecology of this guild of dung exploiters is quite complex. As a way of introducing this crucial part of the energy flow of an ecosystem, we present the dung beetle.

Dung Beetles

Many organisms, for some part of their life-cycle, require a resource that is randomly (i.e., unpredictably) available. That usually means the organism cannot predict when the resource will be available, in what amounts, in what locations, and within reach of how many competitors. Vultures face this problem; so too do plants that require specialized conditions for the establishment of their seeds. A prime example of such a patchily available resource is the dung of large herbivores. As we have seen, herbivores typically assimilate half of what they ingest. That means they are excreting or otherwise ejecting a large proportion of the food they have collected. Their dung is thus a concentrated, somewhat processed source of nutrients and energy for plants (when it has decayed enough to act as fertilizer) and also for some animals that have specialized to exploit this bonanza. Perhaps the most conspicuous of such creatures are the dung beetles.

Beetles occur in fantastic variety and numbers around the world. They often are very beautiful, with wing covers that are jewel-like, metallic, or like porcelain china in a range of colors. Beetles are a very successful group: about 250,000 species have been named, and that is certainly an underesti-

mate, perhaps one-tenth of the existing species. (It is also roughly equivalent to the number of all the world's known plant species.)

Dung beetles are a numerous group within the beetles, numbering about 7,000 species (by comparison, there are about 8,600 bird species in the world). They are rather similar in shape but vary in size. Their lifestyles are also varied. Cambefort and Hanski classify dung beetles into three behavioral or functional groups: the dwellers, the tunnelers, and the rollers.

Dwellers have the most unspecialized habits. They find the dung, then inhabit it, eat it, and lay their eggs in it. They do not construct nests or otherwise defend the dung from competitors. If the dung pat is large, several beetles may use it, in addition to the other insects that exploit this resource. Thus, the adults and the larvae are vulnerable to competition both for food and for space within the dung pat.

Tunnelers adopt a strategy like that of burying beetles: they dig a tunnel below the dung, and transport some or all of the dung into the nest, where it can be eaten and used in incubating the young. This strategy means adults compete for a share of the dung pat, both for food and space, but the eggs and the grubs are protected against competition.

Finally, the most specialized of the beetles, the rollers, rush up to the dung pat, form some or all of it into a ball, then roll the ball to a nest some distance away. That eliminates competition by larvae and also competition among adults for space: the adults take what they need, and it is only in the securing of their share of dung that they compete. (Actually, as we might predict, a few species of dung beetle have evolved a strategy that eliminates this struggle at the dung pat: they find and parasitize the nests of other beetles.)

Dung beetles occur in fantastic numbers—someone once counted 1,600 of these creatures on one pile of elephant dung that weighed perhaps 1.5 kg. The beetles do not know where the next opportunity will come, so they are very sensitive to the presence of fresh dung and follow a scent trail rapidly to its source. Very large beetles, such as *Heliocopris*, can monopolize a small deposit of dung, but at the larger piles there is an amazing competition for the resource.

READING 1B
THE NORTHERN HARDWOOD FOREST

The Northern Hardwood Forest (NHF) is a type of ecosystem that occurs in the United States from Maine to Minnesota and south to parts of Ohio, central New England, Illinois, and Wisconsin—areas of strong seasonal changes, deep winter cold, and plentiful precipitation. It fits in between the spruce-fir (boreal) forests to the north, and the oak-hickory and other forest types to its south. Although it shares many characteristics of each of these other forests, it has a character of its own, which results from the combination of abiotic and biotic characteristics that meet there. This is a layered world where growth has been undisturbed for decades, and a canopy of the tallest trees shades everything else. The light that spills or leaks through the canopy is caught by understory trees, small trees that get by in a dimmer world. Below those trees are shrubs and saplings, and below them the wildflowers and ferns, which somehow must make their living on 2–20% of the light that strikes the area.

In, under, and around all the trees, shrubs, and herbs, animals abound. Most people, however, walking through a forest, do not see any of the animals. The plants get in the way, of course, but the animals specialize in concealment. The average Northern Hardwoods animal weighs less than a kilogram, in fact, probably less than half that—the most numerous and important animals are insects, rodents, birds, and small predators above and below ground.

In contrast to a place like the Serengeti grassland, where the animals account for a high percentage of the total biomass, ecologists of the Northern Hardwood Forest sometimes completely discount the animal biomass in their estimates—the trees are for biomass.

When you walk through the forest, you get a strong impression of differences. Here there is a lot of undergrowth, there almost none; here lots of young trees, there few; here is a hemlock stand, there it is oaks and blueberries. Things tend to be moister toward downhill, drier uphill. The vegetation changes noticeably with each change in the topography, and practically every patch is in the midst of a change as well. The more you look, the more you see the forest as a dynamic mosaic; the animals that dwell there also must participate in these endless developments.

In this, as in earlier chapters, we are working with a (small) subset of Northern Hardwoods animal organisms, so we can study them in more detail. They are already familiar to you from **Chapter 4**. We present the list here, because now we are considering them as an assemblage of interacting organisms, and it is helpful to have an overview of the players.

shorttail weasel	blue jay
red-backed salamander	black-capped chickadee
shorttail shrew	beaver
gray wolf	deer mouse
great horned owl	Eastern cottontail
red squirrel	garter snake
Eastern chipmunk	whitetail deer
gray fox	

THE PLANTS

Forests have a structure, shaped by the competition for light. As they mature, overstory or canopy trees overtop other plants, so their top leaves receive the maximum light available in that location. In the Northern Hardwood Forest, the canopy species include sugar maple *(Acer saccharum)*, American beech *(Fagus grandifolia)*, yellow birch *(Betula allegheniensis)*, mixed with white pine *(Pinus strobus)* and hemlock *(Tsuga canadensis)*. Below the canopy, each layer that develops intercepts more and more light, until at the forest floor the plants may receive less than 15% of the incoming light.

Some of these plants are well adapted to life in the shade—species such as Canada mayflower *(Maianthemum canadense)*, flowering dogwood *(Cornus florida)*, and hobblebush *(Viburnum alnifolium)*. By contrast, some herbs exploit the seasonal leaflessness of the canopy—they sprout, flower, and set fruit before the canopy leaves come out, when the most light is reaching the forest floor. Such species include trout lily *(Erythronium americanum)*, the exotic-looking fringed polygala *(Polygala paucifolia)*, and trilliums *(Trillium)*. Although these herbs catch our eye with their blossoms, they fix a rather small amount of carbon (and therefore energy) in a typical forest (in one study, no more than about 2.7%).

The vast majority (well over 90%) of the biomass and of annual production is in the trees. Not all trees have lifetimes many centuries long; for many trees, the life expectancy is between 100 and 150 years. Still, their strategy is to invest in supporting structure, to get leaves up into the sunlight—that means a big investment in wood (a long-term investment) as well as in leaves and other disposable organs (such as fine roots). They reproduce annually or less often, but many times in their lives.

VEGETATION AND ITS EFFECTS

Much of the primary production is temporary, and the rest is hard to use. For instance, of the sunlight that strikes a forest, perhaps 1% is captured in carbon compounds. Of that, 50–55% is used for the plants' respiration. Of the rest, perhaps 20% is used for wood. The remainder is in leaves and fine roots, which are discarded at the end of the season or even more frequently. The leaves have a life-cycle of their own: when they are young, their metabolism runs fast, and they use a lot of energy in their growth and expansion, often more than they capture. At that time, they are most vulnerable to plant eaters. When they mature and are "paying their own way," they have a higher proportion of fibrous supportive and vascular tissue, and they probably also are producing poisonous or distasteful secondary compounds. Toward the end of the season, they are less efficient at light capture than before, and have less energy to defend, repair, and maintain themselves. And toward the end of that process, the green fades, and the woods change color.

The wood, as we know, is a resource that is exploited only by specialists, such as termites and some other insect species, plus bark specialists such as beaver and other rodents. Therefore, wood is a food source mostly when the plant has died or when a branch or twig has fallen to the ground and the decay process has begun.

CHANGE OVER TIME

Several dynamics are at work in the forest that produce change over time. One dynamic is competition for light. Some plants, such as hemlock and sugar maple, have a high tolerance for shade; others, such as oaks or white pine, need more sunlight to reach maturity. Some species require sunny conditions for their seeds to germinate, but when they reach maturity they can tolerate much shadier conditions. Some species, such as sugar maple, can live as saplings for long periods in the understory, shaded by oaks, other maples, and conifers. When a branch or tree falls and a gap opens, however, they shoot up toward the light; their growth spurt enables them to move into the canopy, thus gaining access to greater resources for photosynthesis. The differing needs of the various plant species for different light conditions mean that changes in a forest site will almost always result in a change in the mix of species there, at least for a while.

Another dynamic is disturbances. Several kinds of disturbance are a permanent part of the forest system, even when no human effects are present. The notion that a forest is unchanging unless humans "damage" it is a fiction. That is not to say that humans do not often create disturbances that change the forest, but it does mean that at a certain scale the ecosystem maintains itself in the face of such changes.

The principal disturbance that triggers others in the forest is the fall of a tree (or many trees). Once a gap in the canopy opens, there is an area of brighter light, more direct rainfall, and greater air circulation. There may be bare soil (where tree roots have tipped up), in which seeds can germinate with little competition from established plants. Birds and other animals may come to such openings, foraging for food, nesting sites, or other resources; preying on plants and seeds; and bringing with them other seeds. Saplings and shrubs may put on a burst of growth and harbor new seedlings in their shadow.

The tree or branch fall that releases all this activity may be the result of disease, snow damage, or high winds. It may be simulated by human activities, such as logging, road building, farming, or wood gathering. It sometimes may result from the other native source of disturbance, fire, which removes litter and undergrowth, lays bare the soil, cracks open or otherwise stimulates some seeds, and weakens some trees, making them more vulnerable to wind damage.

The requirements of a tree species for light and other specific conditions may mean that it is a temporary resident of an area (temporary, that is, as a tree would understand it). Cherry trees and white pine, for example, often establish themselves in old fields, but when other tree species come in, no new cherry trees establish in their shade, and the new recruits are maples, oaks, or birches. When a gap appears, cherry or pine may arrive and settle again. The whole replacement process happens again, in each place a little differently, depending on what vegetation is present at the time and what happens to arrive there. For example, when hemlock establishes in the shade of beeches or maples, it slowly grows and spreads. When it reaches

canopy size, it casts such a deep shade that little except hemlocks can grow there—until one falls, and a maple or beech settles in.

Thus, though we may say that a forest has the same species it had 200 years ago, on the local scale it may look very different from decade to decade. These changes over time are called succession. In each kind of ecosystem, succession has a characteristic shape—the pioneer herbs, the first trees and bushes to come to an opening, then the canopy species that start in the understory layer but later overtop and overshade their competitors. For a time, the canopy species dominate the environment in an area, drawing in the bulk of its resources, producing the bulk of the new plant tissue, and thus playing the central role in nutrient and energy cycling. The trees provide the scaffolding on and around which the other organisms in the forest build their lives.

THE HERBIVORES

Herbivores take little of the energy fixed by the primary producers. In some studies of energy flow in the Northern Hardwood Forest, all the herbivores together used no more than 2% of the energy captured in a year. Nevertheless, the Northern Hardwood Forest has a diverse collection of plant eaters, most of them hard to see. They include such stars as caterpillars (perhaps the most important herbivores), beetles, ants, sap-sucking insects such as aphids, specialists in fruits or seeds (rodents, weevils, birds), and larger animals that eat leaves and new twigs, such as porcupines and deer.

Although the animals account for little of the biomass and therefore are not important in the overall energy accounting for a hardwood forest, they play other critical roles. For example, animals—in these woods, mostly the insects and hummingbirds—are a primary means of communication between plants of the same species, as they carry pollen from flower to flower. Animals also often serve as plants' "legs"—seeds are carried on animals' fur, in their digestive tracts, and in their beaks or mouths and dropped in places where new colonies of the plant can start. In that way, the animals contribute in an essential way to the renewal of the forest.

In terms of energy, of course, the herbivores are the link between the energy gatherers—the plants—and the carnivores, as well as all the creatures that derive their energy from animal tissues and by-products—the carrion feeders, the parasites, the dung users, and so forth. Let's begin with an animal that lives on a scale that is easy for humans to understand—the whitetail deer. Remember, though, that in the forest the large mammals are only a tiny part of the consumer energy picture, and the consumers are a small part of the energy picture for the whole forest.

Whitetail Deer (*Odocoileus virginianus*)

The whitetail deer lives in every one of the 48 contiguous states, as well as in almost all of Canada's provinces. The deer may be the most familiar forest creature, not just from movies and books, but because in many places their numbers are increasing rapidly. Large numbers of them live near big cities—there are thousands in such populated states as New Jersey, Pennsylvania, and Massachusetts. This population boom is taking place in large part because their habitat is increasing (the forests are expanding) and because their principal predators—wolves and cougars—were long ago suppressed by human activity. They are favorite prey for human recreational hunters, but only a small proportion of the population is killed each year.

Deer are social, as are other hoofed animals, but their social life varies with the seasons. During the winter, they gather in groups of a few to a few dozen. The expansion of the woods is crucial, because the deer are forest creatures. Their diet consists largely of leaves, fruit, fungi, young twigs of trees and shrubs, and grasses and other herbs. As you will see in a later activity, these foods are available in different amounts at different times of the year. During the growing season, when food is widely available, deer tend to remain in small groups, either of bucks or of does and fawns, which circulate within a territory up to perhaps a square kilometer in area. Within their territory, the deer wear paths from customary sleeping sites to feeding areas (giving the occasional hiker an impression of a lot of local foot traffic). When winter makes travel more difficult, the small summer groups tend to coalesce into "yards," which contain one or two dozen individuals who huddle for warmth at night and beat paths throughout their area to good food resources.

The segregated groups—buck groups and doe groups—blend together during the fall, when females are fertile. Mature males seek out female groups, sometimes competing with other males, and mate with several females. Females bear one or two fawns the following spring. These "young of the year" stay with their mother during the next two years, even after she has given birth to new young. During this period, the yearlings are increasingly independent, and in their third summer (after their second winter) they leave their mother, the males to join a buck group, the females to join a doe group.

Deer digestion

The whitetail deer are ungulates—hoofed animals—specifically, they are even-toed ungulates. This puts them (with all the Cervidae, the deer family) in the same group as the Bovidae (the cow-sheep-antelope family) and the Suidae (the pig family). Although the group's name refers to the hooves all share, a more important part of their anatomy, ecologically speaking, is their digestive system. The ungulates as a group exploit a wide range of plant material that is high in fiber. The carbohydrate construction materials, such as cellulose, that make up fiber are hard to digest, which means the energy (and nutrients) contained in them is harder to extract.

As you may remember, few organisms have the ability to break down those carbon compounds to extract the energy they contain. Thus, multicellular organisms that eat such foods generally must have developed a partnership with bacteria that can begin the digestion process. Gut-dwelling anaerobic bacteria ferment the vegetable matter and turn the complex carbohydrates into simpler sugars, which the host organism can then metabolize.

Ungulates have two strategies for this digestion process; both strategies have the effect of giving the bacteria time to do their work by retaining the food matter in the gut long enough for the fermentation process to happen. Foregut fermenters, such as cows, deer, and gazelles, have elaborate chambered stomachs, which allow fermentation to take place in a series of stages, each operating on the output of the previous stage. Such animals chew their food twice, first on eating it, and second as "chewing the cud." The bacteria have begun to work during the first chewing, but cud chewing shreds the fibers more finely, creating more surface area for the bacteria to work on. This multistage process allows the animal to extract a higher percentage of the calories from the food. Since the gathering of food takes place at a different time than the cud chewing, it can be done even in risky places, after which the deer can retire to a safer place to chew the cud.

Hindgut fermenters, such as horses and elephants, harbor their bacterial symbionts in the latter part of the digestive tract, after the stomach. They do not chew the cud and do not retain the ingested matter for as long, so their digestion is less complete than that of foregut fermenters. They must, therefore, ingest larger amounts of food for their body size or specialize in new growth, which is less fibrous and also higher in protein and other nutrients per unit weight.

From the point of view of energy capture, these details matter because ungulates are well equipped to eat a diet high in fiber, such as grass and leaves, and to do so they must eat in high volume. Deer are equipped to exploit a wide range of browse (food mostly from above the herb layer) and thus can inhabit a wide range of ecosystem types, including a mixture of broad-leaved forest, old fields, and the patchwork of fields, woods, parks, and gardens that we find on the outskirts of many urban centers.

THE CARNIVORES

The Northern Hardwood Forest is home to a diverse group of carnivores. As with the herbivores, most of them are small. Many are birds—hawks, owls, and many insectivorous birds. There are several members of the weasel family (Mustelidae), from the least weasel (40–70 g) to the river otter (up to around 11 kg). Shrews and moles, salamanders, and the omnivorous bear and raccoon are also widespread and numerous. The bobcat *(Felis rufus)* is found in the northern states, and in many areas the domestic cat *(Felis domesticus)* is an important predator.

In addition, there are four members of the dog (Canidae) family: the gray and the red foxes, the coyote *(Canis latrans)*, and the gray, or timber, wolf *(Canis lupus)*. The coyote, usually thought of as a western animal, is actually found in most of the United States. Like the whitetail deer, the coyote is expanding its range and moving closer to humans—it has been sighted in some city dumps and has been heard howling from the town common of an old village in central Massachusetts. The wolf, once extremely widespread in the northern hemisphere, has been eradicated from most of its former range in the United States. In a few locations in the northern states (and still over much of northern and western Canada), it remains in sufficient numbers that we can see its role as a predator on large ungulates such as deer, which in many places are its principal food source.

The wolf, as with most of the dog family, is a social animal, living in packs of up to a dozen or so when there are young to care for. Such packs may have a range of at least 100 km² or several times that, depending on the abundance of game. As with all dogs, the wolf is an opportunist, catching any kind of animal, from rodents to deer and even (in the north woods) moose. Coordinated hunting groups give it a wider range of possible prey to seek—it does not take a pack to catch a grouse, but the larger prey are impossible for a single wolf to take, even if they are ill or weakened animals. You will hear more about wolves later in this unit, as you investigate the close relations between the wolf and the whitetail deer.

THE INDISPENSABLE CLEAN-UP CREW

Once I was an autotroph;
Earth, air, sun met all my needs.
I'd stand, and catch some rays, and loaf
Unless I felt like setting seeds.

But now I'm a detritivore;
My life of leisure's through.
I chew and chew and chew and chew
And chew and chew and chew.

Energy enters an ecosystem when it is captured by the primary producers—the plants. As you have read, organisms make use of energy in respiration, breaking carbon bonds and using the energy to power various processes, including maintenance and storage. The carbon (and other elements) are not used up, of course, but merely recombined over and over in myriad forms. In every ecosystem, a high proportion of the energy-containing compounds remain unused—vegetable matter that falls directly to the ground or that passes through the gut of herbivores undigested and animal tissue, either directly (through death and decay) or indirectly (as food for a predator). As we have mentioned, in the Northern Hardwood Forest, up to 98% of the energy fixed by plants is not used by herbivores, the primary consumers—it falls to the ground uneaten.

All this matter and energy is not available to the rest of the ecosystem yet, because it is not in a form that many organisms can use. The detritivores and decomposers are the organisms that finally use the remaining energy and release the nutrients and carbon back into the cycle.

Although all these organisms are considered to be part of the decomposition cycle, it is useful to make a distinction between detritivores and decomposers. This distinction is based both on size and on trophic characteristics. By detritivores, we mean multicellular organisms—insects and other arthropods, worms, nematodes—that shred or otherwise break up the organic matter that is their food, increasing the surface area that is available to the decomposers and also making some material available after it has passed through their digestive tracts. The decomposers, especially fungi and bacteria, absorb chemicals from organic matter, rather than ingesting complex pieces of organic matter using a mouth of some kind.

This clean-up crew is small and mostly hidden; the fascinating creatures are largely unknown to most of us. Since they are major players in the energy and carbon cycles, though, it is important to get to know them and understand how they play their role. As a sample detritivore, we introduce the millipede.

Millipedes

Millipedes are among the most numerous largish soil creatures in the Northern Hardwood Forest. In tropical areas, there are millipedes that reach lengths up to 15 cm (6 in.); in the northern forests they rarely are more than 1 to 2 cm in length. Millipedes are arthropods and are thus related to centipedes, spiders, insects, and so forth, but they are a distinct group. Long and segmented, with two pairs of legs per segment (centipedes have one pair per segment), millipedes are vegetarians or detritivores that need moist conditions to survive. Turn over the top layer of leaf mold in the forest, and you will see them moving about or coiling up into a defensive ball. They are not very fast, cannot bite or sting, and are good subjects for terrarium study.

There are many kinds of millipedes; some prefer moister and some drier conditions, some more acidic, some less acidic soil. They are found in the soil and litter and also under the bark of rotting logs and branches. Though numerous and widespread, millipedes do not occur in high densities—sometimes the population level is about one millipede per square meter.

Though we will be using millipedes as examples of the detritivore community, you should know that their ecology is not completely understood. Studies of their feeding behavior and body composition suggest that they may play a role in concentrating certain elements in their exoskeletons—they are higher in calcium, for example, than the food they eat or even other detritivores. That suggests that their body chemistry slows the loss of vital nutrients (at least calcium) out of the ecosystem; since the millipedes make use of calcium, it is not leached away into the lower soil. When a millipede molts or dies, the calcium it picked up during its lifetime slowly is made available in the soil—a time-released effect. Thus, though they are small (up to 2.5 g but often much smaller), their numbers may make them an important player in forest nutrition.

Another fact whose importance is not yet known is this: when you sterilize millipedes' food, they become malnourished or die. That is, if you take soil with all the elements in it that we think of millipedes needing, sterilize it (say, by baking it for a certain length of time), then let them feed on the sterilized plant matter, the millipedes do not thrive. That suggests that the microbes killed by the sterilization are an important source of food for the millipedes and that there are whole sections of the forest food chain about which we might be quite unaware.

Exploration 2
LIFESTYLE: YOUR ANIMAL AT HOME

Since we will be trying to fit together, ecologically, the fifteen animals from each habitat, we need to know as much as possible about their "corners"—what they do, how big they are, what that means—where the animals and their "corners" begin and end.

By now, we know quite a bit about each animal: its size, shape, diet, and other facts. Let's expand on those facts and think about what they might mean for the animal's life in the broadest sense possible. So, with your animal in mind, try to think broadly about each question. Use reference materials if they help. And please write down your ideas about these issues and how they might affect your animal's lifestyle.

Materials
- **Your animal (Chapter 4)**
- **Reference materials**

Procedure

1. **Size: How big is your animal?**
   Relate it to your own size. How does its volume roughly compare with yours? How about its height and length? How long are its legs? How fast do you think it might move? How far might it travel in a day? In its lifetime? What about heat loss or gain? Might it need a nest or den? Why?

2. **Reproduction.**
   We know how many offspring are born each year (on average). What does your animal eat, and how might that affect the number of offspring? What guesses would you make about the population density of your animal? Might rearing the young make small or large energetic demands on parents? (It may be useful to think of other animals you know that are similar to yours in any of these ways.)

3. **Food and other resources.**
   What resources are crucial for the survival and reproduction of your animal on any given day, over a week, over a year, over its lifetime? Where do those resources occur? For instance, are the resources near each other in space (e.g., the animal sleeps where it eats) or in time (e.g., always, sometimes, or rarely available)? How does that affect your organism's behavior?

4. **Other biotic factors.**
   How might other species or even other members of its own species affect your animal? Competition, predation—what other sorts of interactions are possible or might be occurring? (We focus on interactions throughout the remainder of this Unit.)

5. **Abiotic factors: Climate and geography.**
   How might the seasons affect your organism? For instance, when do you think your organism reproduces? How does that relate to the seasonal cycles of, say, temperature or food availability? What seasonal changes have energetic effects on your organism?

Exploration 3
SUN TO WOLF: ENERGY TRANSFER!?

How much solar energy does it take to produce 8 kg of carnivore, say, a wolf or a cheetah (depending on your habitat)? Seriously. Suppose you are an adolescent wolf/cheetah and will finish your growth this year. Given wolf/cheetah growth rates, that means you will be adding about 8 kg, which has an energy content of about 10,000 kcal. To simplify matters, we are assuming that the wolf eats only deer; the cheetah, only Thomson's gazelles.

To solve this problem, we must pull together our knowledge on insolation, plant productivity, and how individual organisms get and spend energy. Those data will help us think about energy movement <u>between</u> organisms (up to now, we pretty much have focused on energy movement <u>within</u> a single organism) and energy flow through the ecosystem in general.

So, how much solar energy is needed for an adolescent wolf or cheetah to grow normally during the course of a year?

Materials
- **Data from previous work** (Exploration 2, and **Chapter 4**) and **animal sheets**
- **Calculators**
- **Graph paper**
- **String**
- **Scissors**
- **Measuring tape or stick**

Procedure

1. **A prediction.**
    How much solar energy is needed for your wolf or cheetah to put on 10,000 kcal of new tissue this year? A silly question, you may think—wolves and cheetahs do not get energy directly from the sun. But these predators <u>do</u> depend on the sun for their energy, via energy flow and transfer among other species.

    Wolves and cheetahs get their energy from the animals they eat (typically deer and Thomson's gazelles, respectively). In turn, deer and gazelles get their energy from plants they eat. And, as we know, plants get their energy from sunlight. In the absence of sunlight, plants do not get energy, so deer and gazelles do not get energy, and wolves and cheetahs go hungry. (We are simplifying a bit here. Some predators also eat other prey species, but here that assumption does not affect the calculations or outcome. Why not?)

    So, let's rephrase the question. Given the chain of energy transfers, from sun to plants to deer/gazelle to wolf/cheetah, <u>how much solar energy must reach the plants for the wolf/cheetah to get enough food to put on 10,000 kcal of new tissue this year?</u>

Predict how many kilocalories of solar energy that would be. Please write your prediction (anonymously if you like) in a corner of a piece of paper, tear off that corner, and give it to your teacher. Also note your prediction in your notebook, to compare with the results of your group's calculations.

2. **Carnivore intake and production.**
   Now let's check our predictions against some real calculations. Remember, we assume that the wolf eats only deer meat and the cheetah eats only gazelles.

   How much energy does the wolf or cheetah need to take in to produce 10,000 kcal of new tissue? (Throughout the calculations, we deal with units of energy, in kilocalories.)

   Look up the energy use equation for wolves and cheetahs in their respective data sheets. We know **Production** is a proportion or percentage of **Intake** (**Chapter 4**, Exploration 2), and we also know that in this case **P** = 10,000 kcal. So what is the wolf/cheetah's total energy intake? Note it in your book, perhaps by copying the following diagram and filling in all the percentages and kilocalories. Remember this figure from **Chapter 3**? We use it to show an organism's energy allocation as energy that is potentially available to others (right of the broken line) and energy that is unavailable (left of the line).

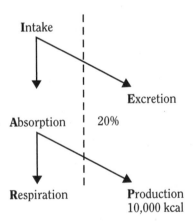

   Now that you have finished the first step of the calculations, would you like to revise your initial prediction?

3. **Ungulate (or prey) intake and production.**
   How much energy must the deer/Thomson's gazelles take in to produce enough tissue for the carnivores?

   We are talking not just about one deer or one gazelle. After all, would one animal last its predator a whole year? We are referring to production by a herd of ungulates. And we assume that the deer/gazelle population is neither growing nor shrinking, that is, all new tissue produced by the herd during the course of a year is eaten by the wolf/cheetah. (This assumption simplifies our calculations and clearly shows the underlying patterns of energy transfer.)

In other words, wolf **I**ntake equals deer **P**roduction, and cheetah **I**ntake equals gazelle **P**roduction. Since we just calculated wolf/cheetah **I**ntake, we substitute it now for deer/gazelle **P**roduction, as shown in the next diagram. And since we know or can find the relationship between deer/gazelle **P**roduction and deer/gazelle **I**ntake, we can calculate the herd's annual **I**ntake, just as we did for the wolf/cheetah. (You may want to use exponents.)

(**NOTE:** This assumption probably is not realistic for Thomson's gazelles, because they are preyed on and eaten by several other predators. It does, however, seem realistic for deer populations that live where there are still wolves. Does that mean the deer and wolf populations are regulating each other? We consider that general question of who controls whom in **Chapter 11.**)

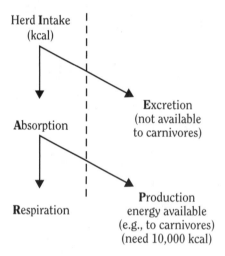

In other words, how much deer/gazelle **P** is necessary for 10,000 kcal of wolf/cheetah **I**?

4. **Calculations: The plant data.**
    How much energy must the plants take in to produce the tissue that the herbivores eat?

    Here we need a different equation, since plants get their energy from the sun and they do not excrete as animals do. Some sun energy that hits a plant gets captured by the plant and is photosynthesized. That amount of energy is called the gross primary production, or GPP. About half of GPP becomes plant tissue, which might be eaten by herbivores; it is called the net primary production, or NPP. (The other half of GPP is used in respiration by the plant.) Overall, though, most of the sun's energy is not absorbed, but is reflected, transmitted, or simply dissipated as heat. So our equation for plants is this: Incoming energy = Production (NPP) + Respiration + Unabsorbed energy, where **P** = 0.5% of **I**, **R** = 0.5% of **I**, and **U** = 99% of **I** (we have rounded these figures for ease of calculation).

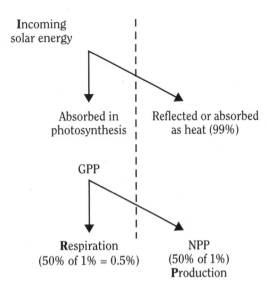

Incoming
solar energy

Absorbed in
photosynthesis

Reflected or absorbed
as heat (99%)

GPP

Respiration
(50% of 1% = 0.5%)

NPP
(50% of 1%)
Production

So we know that **P** = 0.005 × **I**. We know from step 3 that deer/gazelle **P** = X kcal. What is X? In other words, how much plant **P** is necessary for the deer/gazelle **I** we just calculated? And how much solar energy, in kilocalories, is striking the plants (**I**)?

5. **The big picture: How much solar energy?**
   As a result of our three calculations, we now know the amount of solar energy needed to create 10,000 kcal of new wolf/cheetah tissue. How close or far off was your initial prediction? Energy transfer is not an efficient business, is it? (Most people, even biology teachers, are off with their predictions—way off. The amount of solar energy involved is just so enormous.)

6. **Presenting the data.**
   As a group, choose a way of presenting your findings to the rest of the class—a graph or some other representation. You want to show clearly the relationship among the various quantities of energy with which we have just been working. Use 10,000 kcal as your basic unit and express all other quantities as multiples of 10,000 kcal. Possibilities for representing each unit of 10,000 kcal include the following: a small square of paper for each 10,000 kcal, such as a square on graph paper; a short line or measure of string to represent each unit; or some weight or volume measure for each unit (e.g., pennies).

   HINT: Select something small to represent each unit of 10,000 kcal. By the time we get to representing solar energy, we are dealing with large numbers.

   The picture of your data should include, in kilocalories, the energy content of new tissue for the wolf/cheetah; energy content of the deer/gazelles eaten by the wolf/cheetah; energy content of the plants eaten by the deer/gazelles; and energy content of the sunlight hitting the plants that are eaten by deer/gazelles.

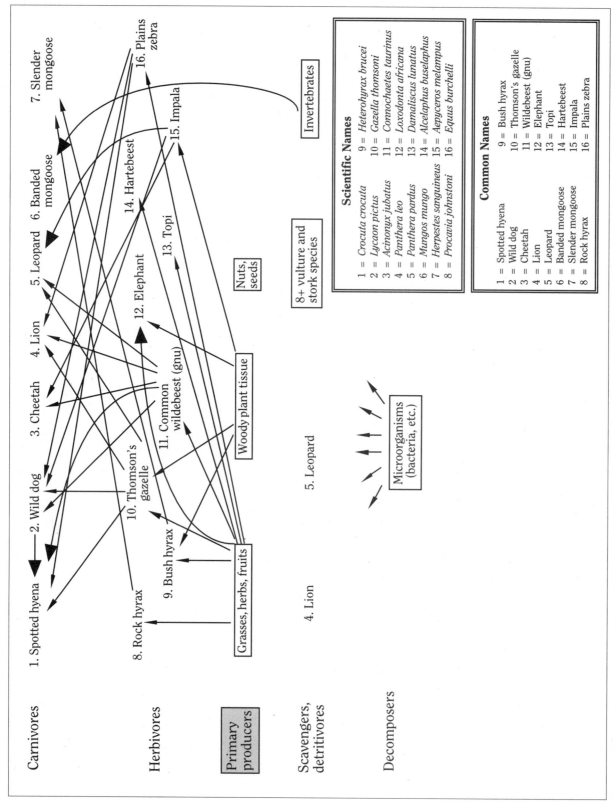

Figure 1. The Serengeti Ecosystem: Partial food web.

Scientific Names

1 = *Crocuta crocuta*	9 = *Heterohyrax brucei*
2 = *Lycaon pictus*	10 = *Gazella thomsoni*
3 = *Acinonyx jubatus*	11 = *Connochaetes taurinus*
4 = *Panthera leo*	12 = *Loxodonta africana*
5 = *Panthera pardus*	13 = *Damaliscus lunatus*
6 = *Mungos mungo*	14 = *Alcelaphus buselaphus*
7 = *Herpestes sanguineus*	15 = *Aepyceros melampus*
8 = *Procavia johnstoni*	16 = *Equus burchelli*

Common Names

1 = Spotted hyena	9 = Bush hyrax
2 = Wild dog	10 = Thomson's gazelle
3 = Cheetah	11 = Wildebeest (gnu)
4 = Lion	12 = Elephant
5 = Leopard	13 = Topi
6 = Banded mongoose	14 = Hartebeest
7 = Slender mongoose	15 = Impala
8 = Rock hyrax	16 = Plains zebra

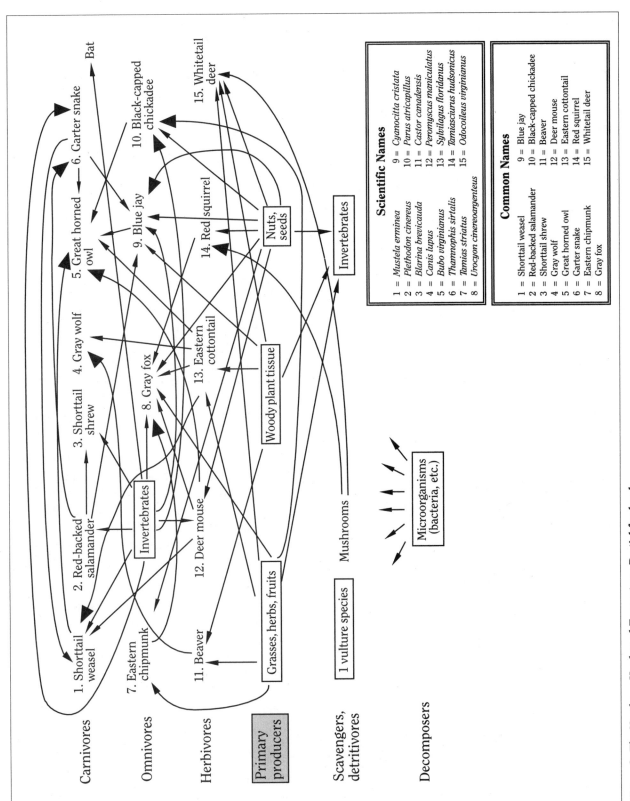

Figure 2. The Northern Hardwood Ecosystem: Partial food web.

Scientific Names

1 = *Mustela erminea*
2 = *Plethodon cinereus*
3 = *Blarina brevicauda*
4 = *Canis lupus*
5 = *Bubo virginianus*
6 = *Thamnophis sirtalis*
7 = *Tamias striatus*
8 = *Urocyon cinereoargenteus*
9 = *Cyanocitta cristata*
10 = *Parus atricapillus*
11 = *Castor canadensis*
12 = *Peromyscus maniculatus*
13 = *Sylvilagus floridanus*
14 = *Tamiasciurus hudsonicus*
15 = *Odocoileus virginianus*

Common Names

1 = Shorttail weasel
2 = Red-backed salamander
3 = Shorttail shrew
4 = Gray wolf
5 = Great horned owl
6 = Garter snake
7 = Eastern chipmunk
8 = Gray fox
9 = Blue jay
10 = Black-capped chickadee
11 = Beaver
12 = Deer mouse
13 = Eastern cottontail
14 = Red squirrel
15 = Whitetail deer

READING 2
WHAT DOES A FOOD WEB MEAN?

A food web, like the one we produced in Exploration 1, is a useful picture of trophic relationships (and thus energy flow) among organisms. It is, however, just a partial picture in terms of species and even of specifics about the trophic relationships represented.

Figure 1 and Figure 2 are summaries of our work from that Exploration, partial food webs for the Serengeti and the Northern Hardwood Forest (with the scientific and the common names). They are partial because they do not represent even all the vertebrates, never mind all the organisms. But what else might they lack? What do the webs not show? Let's consider a few specific cases.

CASE 1: THE WILDEBEEST CONNECTION

In the Serengeti, most of the carnivores in the web in Figure 1 eat wildebeest. What is not specified is that they eat wildebeest calves. Most of the wildebeest females (i.e., some ¾ million females) give birth within a few weeks in January. During that time, most Serengeti carnivores feast on the relatively vulnerable calves. In terms of energy flow and food availability then, the wildebeest account for a large percentage of the intake of many carnivores during a few weeks, but then none of the intake during the rest of the year.

Is that important? Well, yes, for the animals involved but also for our understanding of their interactions, which are especially important if we must manage any of the specifics involved. What if a deadly epidemic disease infects the wildebeest and most of them die? What if we are studying the food habits of jackals, which can kill wildebeest calves but not adults, and we study jackals only during wildebeest calving season? Or only outside that period? What if we study any carnivores that eat wildebeest only during or only outside the calving periods?

Natural systems such as ecosystems are complex, because their components are all interconnected and constantly changing. Studying ecosystems is not easy—things that happen infrequently or briefly, such as wildebeest calving, can be enormously important. If we were to develop a jackal management program but did not know the role of wildebeest calves in the jackal's diet, the program could not be appropriate because we would be leaving out an important component.

CASE 2: SALAMANDER CENSUS

Although they are not as visible as wildebeest, salamanders are a good-sized part of the animal biomass in the Northern Hardwoods ecosystem. They account for more biomass than all the birds together and occur at densities of about $6/m^2$. Worldwide, there currently seems to be a decline in the numbers of salamanders (and snakes, frogs, and toads—in fact, many species of amphibians and reptiles in general). Ecologists and other researchers are concerned about this possible decline and are trying to determine whether it is real and what might be causing it. Candidate causes include acid rain and general levels of pollution.

What do you think might be involved? If you had unlimited research funds and staff, how would you solve the mystery? What would you want to know and how would you find out? Using the Northern Hardwoods ecosystem as your study site, outline a study (in your notebook) by which to test your ideas.

INCOMPLETENESS

Although the webs we have produced here are real, we know they are incomplete, just a tiny part of the whole picture. Each trophic layer includes more species, in some cases thousands or hundreds of thousands of species, with even larger numbers of individuals. A list of all the known species for either ecosystem would run many dozens of pages. There are over a hundred species of birds in the Northern Hardwoods ecosystem alone. And several orders of magnitude more species of insects and other invertebrates. In the Serengeti, most of the invertebrates have not even been identified, so we can only guesstimate at their numbers, which will be orders of magnitude greater than those in the NHF.

The webs in Figures 1 and 2 do not even show all the large vertebrates. In fact, each figure is only a tiny portion of one layer of the real multilayer web for each ecosystem. There are invertebrate and vertebrate omnivores, carnivores, herbivores, and detritivores and scavengers (Figure 3). Among

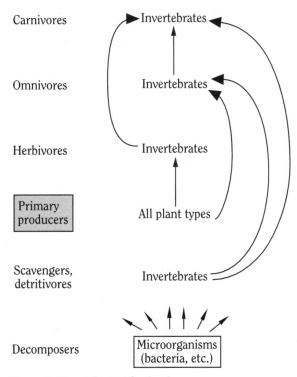

Figure 3. Invertebrates' food web.

the ants alone, there is an entire web of such relationships, with some ant species occupying every trophic level except primary producer. Although ants are not themselves decomposers, some of them farm fungi, growing the fungi on decaying plant matter. Thus, the ants have even that trophic level covered, albeit indirectly.

Imagine how a complete web picture would look—like spaghetti on a plate! Actually, it would be impossible to picture it the way we have done the partial webs in Figures 1 and 2. So our web is a small bit of the whole.

ROLES

Not only are there many more species than we can show in a single web, but members of a single species of different places or roles in a web, depending on season, their growth stage, or age. We have already seen that wildebeest calves have a different role than do adults—that is, the young serve as food to many carnivore species, but the adults do so much less. The foods eaten by organisms can also change as they develop. Most young birds are fed insects and other invertebrates by their parents, even in species where the adults themselves do not eat insects but seeds, fruits, or nectar. The young of carnivorous mammals (like lions, wolves, mongooses, etc.) suckle milk from their adult mothers, although the mothers eat meat. Animals such as the small weasel and mongoose species, which eat invertebrates, change their diet seasonally, as numbers of some insect food species change with cold or drought.

EXTREME EXAMPLES

Some of the more extreme differences in roles held by members of a species are seen in invertebrates, where different-aged members can look and act like wholly different animals. Voracious leaf-eating caterpillars grow and develop into nectar-feeding butterflies. Gound-living, root-eating, soft-bodied grubs develop into hard-winged beetles that can eat many different things. Mosquito larvae can be water-living and carnivorous, killing and eating other insect larvae, including their own siblings, yet adult mosquitoes feed on nectar or, infrequently, blood. In all these cases, the different life stages also look different, have different mouths (chewing mouths vs. piercing, sucking mouths), eat different foods, live in different places—in short, they act like very different animals. Notice the different life stages in the water beetles and their different foods (Figure 4). Yet they are the same species, taking different roles at different times in their development or during different seasons.

All these roles are also part of the big food web. In each case, some species feed on the members of any role. What interconnectedness! What complexity!

To recap, describe at least five things that our partial food webs did not include.

Figure 4

Exploration 4
ENERGY IN POPULATIONS: POOLS AND FLOWS

Another title for this Exploration might be something like "Why Are Chickadees Not Salamanders?"

Researchers in northern New Hampshire have collected a good deal of data on chickadees and salamanders: how many at which times of year. And there are <u>way</u> more salamanders than chickadees. But what do we know about the contribution of either species to the energy flow of the ecosystem?

Materials
- **Chickadee and salamander data (Chapter 4)**
- **Calculators**

Procedure
1. **In groups, collect and calculate the data.**
   Fill in the empty cells of the following table, using data from the animal cards (**Chapter 4**).

NAME	WEIGHT PER INDIVIDUAL	NUMBER PER HECTARE	ENERGY FLOW PER INDIVIDUAL PER YEAR	BIOMASS PER HECTARE, WET WEIGHT; (CALORIC VALUE)	ENERGY FLOW PER HECTARE PER YEAR
Red-backed salamander					
Chickadee					
All songbirds	Not applicable	10	Not applicable	200 g (350 kcal)	75,000 kcal

2. **Examine the abundance data.**
    Which of the two species is more abundant (has the higher number of individuals per hectare)? How does that compare with the biomass per hectare?

    NOTE: Although there certainly is a size difference between a chickadee and a red-backed salamander, both are quite small vertebrates. The size difference is not like that between, say, a chickadee and an alligator or a salamander and a pelican. Thus, we can make these comparisons in a Fermi-like way. (The chickadee weighs about as much as two nickels, while the salamander weighs a bit more than a paper clip.) In other words, individuals of these two species can accurately be described as "small."

3. **Energy flow.**
    Is the picture the same if we consider energy flow? How about by individual per year versus per hectare (ha) per year? How much does one chickadee eat versus one salamander? How do they regulate their temperatures?

4. **Back up to energy expenditures.**
    What do we know about the lifestyles of these two species? Look at their energy use equations. How do their lifestyles fit with the abundance and distribution patterns we have just filled in on the table? Consider the differences per individual of each species. And then look at the total effect of all the individuals of that species.

5. **Discuss and write up.**
    Try to explain the patterns of abundance and energy flow in light of everything you have studied in this Unit. When you have finished discussing, write a paragraph or two explaining the patterns of abundance as best you can.

READING 3
ENERGY FLOW IN THE SEU AND NHF

Which ecosystem do you think is more productive, the Serengeti or the Northern Hardwood Forest? Why? What do we mean by "productive"?

So far, this Chapter has been like making a star, with each arm pointing in a different energy-use direction: interactions among organisms in webs; food chains and the inefficiency of energy transfer across links of those chains; population energy patterns as the sum of species-typical energy-use patterns; and pools and flows of energy through individuals and species. Now we center the star by showing an overview of all those interactions and energy uses. Let's step way back and consider the "big picture": let's compare our habitats in terms of the total energy that moves through them.

In Exploration 3, we did an upside-down trophic pyramid. We began at the top (ecologists usually begin at the bottom), and we did not consider the whole ecosystem, just one food chain in each ecosystem. Following are some data for each entire ecosystem. We do not include carnivores because we cannot find good data. We do know, however, that they take in only a minute proportion of the energy present in an ecosystem. So, although carnivores are important ecologically (perhaps keeping their prey populations in check, for example), in terms of energy flow, they hardly exist at all!

Because the two ecosystems differ in size, we do as ecologists do: standardize and consider energy flow data for a defined area that is the same for each ecosystem. Typically, ecologists consider the average amount of energy flowing through one square meter (m^2) of an ecosystem per year.

Data: Energy flow in the Northern Hardwood Forest

The **herbivores** eat 4×10^1 kcals/m^2 year.

Detritivores and decomposers as a group ingest 5×10^3 kcals/m^2 year.

The **producers** (plants) fix about 1×10^4 kcals/m^2 year (the gross primary productivity, or GPP). Of that total, the plants spend about half on respiration and store the other half in new tissues (the net primary production, or NPP). About 25% of NPP is stored in woody tissue, which cannot be eaten by most herbivores.

Visible solar radiation is 5×10^5 kcals/m^2 year.

Data: Energy flow in the Serengeti Ecosystem

The **herbivores** as a group eat 7×10^2 kcals/m^2 year.

Detritivores and decomposers ingest 3×10^3 kcals/m^2 year.

Producers fix about 9×10^3 kcals/m^2 year (the gross primary productivity, or GPP). Of that total, the plants spend about half on respiration and store the other half in new tissues (the net primary production, or NPP). Only 5% of NPP is stored in woody tissues, which cannot be eaten by most herbivores.

Visible solar radiation is about 7×10^5 kcals/m^2 year.

REPRESENTING THE DATA

Make some schematic representation of the data for each habitat (remember the issues we had with representing such pyramidal information in Exploration 3). If you decide to represent the data literally, it will facilitate comparisons if you chose as your basic unit the smallest amount of

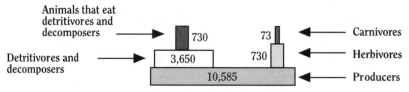

Figure 5. Energy-flow pyramid (kcal per m² per year).

energy flow per square meter (in this case, the amount of energy ingested by Northern Hardwood herbivores) and express all other quantities as multiples of that basic unit. Figure 5 shows one possible scheme illustrating the relative abundance of each trophic level.

COMPARISONS

Look at the two sets of data, and consider these questions. Where does the energy flowing into an ecosystem "go"? What are the similarities between the patterns of energy flow in the two ecosystems? What are the differences between the patterns of energy flow in the two ecosystems?

Please write down your thoughts and bring them to class for discussion.

PREDATOR AND PREY
WHO EATS WHOM?

CHAPTER ELEVEN

CONTENTS

OVERVIEW

The relationship, or "match," between the Intake of an organism and the Production of the organism(s) it eats, is an interesting and important aspect of ecology. Why? Because those matches (or lack of them) are about energy and carbon transfer. An ecosystem can be defined as a group of organisms that live together and are linked by energy transfer. Thus, understanding the energy transfer and energy relationships among the organisms in an area means understanding a primary part of that ecosystem. The match between the **I** of one organism and the **P** of its food organisms is remarkably difficult to understand. Not many examples have been studied; those that have been studied have given variable results.

One question about these interactions is a topic of much study and debate among ecologists: Who "controls" the interaction? It is true that most predator species typically eat prey of several species and that many prey species are eaten by more than one predator species. Nonetheless, especially when a predator gets much of its food by eating a single prey species, it is ecologically interesting to ask, "Does either species affect the other?" Does the predator, through its intake of prey, keep the number of prey (the size of the prey population) about the same over time? Would the prey population keep increasing if there were no predators? Would there be more predators if they had more prey?

Remember that for the NHF deer and wolf populations in **Chapter 10** there is a close match between wolf **I** and deer **P** <u>for those populations</u>, but not for the Serengeti Thomson's gazelle and cheetah populations. (Why can we compare **P** and **I** in this way only for specific populations? Why not compare **P** and **I** for all wolves and deer, for example?)

Exploration 1
THE HARE-LYNX CYCLE

One famous vertebrate study of the interaction between the population of a prey species and its major (but not only) predator is that of the snowshoe hare *(Lepus americanus)* and the Canadian lynx *(Lynx canadensis)*. Between 1821 and 1934, the abundance of both species was tracked using skin counts from fur-trapping records kept by the Hudson Bay Company in Canada. For nearly 100 years, trappers sold skins of both species to the Hudson Bay Company, which, in turn, sold them around the world.

Procedure

1. **The hare data.**

The number of hare skins bought by the Hudson Bay Company is graphed in Figure 1. Study it closely.

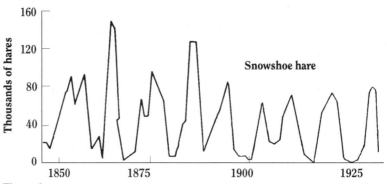

Figure 1

Roughly how many times more hares are there at high densities than at low ones?

How many years pass between peak numbers of hares? Between low, or trough, numbers?

2. **The hare's foods.**

The hare population cycles are synchronous (occur at the same time) across the entire range of the species, from Alaska to Newfoundland. The snowshoe hare feeds on the twig ends of shrubs and small trees. Throughout its area, it is the major herbivore on those foods. In other words, of all the twig ends that get eaten, the hare eats most of them. What effects might high numbers of hares have on their food supply? Make a prediction.

3. **The lynx data.**

Now look at Figure 2, a graph for the same time period that shows the number of lynx skins. What is the approximate time span between peak numbers? Between low, or trough, numbers? Roughly how many times more lynxes are there at peak times than at trough times?

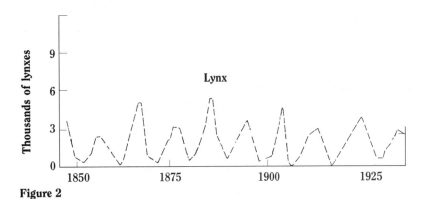

Figure 2

Summarize your findings so far. What do you know about hare and lynx cycles? Support each statement by saying what evidence you have for it.

4. **The hare and lynx together.**

   Figure 3 is a graph of data from both the hare and lynx species together. How are changes in the numbers of the two species related? That is, which rises or drops first, and which second? Which species do you think is "causing" the cycling? Why? How might you test your prediction? What else would you like to know to test your prediction?

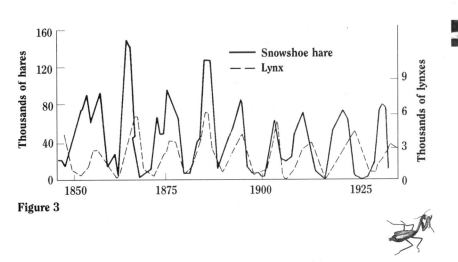

Figure 3

READING 1
HARE AND LYNX: OTHER FACTORS

THE ROLE OF HARE FOOD

In Exploration 1, you made a prediction about possible effects of huge hare (herbivore) populations on their food plants. You may have said something about so many hares using up the food supply, resulting in a food shortage. That is true, but it is even more interesting than that.

Let's step back for a moment and consider just the interaction between the hare and its food plants. As we have said, the hare eats the tips of branches of many different species of shrubs and small trees. That interaction between the hare and its food plants is itself a predator-prey interaction: the hare is a predator of plant prey.

Now, what major difference between animals and plants makes plants easier to "catch"? Yes—plants cannot run away. However, that does not mean they are defenseless. In fact, in this, as in so many other things, all organisms, including plants, have the same categories of behaviors: they take in energy, they grow, they reproduce, they defend themselves against predators, they die. The differences are in how different organisms carry out those behaviors.

PLANT DEFENSES

Plants defend themselves not by running away but by being tough or prickly or unpleasant/poisonous to touch or eat. Have you ever tried to crack a walnut, a butternut, or a hazelnut without a nutcracker? Brushed against a nettle plant, a rose bush, or poison ivy? Or maybe thought of nibbling a locust seed pod or those pretty red berries of the nightshade plant? All those are defenses by plants against some of their predators.

TIMING THE DEFENSES

In some cases, the plant produces its defense all the time. Rose thorns or stinging nettles are present during the plant's entire life, and poison ivy always produces the oils that give humans a rash. But other plants produce chemicals only when the plants need them. This is in response to some attack on the plant, such as lots of predation or predation over an extended period of time. The plants that are preyed on by hares experience both types of attack when hare populations are high. There is a lot of predation on the plants because there are so many hares. And the predation goes on for months, even years.

Some of the plants on which the hares prey (feed) respond by producing chemicals that are unpleasant to the hares. The chemicals are especially likely to be in the hares' preferred food, the newly growing tips of twigs. Once the twigs contain those chemicals, hares tend to avoid them. Thus, food plants respond to the increases in hare numbers by producing unpleasant chemicals, and the amount of food available to the hares drops. To the eye, nothing has changed. Food plants are putting out new growth, apparently as usual. But chemically, that is, to hare taste and digestion, the plants are much changed: they are no longer a good food source.

EFFECTS ON HARE POPULATIONS

As hare numbers soar, their supply of available food drops. More hares are eating the twigs of food plants. That has two likely effects: there are fewer twigs altogether, and, more important, all twigs become inedible in those plant species that respond by producing chemicals that are unpleasant to the hares.

The decreases in available food cause hares to become weaker, to die younger, and to have fewer babies. So the drop in hare numbers actually begins because of a change in their food plants. Moreover, plants continue to produce the protective chemicals for 2 to 3 years after peak grazing by hares. Thus, throughout that period, the hares continue to have inadequate food supplies.

Being weaker makes hares less able to escape from their predators. How does that explain why the peaks in lynx numbers usually happen after the peaks in hare numbers?

In your notebook, diagram the effects in the plant-hare-lynx cycle. Bring it to class.

YET ANOTHER FACTOR: THE GROUSE

Two grouse species, the ruffed grouse and the spruce grouse, are also important herbivores in the same area and are also eaten by lynxes. Go back to the graph in Figure 3, with both the hare and lynx cycles. Lynxes eat snowshoe hares when they can and grouse when there are few hares. Do you think that the grouse cycle peaks before or after the hare cycle peaks? Why?

Which species is "regulating" the cycle? Is it possible to say? Why or why not?

READING 2
WHAT KIND OF DATA AND WHAT DOES THAT MEAN?

Note that the hare-lynx data are observations only; they do not include any experiments. That means, using data on fur numbers, ecologists have shown that the lynx population numbers decline after the hare numbers have declined, and lynx numbers rise after hare numbers have risen. We can describe coincidences between things: the hare cycles coincide with changes in plant defense chemicals; the lynx cycles coincide with the hare cycles; and so on. But there is no direct evidence of causality. No one has carried out experiments changing hare population size to show whether those changes also cause changes in lynx population.

Such experimentation would be difficult and probably unethical, since it would cause serious disruption of the natural populations. But it is important to realize the difference between coincidence and causality. In coincidence, two or more things happen in a way that makes people think they are or may be functionally related. In the case of causality, there is direct evidence that one thing actually causes the other.

ADVERTISEMENTS

Advertisements usually include real or implied causality. And marketers are very careful to differentiate between the two, since the law strictly regulates the former but not the latter. Next time you watch television, notice how ambiguously ads are worded. Do they promise something specific or just suggest things? Will that cold medicine make you less ill or only make you feel cozy? Or read food labels. Is that fruit drink made "with real fruit juice" or "of real fruit juice"? "With" means some real fruit juice in the drink, while "of" means it is all fruit juice. Small words, big difference.

CHANGE OUR CONCLUSIONS?

Does that mean we think lynx population numbers do not follow hare population numbers? No. It just means we are conscious of what kind of data these are and of their possible limitations. In the case of lynx and hare cycles, to be sure of causality, we would need to show cause and effect for whatever part we wanted to test.

A POSSIBLE EXPERIMENT

For example, to test whether the drop in lynx numbers is actually due to the drop in hare numbers, a researcher might run the following test in the wild during a period when hare numbers are dropping. She might compare hares and lynxes in an undisturbed area with hares and lynxes in an area that is the same in every possible way, <u>except</u> that the researcher artificially keeps the number of hares from dropping. Perhaps she releases 1,000 hares every week, so the lynxes still have large numbers of hares to eat. If our hypothesis is correct that hare numbers are the cause of lynx numbers, lynx numbers should stay high in the area where hares are released, while in the other area, lynx numbers should drop with the dropping hare numbers. (For more on this, see the **Technique: Introduction to Research**.)

Exploration 2
ENERGY BALANCE DURING HARE CYCLES

The following factors all contribute to a drop in the population numbers of hares:

- Fewer females give birth.
- Females that do give birth have smaller litters (i.e., fewer young).
- Those young are less likely to survive.
- All animals, young and adult, show weight loss and grow more slowly than usual.

Procedure

1. **Modeling the situation.**
   How would you use the energy use equation to show the change in hare biology? Which terms would change and how?

   Do not worry about having numbers. Use the equation qualitatively, that is, describe the "qualities" you see (as opposed to quantitative descriptions, which rely on numbers or quantities).

   HINT: We are describing two situations for the hare: "normal" and "underfed."

2. **Experimental evidence.**

How might you test the hypothesis that those effects in hares are due to too little food? Design at least two tests. Assume you have unlimited help, laboratory space, funding, and time in the field.

Exploration 3
WHO CONTROLS WHOM: PREDATOR AND PREY?

There are three categories of match between predators and prey in terms of which one seems to "control" their interaction:

1. The prey can regulate the predator (if prey numbers drop for some reason such as disease or starvation, predator numbers also drop).

2. The predator can regulate the prey (if the predator is removed from an area, prey numbers increase).

3. Neither the predator nor the prey apparently influences the other (a change in the numbers of either causes no apparent change in the numbers of the other).

Procedure

1. **Examine the data.**

Your teacher assigns each group of three to five students a few examples from one of those three predator or prey categories. Examine the data carefully for your set. To which category do its examples belong? Why?

2. **Class discussion.**

Each group describes its predator-prey interactions: who do you think is "running" the interaction and why? The class discusses the implications of each type of interaction, including the following considerations:

So what is a predator?

Why does it matter which species regulates which?

In a more complex situation, does competition between species regulate the population size of either species? For instance, two predator species might compete for the same prey species. Might the predator species then regulate each other?!

EXAMPLE SET 1

The Wolf and the Deer

In our study populations (the Northern Hardwood Forest) are 6 wolves and 500 deer in an area of about 115 km². The yearly intake of each wolf is equivalent to about 30 deer. When the deer population drops because of snow or disease, wolves have a hard time finding alternative food.

The Bean Weevil and the Wasp

Another classic study is that of the adzuki bean weevil and its "predator," a wasp. According to Figure 4, who seems to be ahead of whom?

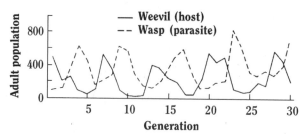

Figure 4

EXAMPLE SET 2

Sea Urchins: Their Prey and Their Predators

On some rocky seashores, sea urchins, otters, and algae, including kelp, all coexist. When sea urchins are removed or excluded from an area, algae populations quickly increase, but some species are affected more than others. Large brown algae begin to take over and crowd out two other algae species that normally coexist with the brown algae and the sea urchins.

Kelp, a brown alga, is harvested by humans because it is an important source of iodine and fertilizer.

Sea otters prey on sea urchins. Humans are the major predator of sea otters.

Draw a diagram of who eats whom and who controls whom.

The East Coast situation

Along the Atlantic coast of Canada and the United States, the situation is slightly different. Urchins prey on brown kelp, crabs (not otters) prey on urchins, and lobsters prey on the crabs. Where lobsters have been over-fished, crab numbers are high.

Again, draw a picture of who eats whom and what effects they have on each other.

The Cyclamen Mite and the Predatory Mite

The cyclamen mite is a pest of strawberry plants in California. Mites usually invade a field shortly after the berry plants are planted but usually do not damage the crop until their second year. Typically, that is also when the predatory mite species (a mite species that preys on cyclamen mites) invades the field. Once the predatory mite is present, it remains.

According to Figure 5, who regulates this interaction?

In an ironic twist, fields treated with the insecticide parathion (note the "p" and the arrows in Figure 5) lost their predatory mites but still had pest mites at damaging levels. In fields not treated with the insecticide, the predatory mites remained at their usual numbers.

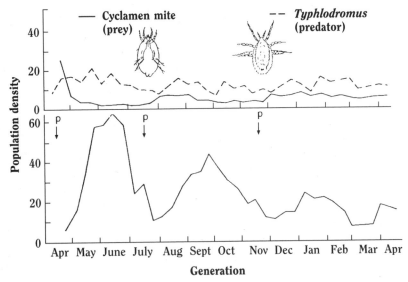

Figure 5

EXAMPLE SET 3

Tawny Owls and Two Prey Species

From Figure 6, which species seems to be influencing which?

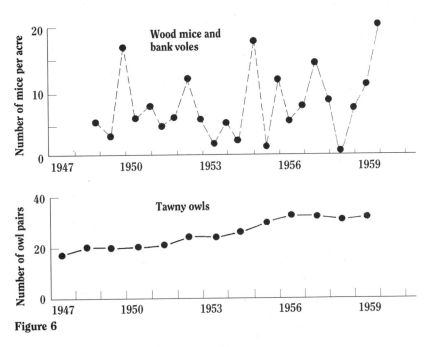

Figure 6

Make a diagram of who affects whom. How do you think owls are eating when their prey species numbers are low? What seems to be going on with the owls?

READING 3
EPILOGUE

Let's look in more detail at the cases we have examined. What else might we like to know about them?

PREY APPARENTLY REGULATE THE PREDATOR (CATEGORY 1)

Hare and Lynx, Deer and Wolf

The hare-lynx case is a long story about a simple question—whose numbers start the cycles? The hare.

The "match" between wolf **I** and deer **P** in the Northern Hardwoods ecosystem is so close that in areas where the primary prey of wolves is deer, some ecologists believe that the deer regulate the wolf population. That example, however, is less well studied than the hare-lynx case. Hare-lynx cycles occur throughout the entire geographic area where both species are present, while deer-wolf interactions have been studied in just a few places. (Now, of course, there are very few wolf populations anywhere in the United States.)

Hare-lynx data also cover nearly 100 years, while data on wolf-deer populations cover just some 20 years. And tens of thousands of hare and lynx pelts are the database for those interactions, while our picture of the deer-wolf cycle is based on just a few thousand deer and wolves.

Does that mean we do not think deer numbers influence wolf numbers? No. But, as always, it is important to know as much as possible about the data from which we draw conclusions. For instance, if the average wolf life span is 35 years, data from just 20 years is not very useful for deciding whether wolf numbers cycle—we do not have a complete picture of the lifetime of an average wolf.

The Bean Weevil and the Wasp

The adzuki bean weevil and its wasp "predator" show oscillations in animal numbers similar to those oscillations for the lynx and the hare. So it seems that predator and prey populations can interact in similar ways whether the organisms are large vertebrates, tiny invertebrates, or even plants.

PREDATORS REGULATING PREY POPULATIONS (CATEGORY 2)

Sea Urchins: Their Prey and Their Predators

On some rocky seashores, sea urchins apparently regulate populations of their algae prey. In the simplest experiments, sea urchins are removed or excluded from an area. After their removal, algae populations quickly increase. Actually, large brown algae crowd out two other algae species that normally coexist with the brown algae and with the sea urchins. (The coralline algae have a hard covering, which deters grazing by sea urchins. Small green algae have such a short life-cycle and fast rate of reproduction that they can stay ahead of grazing by sea urchins.)

Removal of predators (sea urchins) disrupted the algal community by causing that predator's major prey species (brown alga) to outcompete other algae species with which the prey coexists when the predator is present. Kelp, a brown alga and an important source of iodine and fertilizer, is also harvested by humans.

The sea otter is the major predator of sea urchins; humans are (or were) the major predator of sea otters. (Sea otters were nearly wiped out by humans in the late nineteenth and early twentieth centuries. Closely protected since the 1960s, the otters have come back successfully along parts of their former range.) Because sea otters prey on sea urchins, wherever the otters are in their original numbers, brown algae flourish and the harvesting of kelp can continue.

The East Coast situation

Along the Atlantic coast of Canada and the United States, the major predator of urchins is crabs (not otters), and lobsters prey on the crabs. Where lobster have been overfished, the crabs keep urchin populations low, which keeps kelp biomass up.

The Cyclamen Mite and the Predatory Mite

Mites usually invade a field shortly after berry plants have been planted. The mite population increases but usually does not achieve levels at which they damage the crop until the second year.

Typically, that is when predatory mites invade the field and rapidly subdue the pest mites. Moreover, once the predatory mite is present, it remains, and pest-mite levels never again become sufficiently high to cause damage to the strawberry plants.

In experiments, plants without predatory mites had up to twenty-five times as many pest mites as those with predator mites.

PREDATOR AND PREY NUMBERS SEEM INDEPENDENT (CATEGORY 3)

In some cases, the interactions between species seem clear, as in categories 1 and 2. But those are only a very small minority of the cases that have been studied.

A particular form of seeming independence between predators and prey is that in which prey populations cycle without their predators. Certainly, populations of some prey species cycle, including (among vertebrates) grouse, lemmings, and voles, and (among invertebrates) locusts and gypsy moths. Those cycles, however, do not seem to have direct effects on their predator populations. Nor are the cycles as clearly linked to an explanation as is the hare cycle. In fact, lemming and vole cycles are so complicated they are believed to involve at least ten major factors.

What are the possible differences between a predator that is and one that is not independent of changes in the population size of one of its prey species? (For one possibility, compare wolf and cheetah diets.) List a few possibilities in your notebook for discussion in class.

CHARACTERISTICS OF PREDATION: SOME TIDBITS

Here are a few interesting things that have been discovered in studies of predation.

When a prey species is abundant, its predator(s) might eat more of it—that seems obvious. But the predator will eat disproportionately more of the common prey. For instance, if a sudden hot, humid spell causes a lot of mosquitoes to hatch, little brown bats eat lots of mosquitoes. If mosquitoes usually make up 85% of the flying insects from which the bats are eating during a mosquito "boon", bats actually choose mosquitoes preferentially, so their intake is more like 100% mosquitoes. Why? Ecologists do not really know. Maybe the bats are capitalizing on the sudden mosquito bonanza.

Predators also switch prey, that is, they switch from eating one species to another, for various reasons. Perhaps their preferred prey is less abundant (as in the lynx-hare-grouse example). Perhaps the predator has nutritional needs that are not adequately met by its current prey; say, the prey population is suffering an illness or is itself lacking food, so its members become less meaty and less energetically worth the effort. Or if the prey species is a plant, it may be drying out from drought or age or producing defensive chemicals.

CONCLUSION

Besides showing that predator-prey interactions are complex, the different manipulations and their effects nicely illustrate the complexities of environmental management. In the case of the sea otters, urchins, and kelps, fur trappers and kelp farmers would be at odds; urchin farmers and fur traders would be on the same wavelength; lobster and crab fishermen would have opposing wishes; and environmental purists might be at odds with everyone.

Is there any succinct moral or neat upshot to this story? Unfortunately, no, as is often the case in managing the environment. There are too many different and even opposing interests for each to get its wishes met. Good management takes into consideration all the wishes and their likely effects in the future as well as in the present. Too often, management decisions are made considering only their effect in the present. And as we are seeing, choices on ecological issues can have consequences throughout an ecosystem and even to other ecosystems, not only in the present but into the future.

INTEGRATION
Perturbations: Events That Disturb Ecosystems

There is no undisturbed, perfectly steady-state region on earth. Simply put, to exist anywhere on this planet is to suffer perturbations. "Perturbation" is not the same as "human disturbance"—in every ecosystem, rare or occasional events have important effects on energy or nutrient cycling, on primary production, on species diversity, or on other aspects of the system.

HUMAN EFFECTS

Human activities also may be present, interacting with the perturbations that are natural to the system. Depending on the scale of the human activity, the effect may be more extensive than you might expect, because it is affecting a system already under some nonhuman stress. For example, droughts are not a human-caused event, but the catastrophe in the Sahara region over the past two decades was worsened by human behaviors: wars in several nations there displaced many farmers and herders, who were pushed into areas where the system could not provide them sustenance. Their flocks overgrazed the land, and the desert spread.

"NATURAL" PERTURBATIONS

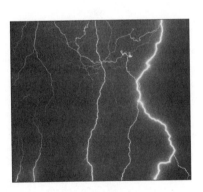

Even in the absence of humans, some regions are less perturbed than others. For example, organisms living on the ocean floor may experience only perturbations such as occasional seaquakes or drifting matter raining down on them. But for the most part, organisms receive many types of large and small perturbations. Fire, wind, floods, and drought are features of many systems, and organisms react to them, more or less well, depending on their genetics, physiology, and so on (remember the finches from **Module 1**?). Fire is a good example—many ecosystems are fire-based. Fires from spontaneous combustion or lightning are regular, frequent, and, by now, necessary parts of those ecosystems. Without fire, underbrush builds up and prevents plant regrowth; some plant seeds require fire to mature; some conifer species that are adapted to withstand fire get displaced if deciduous tree seedlings are not regularly burnt down in natural fires.

FREQUENCY OF PERTURBATIONS

Some perturbations occur in patterns that cycle at the rate of decades or centuries. Many perturbations have a human component; unfortunately, those often occur at much faster rates or are more intense and far reaching than any natural perturbations. Species thus do not necessarily have enough time to "respond"—to be selected, to adapt. Which is not to say that extinction is an unnatural process. But the rate of species extinction currently is at one of three all-time highs. (The other two were not due to human perturbations.)

Materials

- One or more **Perturbation Case Studies**
- **Reference materials** (from the library or other sources)
- **Your wits**
- **Whatever you have learned from this Unit**

Procedure

1. **Types of effects.**

Consider the effects that the perturbation might have on specific ecosystem: Consider also the effects that those effects have—the second-order effects. What is a second-order effect? Imagine the following scene.

Standing at a street corner, you see a fast-moving car with malfunctioning brakes slam into a car waiting at a stop light. The damage suffered by both cars is an effect of the initial cause, the bad brakes. But the stationary car was not the only car waiting at the light. It was hit so hard by the malfunctioning car that it shot forward and hit another waiting car. The damage to the third car is a second-order effect, an effect of the first effect.

2. **Levels of effects.**

In your discussions, try to consider both the direct (or first-order) effects of perturbations and the second-order effects. If you have time, consider the third-order effects—those caused by the second-order effects.

It is difficult to predict specific results of a given perturbation, but we can consider the possibilities. Use the knowledge you have been acquiring during this course to think about some of the possible results of your perturbation.

CASE STUDY: DEADLY VIRUS SWEEPS SERENGETI

In 1890, the viral disease rinderpest reached the Serengeti. The disease was carried by domestic cattle, for whom it was deadly. Unfortunately, it also proved fatal for several wild species; in two years 95% of the wildebeest and buffalo were dead, as were 95% of the domestic cattle.

Consider the effects of this perturbation on the many levels you have been considering during this course.

Procedure

1. **Effects at various trophic levels.**

Discuss possible effects on populations of organisms on all trophic levels: producers (plants), herbivores, carnivores, detritivores, and decomposers.

2. **Abiotic factors.**

Can you think of any possible effects on abiotic features of the ecosystem?

What might have happened to the Maasai people living in the area whose livelihood depended on their herds of cattle?

3. **Second- and third-order effects.**

Consider the second-order effects that might occur in the ecosystem. What might those second-order effects be? Can you imagine any third-order effects?

CASE STUDY: IMPORTED CATERPILLAR DEFOLIATES FORESTS

In the late 1860s, a U.S. businessman brought a number of gypsy moths to Massachusetts from Europe, in an attempt to establish a silk industry. His venture failed. A few caterpillars escaped from his study window, though, and made themselves at home in the woods of New England.

The caterpillars of these moths eat the leaves of several deciduous trees of the northeastern United States. In some years, they achieve very large populations in some local areas, perhaps covering most of a town or a few towns. The devastation they cause can be staggering. Walking through an infested forest in early summer is a strange experience—it feels like autumn, since most of the trees are virtually leafless. During such outbreaks, however, nearby areas typically are much less heavily hit. In addition, outbreaks, as the name suggests, are temporary. It is rare for a given area to be heavily affected by gypsy moths year after year.

Please consider the effects of this perturbation on the many levels you have been considering during this course. Be sure to consider different physical scales, such as an area the size of a football field and an area of several thousand square miles.

Procedure

1. **Effects at various trophic levels.**
   Discuss possible effects on populations of organisms on all trophic levels: producers (plants), herbivores, carnivores, detritivores, and decomposers.

2. **Abiotic factors.**
   Can you think of any possible effects on abiotic features of the ecosystem?

3. **Second- and third-order effects.**
   Consider the second-order effects that might occur in the ecosystem. What might those second-order effects be? Can you imagine any third-order effects?

CASE STUDY: THE MOUNTAIN LION DISAPPEARS—AND MAYBE RETURNS

While never common, mountain lions (also known as cougars or pumas) were found throughout much of the continental United States when the first settlers reached this country. In northern New England, these magnificent cats were almost certainly wiped out by some time in the late nineteenth or early twentieth century due to a combination of hunting by humans and loss of habitat (as farms replaced forests). All that remains is place names, such as "Panther Caves," to mark a place where the cats once were found.

Something odd has happened recently, however. There have been a number of sightings of large cats in northern New England. Some degree of doubt exists whether these are mountain lions; none of the observers has been a trained biologist, and there is, as yet, no concrete evidence from clear tracks or authenticated photographs. One theory is that these were captive animals that were released or escaped (some people keep these 40-to-90-kg animals as pets). Certainly there is a lot of forest in northern New England these days—many farms that were abandoned in the last century have given way to forest—and deer (a major food source for mountain lions) are plentiful. Perhaps the cats are back.

Suppose a small population of cougars were to become established in a Northern Hardwood Forest in New Hampshire or Minnesota. What effect might this have on the system?

Procedure
1. **Effects at various trophic levels.**
Discuss possible effects on populations of organisms on all trophic levels: producers (plants), herbivores, carnivores, detritivores, and decomposers.

2. **Abiotic factors.**
Can you think of any possible effects on abiotic features of the ecosystem?

3. **Second- and third-order effects.**
Consider the second-order effects that might occur in the ecosystem. What might those second-order effects be? Can you imagine any third-order effects?

CASE STUDY: VOLCANO ERUPTS–COOLS AND DIMS ENTIRE EARTH

In June 1991, Mount Pinatubo erupted, spewing about 20 million tons of sulfur dioxide and vast quantities of ash high into the atmosphere, 20–30 km above the earth. The sulfur dioxide cloud eventually spread to cover the entire earth. The gas mixed with water, creating tiny droplets of sulfuric acid. Those droplets reflect significant amounts of sunlight. Scientists estimate that the result of this one volcano's eruption in the Philippines will reduce temperature by about 0.5°C all over the earth for 2–4 years. In addition, the amount of the sun's energy that reaches the earth's surface will noticeably decrease.

Please consider the effects of this perturbation on the many levels you have been considering during this course.

Procedure
1. **Effects at various trophic levels.**
Discuss possible effects on populations of organisms on all trophic levels: producers (plants), herbivores, carnivores, detritivores, and decomposers.

2. **Abiotic factors.**
Can you think of any possible effects on abiotic features of the ecosystem?

3. **Second- and third-order effects.**
Consider the second-order effects that might occur in the ecosystem. What might those second-order effects be? Can you imagine any third-order effects?

CASE STUDY: NATIONAL PARK CREATED, CREATING AN ELEPHANT PROBLEM

One of Africa's finer national parks, Tsavo, was the site of an ecological disaster in the 1970s. Elephants are large and powerful animals. They eat both grass and leaves off trees, often tearing up small saplings in the process. Large bulls can knock over mature trees to get at the leaves. In general, these destructive actions are not a problem—the elephants merely help to create and maintain patchy woodlands that also contain grass. When an area begins to run short of food, the elephants move on to other areas. So, what happened in Tsavo?

As often happens, human development continued rapidly around the boundaries of the national park. The elephants were prevented from roaming across the park's borders into neighboring agricultural lands. Confined to the park, the elephants flourished for a while. As they began to deplete the trees, however, they had nowhere to go. There were fewer and fewer trees in the park but still a large population of elephants to be supported by the remaining grasslands. Then a drought hit, decreasing the production of grass.

Please consider the effects of this perturbation on the many levels you have been considering during this course.

Procedure

1. **Effects at various trophic levels.**
   Discuss possible effects on populations of organisms on all trophic levels: producers (plants), herbivores, carnivores, detritivores, and decomposers.

2. **Abiotic factors.**
   Can you think of any possible effects on abiotic features of the ecosystem?

3. **Second- and third-order effects.**
   Consider the second-order effects that might occur in the ecosystem. What might those second-order effects be? Can you imagine any third-order effects?

HOW PLANTS CAPTURE AND ALLOCATE ENERGY

HOW PLANTS CAPTURE AND ALLOCATE ENERGY

UNIT 3 CONTENTS

UNIT 3 OVERVIEW

HOW PLANTS CAPTURE AND ALLOCATE ENERGY

Plant forms have fascinated people for centuries. Their stationary lives between soil and sky would seem to put them at the mercy of the dynamics of climate and of animal life passing around and through them, preying on them, and otherwise controlling their destiny. Yet they are far less passive than first appears. Plants have the same "tasks" as animals: they forage for resources (above ground for light; below ground for water and nutrients); they mate, bear offspring, and release the offspring to establish themselves. Not only are plants affected by climate and by animals (including *Homo sapiens*), they pursue all those activities surrounded by other plants, that may be competing for space, for water, for nutrients, for light.

Plants are responsive and sensitive, and almost all their responses are expressed in patterns of growth. Those responses often are so unlike animal responses (such as our own) that we may find it hard to recognize them. The following quote captures the similarities and differences between plants and animals nicely:

> In any densely vegetated environment, leaves serve both as the plant's solar collectors (its "jaws") and as its weapons for interfering with the growth of neighboring plants (its "claws"). In the absence of neighbors, a plant is free to grow sideways, investing minimally in structural tissue for support and supply. However, once plants begin to encounter neighbors, they gain a distinct competitive advantage by growing taller, so that a small size difference can be amplified into a continuing competitive advantage.

—Donald Waller, in <u>Plant Ecology</u>, (M. Crawley, ed.)

This "plastic" (i.e., flexible) response of plants to environmental conditions leads to the great variety that we can see even in individuals of the same species. A plant may grow more or less tall, have different-shaped leaves on different branches, flower on one side and not another, or produce different kinds of flowers depending on the availability of light or other resources. And plants of the same species living in very different regions may look remarkably different.

Within this riot of variety, however, are patterns of growth and strategies for survival. As we have begun to see, the ways plant communities and species have been shaped by environmental constraints have important implications for energy capture (as well as other aspects) of a system.

In this Unit, we explore how environmental forces and plants' responses to them have resulted in characteristic plant formations in each biological region of the earth, including where you live. And, since these plant formations are a foundation for all other life in an ecosystem, we study the interaction between energy capture and the architecture of plants and plant communities.

DESIGN A PLANT
ENERGY CAPTURE AND ALLOCATION
CHAPTER ONE

Exploration 1
DESIGN A PLANT

What is a plant's "job," its role in nature? It sometimes seems that plants are there to provide food and lodgings for the rest of us, the heterotrophs of the world. But that is like saying that birds have feathers so we can make pillows. How do things look from the plant's point of view?

Plants, like animals, must gather energy, use some part of the energy for growth and maintenance, and reproduce. Because plants do not move and because their energy source is sunlight, the resources of vertical and horizontal space and environmental conditions play a very different role than they do for animals.

The Explorations in this Chapter help us investigate the role of plants as collectors and users of energy, in the same way that **Unit 2: How Organisms Acquire and Use Energy** explores animals as collectors and users of energy. We see that plants assimilate some of the energy that pours on them from the sun and that they cannot use other portions of it. Although their life seems very different from that of animals, we also see how plants solve the same life tasks, sometimes in similar ways, sometimes in very different ways.

Materials
- **Green construction paper**
- **Transparent tape**

- **Scissors**
- **Scales**
- **Graph paper**
- **Desk lamp** (optional)

Procedure

For this activity, we recommend working in groups of two or three, so you can discuss your decisions and share data-collection duties.

1. **Design a single plant module.**
    Using green construction paper, design a module that consists of a solar (sun energy) collector (a model of a leaf) and a supportive structure (corresponding to stems and similar tissue in a plant). The module should be self-supporting.

    Remember, a plant does not have unlimited materials for growth. Your model should provide maximum area for solar collection and use the minimal amount of materials.

    If you use tape to fasten parts together, keep a record of the amount of tape you use (by length). Keep separate records by weight of the amounts of paper you use for the leaf and for the supporting structure.

2. **Evaluate the size of your collector.**
    Estimate the area of your solar collecting module: stand it on a piece of paper (graph paper would be handy), with the main light source coming from directly overhead, and trace the shade it casts. Estimate the shaded area. You can do that either by counting the squares of the graph paper or by cutting out the shaded area, weighing the cut-out silhouette and comparing it to the weight of a known area of the same kind of paper.

3. **How good a model (part 1)?**
    Have you ever seen any plants with leaves that are like your design? If not, can you think of any engineering drawbacks your design might have?

4. **Design a whole plant.**
    Now take your module and replicate it. That is, build a plant that includes at least five replicas of your modules in a free-standing structure (more is OK!).

5. **How good a model (part 2)?**
    Use the following questions to evaluate your module, then prepare a brief report to the class:

    What is the total surface area of the "leaves" of your plant?

    Does your five-unit model of a plant intercept five times as much light as the single-unit model? (Or a seven-unit model intercept seven times as much light, etc.)

    Do any of the leaves shade any other leaves?

    As you built up your "plant," the total weight increased. Does the proportion of leaf material versus the proportion of support material also change with different sizes of plant?

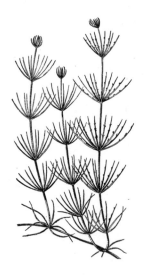

How might you increase the amount of surface area that intercepts sunlight?

How well does your design function if sunlight comes in at a different angle (say, at 45° rather than 90°)?

6. Wrap-up report.

Write a short report discussing your design and describing why you made it as you did. What are its strengths and weaknesses as a system for intercepting light? What would happen if several such plants lived closely together?

As part of the report, also answer the following questions:

Look at the design of any two plants growing outside. What about how they have solved their light-collecting and other problems?

What physical factors does a plant have to contend with that you have not included in your design? How do plants that you have observed appear to solve those problems?

READING 1

SUN LEAVES, SHADE LEAVES, AND TREE SHAPES

Leaves and trees come in a great variety of shapes; even within the same species, they can be confusingly different. Variety in leaf shape is the result of a balance among several factors arising from the leaf's several functions—energy capture, heat dissipation, and gas exchange (CO_2 intake and water loss). In turn, the arrangement of leaves so that they do those tasks effectively has a lot to do with how their tree is shaped.

THE CHALLENGE FOR THE LEAF

A plant's critical above-ground resource is, of course, light. Although light falls abundantly on the surface of the earth, space is limited. The solution that terrestrial plants have evolved is the leaf, which can be replicated and modified, replaced one at a time, and stacked in various arrangements. The arrangement of these replaceable solar collectors has an important relation to the shape of plants. This is seen most dramatically in the shapes of tree species.

Three important features of leaves have enabled trees to maximize use of the light available and to exploit three-dimensional space to that end.

- **Leaves are translucent.** Not all light striking a leaf is absorbed or reflected; some passes through leaves. Sunlight can even pass through several layers of leaves, before all the photosynthetically useful light is "used up."

- **Leaves on the same tree are not all the same.** New leaves can be produced to respond to local conditions. Old leaves can be shed in response to stress, such as drought, unusual cold, or an attack from insects or disease.

- **Each leaf is relatively low-cost to build.** If you need a leaf of a different shape or thickness, you can grow them—that is, you do not need to grow leaves of only one shape or size, and different leaves can be more or less effective at light capture, reflectance, transpiration, and CO_2 capture.

SUN LEAVES AND SHADE LEAVES

Once it reaches maturity, each leaf on a tree must make an energy profit. As the new leaf is growing, it gets a "sugar subsidy" from the other leaves in the vicinity. But once it reaches full size, a leaf needs to make more sugar through photosynthesis than it uses in metabolism. If it does not, it will not be able to replace its metabolic and structural elements—chloroplasts, for example—and will die. (Remember the idea of basal metabolic rate, or BMR, used in **Unit 2**? Plants are sufficiently different from animals that this term is not used by botanists, but the basic idea is similar.)

Now, the amount of sugar a leaf can manufacture is not under just that one leaf's control. If temperatures are very low or if a large proportion of it is eaten by caterpillars, a leaf may not be able to photosynthesize enough to supply its needs. Or a leaf that is shaded may have a hard time photosynthesizing enough sugar.

Most broad-leaved trees can respond to changing lighting conditions by producing different kinds of leaves for high- and low-light conditions. When a leaf is developing, if the light in its area on the tree is high, the leaf will develop into a "sun leaf"; if the light is low, it will develop into a "shade leaf."

Sun Leaves

A sun leaf is adapted for high-radiation life in several ways. First, it has more chloroplasts, to harvest more light; such leaves are also darker green than shade leaves from the same species.

Heat

More solar radiation means more heat, so a sun leaf must have enhanced defenses against overheating and water loss. For that reason, a sun leaf has a thicker cuticle (the waxy covering that protects the leaf against dehydration). That increases the leaf's reflectance (its ability to reflect light), so a higher proportion of light (in the wavelengths not used in photosynthesis) is not absorbed by the leaf. Sun leaves also have more stomata per unit area, allowing for more transpiration, which carries away heat (and a higher rate of CO_2 intake). Sun leaves usually are noticeably smaller in total area and stiffer (because of the thicker cuticle) than shade leaves. (See Figure 1.) Having a smaller area means there is less surface to collect energy, which is balanced by their having more chloroplasts and receiving more sunlight.

Surface area

Another factor is hard to see: on a leaf's surface (as on any other object), a very thin layer of relatively stagnant air is held there by friction against the leaf's surface. That layer acts as insulation against heat loss and

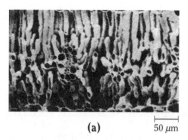 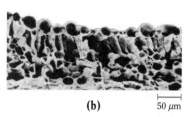

(a)   50 μm   (b)   50 μm

Figure 1. Sun (a) and shade (b) leaves of a member of the pea family. The scanning electron micrographs show the greater thickness of the sun leaf, due to increased thickness of the palisade layer.

against the loss of water vapor. However, if the leaf is under chronic heat stress and that layer is too persistent, mixing only slowly with the surrounding air, the leaf may not be able to rid itself of heat fast enough. The broader the unbroken area of the leaf, the less accessible the boundary layer is to mixing. Therefore, sun leaves' smaller area leads to faster mixing of the boundary air with the surrounding air, allowing faster evaporation. Many species have deep lobes, teeth, or divisions of the leaf edge, so the average distance to any edge from any point on the surface is reduced, which also means that the boundary layer is broken up much more quickly (another example of the importance of the relation between surface area and volume).

Shade Leaves

By contrast, shade leaves are (relative to the sun leaves) paler, less stiff, broader, and longer and have a thinner cuticle. They have fewer chloroplasts and less structural material, so they require less energy to maintain themselves. Thus, the dimmer light they receive is enough for them to turn an energy profit. Their lobes or teeth usually are shallower than those of sun leaves, so the average distance from any point on the surface to an edge is greater.

Checking with Nature

You can see the differences between sun leaves and shade leaves on trees in your area. Find a tree that stands along the edge of a field or a lot, so that part of the tree gets a lot of sun over the course of the day, while part stays mostly in the shade. Compare leaves from different parts of the tree—look at color, texture, and weight. In the same way, compare leaves from trees of the same species that inhabit very sunny and very shady locations.

TREE SHAPES

Multilayer

Tree species have different ideal conditions for growth. One way in which they differ one from another is in the placement of leaf-bearing twigs. Trees that grow in full sun tend to be bushier and with smallish leaves, often with many lobes. The tree crown's shape is more like a cone, and leaves are found at all distances from the trunk. Thus, the abundant

Silver maple

Dawn redwood

Figure 2. Examples of multilayer trees.

Sugar maple

Hemlock

Figure 3. Examples of monolayer trees.

light strikes the outer leaves, which are saturated quickly—their photosynthetic machinery cannot make use of it all. That is where leaf size and shape come in. Some unfiltered light passes between the leaves. That, plus the light passing right through the outer leaf layers, is enough for inner leaves to turn a profit. Because the tree uses several light-harvesting layers, it can capture a high proportion of the light available to it. This design is called the "multilayer strategy." Figure 2 shows two examples of multilayer tree species.

Monolayer

By contrast, a tree growing in the interior of a forest does not have as much light available to it. Light does not cascade onto the tree, pouring through and bouncing off the leaves. Instead, the light is weakened and filtered by the leaves of neighboring trees and the tree's own higher branches. Often there is barely enough light to supply a leaf with energy. A tree cannot afford to waste any light, nor can it afford for any leaf to be shaded by another leaf on the same tree. So the leaves are arranged in a thin layer, like a shell around the tree, with lots of bare branch inside. This design is sometimes called a "monolayer strategy."

A tree that grows in shade thus tends to have a more spherical-shaped or very irregular crown. Leaves are arranged only on the outside surface of the crown and at the ends of branches, with none near the trunk (Figure 3).

Either or Both

Some species of trees thrive in only one condition or the other. Others are more flexible, so that trees growing from seeds from the same mother will be more multilayer or monolayer, depending on the conditions in which they grow.

Exploration 2a
TRANSFORMING LIGHT TO HEAT ENERGY

The sun constantly radiates billions of calories of energy toward the earth. From the stream of light that strikes the earth, living creatures sip just a little, the plants catching it and passing it on to the rest of us.

The sun is a constant source of energy for the earth as a whole. The energy received at any one place, however, varies with the rotation of the earth on its axis (night and day) and the revolution of the earth around the sun (seasonal changes in day length and other factors). In **Chapter 2**, we explore those changes in the amount of energy that reaches the earth, but for now let's assume that solar radiation arrives at the earth's surface at the constant rate of 1,000 watts per square meter (W/m^2). One watt = 0.238 calories per second (cal/sec).

During its journey from the sun through living tissue, this energy gets transformed many times. As we saw in **Unit 2**, each transformation has ecological consequences and is highly inefficient.

Here we use a standard scientific technique—modeling—to explore some aspects of energy flow through plants. A scientific model looks at some specific part of a complex system and, bit by bit, builds up an understanding of the whole based on the study of the parts.

This Exploration opens the way to other investigations, as your class explores what the basic energy budget of a plant might look like. In this Exploration, half the class works with the transfer of light to heat energy, while the other half works on the transformation of light to electrical energy. The two groups then come together to describe what happens to the light striking a plant and to see just how limited light is as a resource.

Materials

- **Thermometers** (2)
- **100- to 150-watt lightbulb**, with **lamp shade** or **reflector**
- **Clamp lamp**
- **Construction paper** in assorted colors
- **Meter stick**
- **Corrugated cardboard**
- **Masking tape**
- **Clock** or **watch**

Procedure

1. **Predict and plan.**
First, choose paper that will give you the maximum and the minimum changes in temperature. ·

    What colors of paper did you choose and why? Write a short paragraph that explains your choice of colors. When explaining your reasoning, be explicit about any ideas you have about the interaction between the color of paper and the light from the bulb.

2. **The setup.**
Without turning on the lamp, position it so light rays will travel 30 cm from the bulb and strike the table at approximately a 90-degree angle. Use a ruler or piece of string to simulate the rays of light. Place a piece of tape on the cardboard where the rays will strike.

    Place the two thermometers end to end on top of the table at the piece of tape so that the bulbs of the thermometers face each other and are equidistant from the lightbulb. See Figure 4.

3. **The experiment and data collection.**
To begin the experiment, cover each thermometer with one of the colors that you chose to test. Record the colors of paper you are testing and the starting temperature under each piece of paper.

    Turn on the light, then record the temperature under each piece of paper every 3 minutes for a period of 12 minutes.

    If there is time, repeat the experiment several times using different-colored paper.

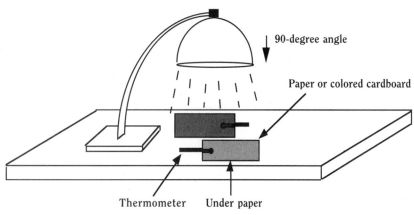

90-degree angle

Paper or colored cardboard

Thermometer   Under paper

Figure 4

4. **Analyze the data.**

Summarize your results, using graphs and tables to represent your data. Prepare a short presentation to the class, beginning with your choice of colored paper and including a discussion of light, reflection, absorption, and energy. Discuss anything that surprised you. (You may find the **Technique: Preparing a Presentation** helpful.)

Be sure to discuss the following:

Under what color of paper was the temperature highest and lowest at the end of the experiment?

What color of paper absorbed the most light energy (converting it into heat)? Which absorbed the least?

Where did the rest of the light go? Can you estimate what proportion of light traveled along each path?

Keep in mind these points: light is a form that energy can take; energy can be converted from one form (e.g., light) to another (e.g., heat); and all transfers of energy are inefficient to some degree. In other words, all transfers of energy involve a loss of some of the energy, usually as heat. For example, when wood is burned, 80–90% of the chemical energy in the wood's carbon compounds is emitted as heat (infrared radiation); only 10% is emitted at visible frequencies. Thus, a wood fire is not an efficient way to get light to read by! Recall from **Unit 2** how little total energy animals get from their food intake and how inefficient the transfer of energy between trophic levels is.

Exploration 2b

TRANSFORMING LIGHT TO ELECTRICITY

All life depends on the tiny, tiny electrical current by electrons flowing one at a time from one molecule to another in the photosystems of plant chloroplasts. The energy of sunlight triggers the complex machinery of photosynthesis, by which electromagnetic energy is stored as chemical energy.

How much energy can a plant actually capture in this fragile system? How much energy is lost? How does it compare to human-designed solar collectors?

The sun is a constant source of energy for the earth as a whole. The energy received at any one place, however, varies with the rotation of the earth on its axis (night and day) and the revolution of the earth around the sun (seasonal changes in day length and other factors). In **Chapter 2**, we explore those changes in the amount of energy that reaches the earth, but for now, let's assume that solar radiation arrives at the earth's surface at the constant rate of 1,000 watts per square meter (W/m²). One watt = 0.238 calories per second (cal/sec).

Here we use a standard scientific technique—modeling—to explore some aspects of energy flow through plants. A scientific model looks at some specific part of a complex system and, bit by bit, builds up an understanding of the whole based on the study of the parts.

This Exploration opens the way to other investigations, as your class explores what the basic energy budget of a plant might look like. In this Exploration, half the class works with the transfer of light to heat energy, while the other half works on the transformation of light to electrical energy. The two groups then come together to describe what happens to the light striking a plant and to see just how limited light is as a resource.

PHOTOCELLS

By the late nineteenth century, scientists realized that it was possible to use light energy to produce electricity. The technology to produce photocells—materials in which light produces an electric current in usable amounts—was not, however, advanced enough to make practical use of that knowledge.

It was not until the 1950s that scientists were able to produce photocells in enough quantity for their use to be widespread. Today, photocells are most important for production of electricity in remote locations (e.g., islands, remote field stations, and space). However, with the costs of production dropping, they soon could generate much of the electricity we use.

In this Exploration, we use the photocell to illustrate several concepts that are critical to life: light is a form that energy can take; energy can be converted from one form (e.g., light) to another (e.g., heat); and all transfers of energy are inefficient.

Using simple instruments and a photocell, we explore those concepts. By comparing the amount of power we get from the solar cell to an estimate of the power of the sun, we can calculate how efficiently the solar cell converts light into electricity. This basic design allows us to study how efficient living plants are as collectors of solar energy.

Materials
- **Multimeter with leads** (A multimeter measures voltage produced by light's effect on the photocell. This voltage represents a portion of the energy striking the light-sensitive surface.)

- **1-ohm (Ω) resistor**
- **Solar cell**
- **A sunny day**

Safety

> **WARNING**
> When taking solar measurements, do NOT look at the sun directly! It can damage your eyes!

> **WARNING**
> Never set the meter to read ohms (Ω) when it is attached to the photo-cell. Doing so can cause permanent damage to the multimeter.

Procedure

1. **Setting up the multimeter.**

In teams of two or three, prepare your simple instrument. Set the dial to 2 DCV (Figure 5).

Put the red lead in the V jack and the black lead in COM. Do not worry about exceeding the maximum voltage for this scale, since the maximum voltage output of the photocells is around 0.5 volts (V).

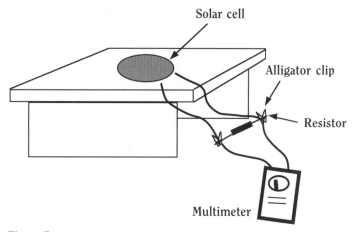

Figure 5

2. **Setting up the photocell system.**

You are going to measure the photocell's output in volts. To measure voltage, you need to set up a pathway that has two points at which you can measure the voltage (physicists say "measure the voltage across the two points"). A 1-Ω resistor is the right size to provide a good path and to allow a simple conversion from the measured voltage to the power output you are looking for.

The basic idea is to create a pathway by attaching one lead from the photocell to each side of the resistor. The reading on the multimeter then indicates the voltage difference between the contact points. See Figure 6.

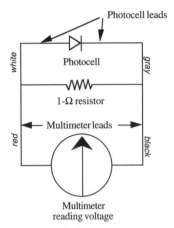

Figure 6. Connecting the multimeter, the resistor, and the photocell.

3. **Trying out the equipment and preparing a data table.**
    Try making some sample measurements with the solar cell facing a window and then away from a window; tilt the solar cell at various angles and see what happens. Practice reading the meter and recording the data. Make sure to use the proper units (volts) when you record the data.

4. **Preparing to take measurements from the sun.**
    Make your measurements as close to the middle of the day as possible, when the sun's power is closest to the 1,000 W/m² that we are assuming to be the input for the photocell.

    To make your measurements, find a sunny place outside or a place inside that has a direct, unobstructed view of the sun. Avoid places where trees, buildings, or other structures block your view of the sun.

    Orient the photocell until the current reading is at its maximum. At what angle is that likely to be?

5. **Voltage readings.**
    Take three or four measurements, each time making sure you orient the solar cell to maximize the current and then get a voltage reading without moving the cell. Record your voltage data and the time in your notebooks.

6. **Calculating power readings from the voltage data.**
    For a system like this, which uses a 1-Ω resistor, the relation between power and voltage is simple:

    $$power = voltage^2$$

    For each reading you took, calculate the power as the square of the voltage and record the values in your notebook. Calculate the average power and record that.

    The values you have recorded are the amounts of solar energy that the photocell was able to convert into electrical energy. The next step is to calculate the efficiency of transfer: what percentage was converted to electrical energy and what percentage was lost in the transfer.

7. **Calculating the area of the collector.**
    The estimated solar input is in watts per square meter (W/m²). To calculate

how much light actually struck your collector, you need to figure its area in square meters. Remember to calculate only the area of the sensitive surface. Make your measure in meters, so you will be using comparable units (W/m^2) to compare input and output.

Divide the power that the cell produced (W) by the area of the cell (m^2), to get an output quantity you can compare with the input value.

8. **Combining your data to calculate the efficiency in watts per square meter.**
    Now calculate the efficiency of energy transfer from the energy in solar radiation to electricity. Efficiency is calculated as the output divided by the input, that is,

    efficiency = output/input

    In this case, use your measure of the power from the solar cell divided by the actual (estimated) solar radiation ($1,000\ W/m^2$).

9. **Reporting your results.**
    In the process of preparing to share your work and results with the class, consider the following:

    Given your experience, how much power would you expect to get from a solar cell that has a sensitive surface of $1\ m^2$?

    If the actual input to your solar cell were only $750\ W/m^2$, what would the efficiency of the photocell be?

    Collect several leaves from outside and estimate their surface area. How much energy strikes each leaf, given a power input of solar radiation of $1,000\ W/m^2$?

    What proportion of the solar input was not converted to electricity? Where did it go?

10. **Class discussion.**
    Were your results different from other groups' results? Why might that be? After all teams have presented, as a class discuss how you could calculate the efficiency of energy capture by a plant.

READING 2
LIGHT STRIKING VEGETATION: REFLECTION, TRANSMISSION, AND ABSORPTION

When radiation strikes a surface, it has three fates. The radiation may be absorbed, reflected, or transmitted. How the incoming radiation is apportioned among the different pathways is controlled in part by the quality, or wavelength, of radiation and the qualities of the material.

REFLECTION

The amount of radiation reflected is a function of the material it strikes. The percentage reflected is commonly referred to as the albedo. Table 1 lists average values.

Table 1 **Average Values of Albedo**

SURFACE	ALBEDO, PERCENTAGE
New snow	90
Old snow	50
Average cloud cover	50
Light sand	40
Light soil	25
Concrete	25
Green crops	20
Green forests	15
Dark soil	10
Asphalt	8
Water	8

TRANSMISSION

Radiation is transmitted through surfaces that are transparent to those wavelengths of radiation. For example, clear glass and plastic are nearly transparent to wavelengths of light that are visible to humans; in contrast, ultraviolet light (the wavelengths that cause suntans) is not transmitted through glass. Obviously, if light passes through more than one surface, some is absorbed by each surface. Thus, radiation that passes through leaves in a forest canopy is weaker than direct sunlight. The light on the forest floor may be as little as 2–10% of full sunlight. That light also differs from full sunlight in its wavelengths: much of the photosynthetically active wavelengths (red and some blue-violet) already have been absorbed by the chlorophyll in leaves. As a result, the light environment below a leaf canopy can be quite different from that outside the canopy. Plants in this dimmer, lower-energy environment have been selected to do most of their light gathering before the upper leaves emerge and cast their shade; some also use light more efficiently and have a lower compensation point.

This means there can be more than one layer of plants per square meter of land surface, which means a higher proportion of the available light is used, which enables a higher productivity—new plant tissue produced per square meter—than would be possible otherwise. The ability to respond flexibly to levels of light availability is a characteristic open to evolutionary design.

ABSORPTION

If you subtract from total incoming radiation the amount reflected and the amount transmitted, you are left with the amount absorbed. A small percentage (1–10%) of light striking a leaf is absorbed by the photosynthetic system. The bulk of it is absorbed as internal energy in the form of heat. Leaves have to dissipate a lot of heat: a leaf with a 300-μm thickness of water would heat up to 100°C if all solar energy were absorbed and no heat lost.

The large amount of radiation absorbed as heat plays an important role in the plant's circulation, since it causes the evaporation of water through the leaves, which drives the flow of water from root to leaf. (This is taken up in **Module 3: Water**, in which energy that plays little part in **Module 2: Carbon and Energy** becomes a central topic.)

Exploration 3a
FIGURING THE ANGLES IN YOUR LOCATION

The sun moves across the sky during the day; during a year, the sun's course is lower or higher in the sky (what is the exception?). Therefore, the sun is sometimes higher and sometimes lower in the sky. You can feel how this change of position affects the strength of the sunlight striking you. How big is the actual difference? How might it affect plants' energy harvest?

NOTE ON SUN ANGLES

The height of the sun above the horizon is called its altitude. It makes no sense to measure this height in meters since it is so <u>far</u> away. Instead, it is customary to measure altitude as an angle from the horizontal surface of the earth. When the sun appears at the horizon, its angle is 0°.

What are the minimum and maximum sun angles at this time of year? What is the angle of the sun at 10 A.M.? At 2 P.M.? Sundown? What effect does this time of year have on the amount of insolation striking a given area of the earth's surface?

To investigate something we cannot measure by counting, we need an instrument that changes in a regular fashion as the phenomenon changes in intensity or quantity, producing an output that you can count. For example, as temperature increases, mercury expands at a regular rate. When the mercury is confined to a narrow tube as in a thermometer, we can lay something like a ruler alongside the column and read off numbers to measure changes in temperature.

For sunlight, there are many ways to measure the quantity striking a unit area. In Exploration 2a, we measured the change in temperature of a piece of paper left in simulated sunlight. Now let's use the solar cell to measure the same phenomenon.

In this Exploration, half the class will be figuring the relation between sun angles and the strength of solar radiation, while the other half relates sun angles to geographical location, specifically latitude.

Materials
- **Desk lamp**
- **Multimeter setup** used in Exploration 2b
- **Carpenter's level**, if possible, or **homemade level** (e.g., glass of water)
- **Protractor**
- **Measuring tape** or **meter stick**

Safety

> **WARNING**
> When taking solar measurements, do NOT look at the sun directly! It can damage your eyes!

> **WARNING**
> Never set the meter to read ohms (Ω) when it is attached to the photo-cell. Doing so can cause permanent damage to the multimeter.

In Advance

Since your group will be taking data at several points throughout the day (step 4), make sure each group member knows when, where, and how he or she will be doing the measurements that he or she is responsible for.

In selecting a site to take data, make sure your location will not be overtaken by shadows early or late in the day and that the sunlight will not be blocked in other ways (by trees, buildings, or whatever).

Procedure

1. **Make some predictions.**

    At what angle will the sunlight be strongest? At what angle will the sunlight be weakest? What difference (in percent) is there between the maximum and the minimum? Write your expectations in your notebook.

2. **Test 1: A model.**

    In this test, use a lightbulb as a model sun. Adjust the lamp head to different angles. In all cases, keep the solar cell at a standard distance from the light, say 30 cm. See Figure 7.

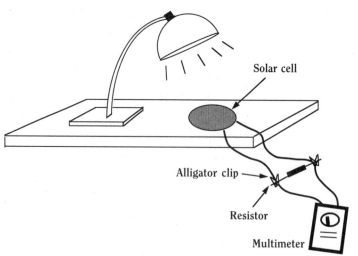

Figure 7. A model light-collecting system.

3. **Collecting data.**

    Note the power reading on the multimeter for each lamp angle you test. What is the maximum reading you attain? At what angle to the light did you get that reading?

What minimum reading did you get? At what angle was that? What is the range between the maximum and the minimum?

4. **Analyzing the data.**
What percentage of the maximum is the minimum?

Does the strength of the light parallel the change of the light's angle?

How do you think this relates to changes in the strength of sunlight during the day? For example, suppose you measure angle versus strength over a 45-degree difference in angle. How would you use these data to predict the relation of changes in sun angle to sun strength over the course of a day?

5. **Revise your predictions.**
Now that you have worked with the model, you can make some predictions about what you will find in the sunlight. Write your predictions for these questions in your notebook:

At what angle will the sun be strongest? At what angle will the sun be weakest? What difference (in percent) is there between the maximum and the minimum? If your predictions are different from those you made in step 1, explain why you changed them.

6. **Test 2: The real thing at your test site.**

Safety

> **WARNING**
> When taking solar measurements, do NOT look at the sun directly! It can damage your eyes!

> **WARNING**
> Never set the meter to read ohms (Ω) when it is attached to the photocell. Doing so can cause permanent damage to the multimeter.

Your group needs to be prepared to take solar readings over the course of one day, such as who will take which reading when. About five readings will do; if you can arrange to do more, so much the better.

Find a place where you can lay the solar cells absolutely flat on the ground; use a carpenter's level if you can. Otherwise, find as level a place as possible (eyeball it, see if a marble sits still on the spot, or see how level the water is in a straight-sided glass there). This is your piece of the "horizon." Mark it with tape or some other way, so each time you take a measurement you do it from the same spot.

Take data at several points in the day: as early as possible, as late as possible, around noon, and another one or two times in the morning and again in the afternoon. Note the voltage reading, the time of day, and the sun's approximate angle above the horizon (noon is 90°, dawn is 0°, sunset is 0°).

7. **Data analysis and presentation.**
As a team, prepare a report of all your findings and explore their meaning for plant energy capture. You may find it helpful to refer to the **Technique:**

Data and the **Technique: Preparing a Presentation**. Include the following information:

Describe where and how you made the measurements. Mention anything that surprised you, including predictions your team made that turned out to be wrong. What was the difference between your prediction and reality?

What differences did you notice between the measurements with the lightbulb, and the measurements with the sun? Were there unforeseen problems in getting results?

When is/was the next/most recent equinox or solstice? How do you think your results will differ at the other three seasons?

What do your results have to do with day length?

Why is this relevant to plants in your area? How does this behavior of the sun affect primary productivity? What else besides solar angle can affect the angle at which light strikes a plant?

8. **Class discussion: Integrating the data.**
The two groups have explored sun angles during the day and on different spots on the globe (and under different geographical conditions).

After each group has reported to the class, discuss the following questions. Refer to your own and the other group's report in raising questions or suggesting answers or conjectures.

What factors limit the light available for primary producers?

At what time scales do these factors operate?

How different are the light environments at the equator and in Alaska? Where in the continuum from equator to pole does your school fall?

What other factors may interact with variations in insolation to limit plant growth (and other processes dependent on it)?

What do the seasons look like in your location? In Hawaii? In Alaska? What does that have to do with variations in insolation?

Exploration 3b
GEOGRAPHY AND PLANT GROWTH

The sun moves across the sky during the day; during the course of a year, the sun's course is lower or higher in the sky (what is the exception?). Therefore, the sun is sometimes higher and sometimes lower in the sky. You can feel how this change of position affects the strength of the sunlight striking you. How big is the actual difference? How might it affect plants' energy harvest?

In this Exploration, half the class will be figuring the relation between sun angles and the strength of solar radiation, while the other half relates sun angle to geographical location, specifically latitude.

WHAT IS AT STAKE?

As we saw in **Unit 2** (especially **Chapter 10**), the productivity of plants in an ecosystem determines the amount of other kinds of productivity in the ecosystem. That is, the energy captured by plants is all the energy that is available to the organisms of that ecosystem. To understand how much life an ecosystem can support, therefore, we need to know the amount of energy that can be captured. And since the sun is the source of electromagnetic energy of the kind plants can use, sunlight is the key here—we need to know how much sunlight is available.

How much sunlight strikes a spot over the course of a day? A year? What factors other than the solar supply affect how much energy is available to the plants (primary producers) on that spot?

Although the sun's output varies for many reasons (e.g., cycles, such as the sunspot cycle), these variations are rather small from our point of view. The amount of radiation reaching the outer limits of the earth's atmosphere often is referred to as the "solar constant," which is about 334 cal/m^2/sec, or 1.4 kW/m^2.

The earth's atmosphere filters this radiation in several ways (what are the two most important?). That means the amount striking the earth's surface, on average, is 238 cal/m^2/sec (about 1 kW). Why is it not a constant? This Exploration will help us begin to answer that question.

Procedure

1. **Look at the data in Table 2.**
    All measurements were taken on cloudless days, so they represent a good sample of the maximum solar energy available at those locations.

Table 2

Sun Energy at Different Locations, Average kcal/m^2/day

	MASSACHUSETTS	GEORGIA	NEBRASKA	IDAHO	ARIZONA	ALASKA	HAWAII
January	1,250	2,000	2,000	1,500	2,750	160	5,220
February	2,250	2,750	2,750	2,250	3,750	710	5,760
March	3,000	3,500	3,750	3,500	5,000	2,130	6,800
April	3,500	4,750	4,500	4,750	6,000	3,760	6,890
May	4,500	5,500	5,250	5,500	6,750	4,610	7,270
June	5,250	5,500	5,750	6,000	7,000	5,040	7,270
July	5,250	5,500	6,000	6,500	7,000	4,340	7,030
August	4,500	5,000	5,250	5,500	6,000	3,170	6,420
September	3,500	4,250	4,250	4,500	5,500	1,800	6,020
October	2,500	3,250	3,250	2,750	4,000	820	5,600
November	1,250	2,500	2,250	1,750	3,000	260	5,040
December	1,250	2,000	1,750	1,250	2,500	60	4,810
Mean kcal/m^2/day	3,200	3,900	390	3,800	4,900	2,240	5,828

2. **Patterns.**

What patterns do you see in the numbers in Table 2? What factors might produce those patterns? Can you think of a physical explanation for the patterns? You may find it helpful to use a globe or an atlas to locate each site.

3. **Presentation and class discussion: Integrating the data.**

The two groups have explored sun angles during the day and on different spots on the globe (and under different geographical conditions).

After each group has reported to the class, discuss the following questions. Refer to your own and the other group's report in raising questions or suggesting answers or conjectures.

What factors limit the light available for primary producers?

At what time scales do these factors operate?

How different are the light environments at the equator and in Alaska? Where in the continuum from equator to pole does your school fall?

What other factors may interact with variations in insolation to limit plant growth (and other processes dependent on it)?

What do the seasons look like in your location? In Hawaii? In Alaska? What does that have to do with variations in insolation?

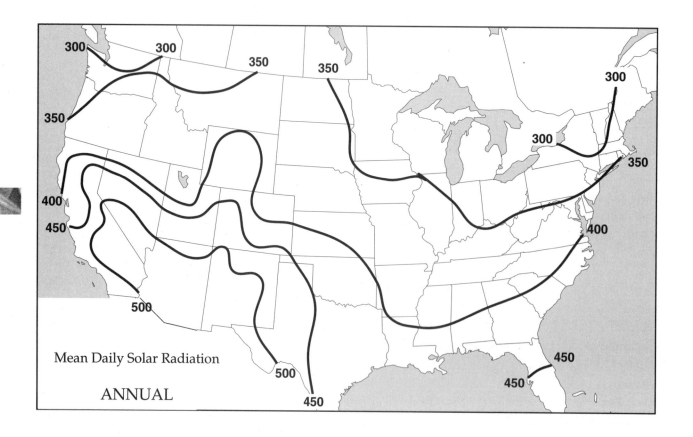

Mean Daily Solar Radiation

ANNUAL

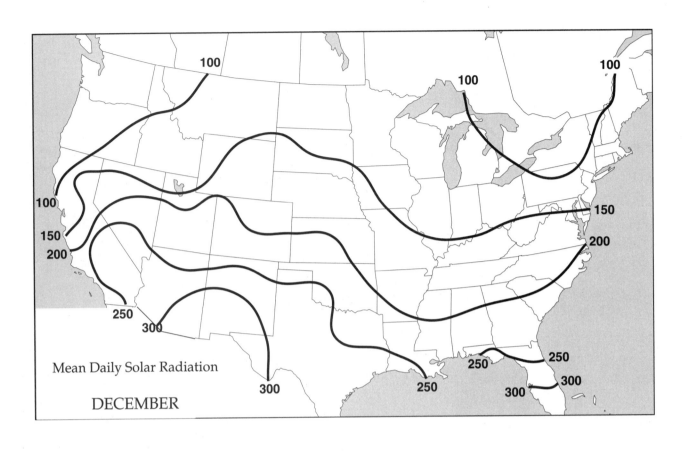

Mean Daily Solar Radiation

DECEMBER

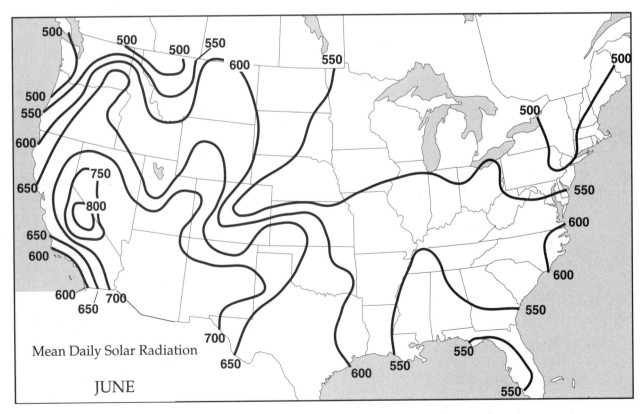

Mean Daily Solar Radiation

JUNE

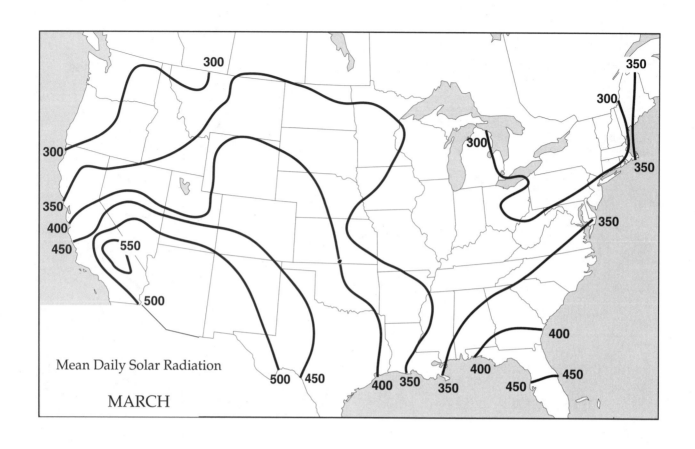

Mean Daily Solar Radiation

MARCH

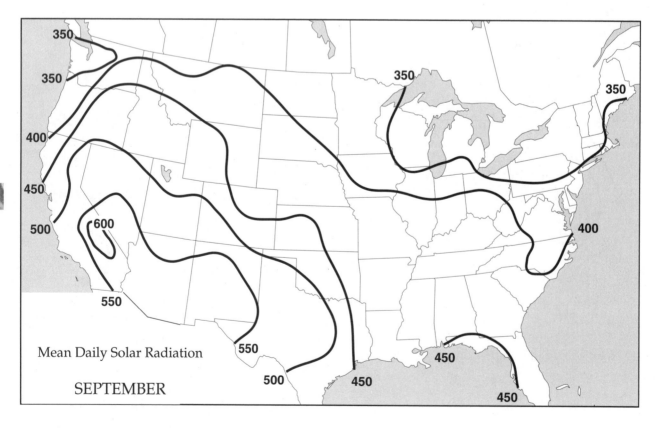

Mean Daily Solar Radiation

SEPTEMBER

ABIOTIC FACTORS AND PLANT DISTRIBUTION

CHAPTER TWO

CONTENTS

OVERVIEW

Do all plants look alike? Clearly not—no more than all animals look alike. But how a plant looks—how it is shaped, built, formed—tells us about where it lives, how it lives, and about its genetic "family history," or evolutionary background. Let's consider differences and similarities among plants—a tulip and a tulip tree, a marigold and a metasequoia—how and where each lives, its lifestyle or life strategy.

READING 1
READING THE SIGNS

In <u>Exploration 1</u>, you take a field trip to gather data you will use later on. Even more important, you get to know plants "in the wild," so here are some pointers on looking at plants and plant communities.

The initial information you gather at the field site can tell you a lot about the history and the present status of the ecosystem there. More layers of plants mean more plants fixing carbon, thus potentially more energy available to the rest of the organisms in the system (in addition to habitat, shelter, etc.). Layering takes time to develop, and many factors contribute to the development of a forest structure. You may see only the beginnings of such layering at your study site. The changes that take place over time in an ecosystem (or part of an ecosystem) are often called succession.

Succession looks different in a forest, a grassland, an abandoned field, a tide pool, and a pond. It always involves a change in the biomass of the life and in the amount of energy flowing through the area; that usually also means a change in the species that are present. Other things happen in an ecosystem, though, most of which fall under the general category of disturbance. That might mean a fire, a tree blown over by the wind, an animal digging a hole, or humans trampling across the area. Some disturbances are part of the system, like wildfires on the prairie or hurricanes in the Caribbean; others, like the clearing of a site for farming, have not been part of the evolution of life in that area. Either way, the things that happen in any ecosystem leave their traces. These abiotic events affect succession—slowing it down, speeding it up, or changing its course.

SUCCESSION AND ENERGY USE

When an area is first colonized by plants (e.g., on an abandoned lot in the city), the "system" is not making full use of the potential energy or nutrients present there. For example, there is a lot of bare ground, which absorbs and reradiates (or reflects) much of the insolation striking it. If we were to calculate the total area of leaves on the site, we would find less than one square meter of photosynthesizing tissue covering each square meter of soil. The bare soil dries out more easily, gets hotter than the soil under the plants, and often is packed down, which makes it difficult for plants to get started.

THREE-DIMENSIONAL COVERING

As time passes, the bare spots get covered by species well adapted to such conditions; there comes to be a fairly continuous layer of grasses and weeds. The plant community now catches a lot more of the sunlight that arrives on the site—the total area of leaves is more than the surface area of the site. In addition, fallen leaves and stems feed a multiplying community of soil creatures, enriching and loosening the soil, making it ever more hospitable to plant life.

The addition of further layers of vegetation usually means a greater and greater variety of types of plants—not only more species, but also species with many kinds of lifestyles, or life strategies. Each of these strategies includes some results of natural selection, responses to the conditions encountered by the plant's ancestors. Some species specialize in putting out leaves and flowering early in the year before other plants' leaves can shade them. Some put a lot of energy first into growing higher, then flowering later in the year. Vines take advantage of other plants' stems to get up to the sun. Trees year by year reach higher and wider, above other plants.

SITE AGE

The amount of vertical space filled by plants on your study site tells you something about how long plants have been establishing themselves, in waves of colonization and (local) extinction, since the last time the site was disturbed in a major way. It is not only time that is at work here, however; the species that happen to arrive at a site interact in complex ways with each other and with the physical environment. As a result, it is hard to generalize about vegetation structure: each location has its own history and dynamics to be deciphered. From the point of view of energy cycling, however, the ratio between an area of leaves and the area of ground below those leaves is the greatest single indicator of the productivity of the system—of the energy captured and available to other life forms.

PATTERNS AND PATCHES

Think about a well-kept lawn or a field of corn. What does it take to maintain a lawn as an even green carpet? What kinds of work does a farmer have to do to make sure his field is covered with corn rather than with a mixture of corn and other plants? How does a farmer get an even stand of corn, all about the same height? How does that compare to the way a forest gets established?

Even if your site started out with just one species of plant, say, all oak trees or all dandelions, over the course of time things happen that make openings in the cover. Some of these openings are very small. A wildflower is eaten off at ground level by a caterpillar, and before it can grow back, the bare spot has been covered by the shoot of its neighbor. Or a seed sprouts, triggered by the extra light admitted when the plant was eaten. Sometimes the gaps are larger. A tree branch or the whole tree falls; a fire burns the vegetation so that bare soil is visible; a large mammal, such as a cow or a goat, begins to eat the plants in one area regularly. In each case, the light environment (as well as the nutrient and water resources) changes, and the plant community's use of available resources changes. Such changes represent opportunity for other plants.

Be on the lookout in your study area for evidence of such changes in the past or changes that started in the past and that still affect the present.

Exploration 1
DESCRIBING A PLANT COMMUNITY: A FIELD TRIP

This activity lays the groundwork for several later activities on light and energy capture. You begin to look at plant communities: working in groups on different parts of the study site you describe the vertical and horizontal arrangement of the vegetation and count or estimate the proportions of plants with one of several life forms.

FIRST IMPRESSIONS

It is no good talking about "ecosystems" in the abstract; you have to be looking at real things around you, plants, animals, and all. You can go a long way in thinking about the ecology of a place by beginning with "first impressions"—that is what you will be gathering during this field trip. If you already know a lot about your study site, you may see it from a new perspective by the time you are through. If you have never learned tree or flower names, you will meet the major players of energy capture in your study area by shape and structure first. You will do some counting, and you will do some drawing.

WHAT ARE YOU LOOKING FOR?

In this field excursion, you gather several kinds of data, each of which allows you to understand different aspects of the ecology of the site. You use your observations from this field trip later, when you study the productivity of ecosystems and the ways that plants are arranged to get maximum use of sunlight.

At this stage, you do not need to identify the species of plants that occupy your study site. But if someone in the class does know the names of some plants you see, note them for later use.

Materials
- **Notebook**
- **Pencil**
- **Strips of sheeting, colored string, or colored tags** to mark boundaries of study areas
- **Compass**

Safety

WARNING

If you are allergic to any plants or insect bites or stings, take precautions as necessary. **IF YOU ARE ALLERGIC TO BEE STINGS, BE SURE TO BRING A BEE-STING KIT WITH YOU.**

WARNING

When you first arrive at the site, note possible safety issues, such as piles of broken glass, abandoned buildings or wells, cliffs, hornets' nests, and plants such as poison ivy or poison oak.

NOTE: When someone says, "Why don't you sketch it for me?" do you get tense? Do you ever say, "Well, I can't draw"? Well, do not panic. The drawings you need to do for this study serve two purposes: they help you look more closely at what is before you, and they are a record of what you see for you to use in later studies.

An artistic, careful rendering of all the details of the vegetation actually is not very helpful at this stage. Concentrate instead on just the information you need. Record the geometry of the vegetation, which you can do with rather abstract figures. Grid lines help you keep things roughly to scale and at about the right distance from each other.

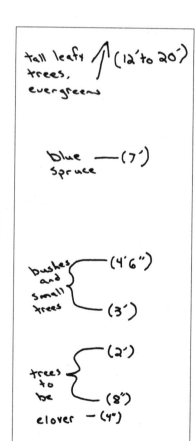

Sketch 1

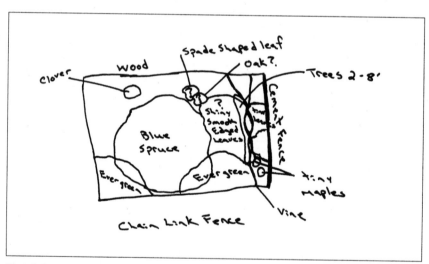

Sketch 2

Procedure

1. **Mark the boundaries of your study area and begin your notes.**

    Make sure you can tell the boundaries of the area you are to study. Use strips of sheeting, colored string, or colored tags to mark the corners or other boundary features.

    In your notebook, note the date and time of the visit, name the location, name your group, and sketch your area in outline. Mark on your sketch prominent geographical features, such as streams, outcrops, roads, or paths.

2. **Survey the area.**

    Walk around, being careful not to trample the vegetation more than absolutely necessary. Look carefully at the trees, shrubs, and herbs. Are there signs of human construction? Trash or other human artifacts? Fire or other destruction of vegetation? Animals? Does it seem to be dry or moist? On a hillside or flat? Does it get a lot of sun, or is it shady? (Check compass orientation if possible.) Is there a lot of undergrowth? Is any bare soil visible?

3. **Where are the animals?**

    During this field session, most of the questions relate to the plant life, which is the scaffolding on and around which the animal life moves. While you are looking at the plants, keep notes on the evidences you find of animal life, for example, dung, feathers or hair, tracks, nests or burrows, leftover food. To see the animals themselves, you may need to come back at different times of day (twilight is good) and watch quietly for a while.

4. **The vertical structure: Seeing in 3-D.**

    Estimate the height of the canopy—the layer of trees closest to the sky. Estimate the height of the tallest trees and the distance to the lowest branches on the canopy trees.

    Sketch the vertical space and divide it into zones. Label the zones, sketching them roughly to scale; for example, 0–1 m, 1–3 m, 3–5 m, 5 m to just under the canopy, canopy. Sketch where plants are growing, and note special features (rock outcrops, human structures, streams, etc.).

5. **The horizontal structure.**

    Note large trees or plants that grow in large clumps (such as some ferns). Put these large features on your map. Estimate the area of the site covered by those large individuals or clumps. For a tree crown, stand under the outermost leaves on one side, then pace across to the other side of the tree, "east to west," and then "north to south" to estimate the amount of surface area over which the leaves are growing (treat the tree's cover as roughly circular for the purposes of this study).

    Mark bare patches, rocks, ledges, and other places with little or nothing growing. Make sure these drawings are also roughly to scale.

    Do any plants grow in carpets or other large populations all together? If so, put those features in. Or do the plants occur mostly as scattered individuals, or in twos or threes? Note that too.

Can you identify any of the plants on the site by common name, at least to the genus level? For example: oak, maple, tulip tree, blueberries, dandelions, and so forth. If so, note the species on your distribution sketch.

6. **Characterize the vegetation types: The whole picture.**
You have looked at the 3-D structure of the field site and noted things of different sizes. Now think: what kinds of plant shapes or designs do you observe there? For example, there may be trees, shrubs, or herbs of various kinds. Size is one factor in deciding a type, but there may be other characteristics that some species share.

When you have decided on the general classes of plants, look at the site one more time. Of the individuals on the site, what proportion belong to each type you noted? (Exact numbers are not necessary, especially for plants that are very numerous. You can say, "about 100," "500 or more," "1,000 or more," and so on. If your plot has a section covered by grasses, do not try to count the individual blades of grass!)

7. **Wrap-up.**
We use the data in later Explorations, so make sure you have recorded them clearly enough so they will make sense later.

Make some notes about the whole site, including what surrounds your marked-off study site. Consider the following questions: Does your area seem typical of the entire field area? Why or why not?

Compare your notes with those of other groups. What differences or similarities do you see? What surprises you?

What questions remain about the kinds and distributions of plants on the site? How might you answer your questions? If someone asked you how the site got that way, what ideas do you have about that? What do you think it will look like in 10 years?

READING 2
ABIOTIC FACTORS CONSTRAIN LEAF AND PLANT SHAPES

Plants have evolved several strategies to capture light, but, as we know, they actually capture only a small proportion of the light that reaches them. The amount of light captured sets a limit on how much carbon can be fixed, so it is advantageous for a plant to grow in ways that maximize light capture. One important strategy by which plants accomplish that is to increase their leaf area per unit of the earth's surface area. As with any design component, however, costs have to be reckoned, and there are limits to the performance of the materials being used. In Exploration 1 in **Chapter 1**, we encountered many of the challenges plants face, but the story is even more complex. Three characteristics have been influenced by plants' evolution as solar collectors: leaf size, leaf shape and type, and tree shape or architecture. Here we consider a few of the major factors and show how some plants have responded to often contradictory forces with geometric solutions.

HEAT

As a leaf absorbs more light, it also absorbs more heat. Above a certain level, heat energy can be damaging to plant cells and cause (among other things) photosynthesis to slow down or stop. Figure 1 shows how photosynthetic rate is affected by temperature.

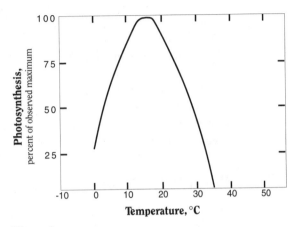

Figure 1

LIGHT OVERLOAD

Although capturing more light means more growth, there is a limit to how much light a leaf can capture. Thus, even though only 50% of incoming light is of the right wavelength for photosynthesis, leaves cannot make use of all of it—the photosynthetic system becomes saturated. The saturation point varies somewhat depending on the species (some can use a higher proportion of available light than others). Under sunny conditions, some species produce leaves that are richer in chloroplasts, so they can make better use of the high-energy conditions. But even those sun leaves have an upper limit.

Figure 2 relates average photosynthetic rates to light levels (actual saturation points depend on the species).

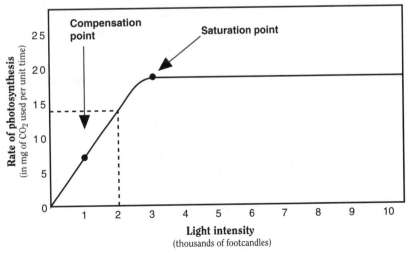

Figure 2

ENERGY UPKEEP

Each leaf has to turn an energy "profit." That means each leaf must take in more energy than it expends. Leaves, like anything else alive, use their energy reserves to perform metabolic respiration all the time, day and night. For a leaf to survive, it must take in at least as much energy as it uses. And if it is to be able to grow, manufacture protective chemicals, or export sugar to the rest of the plant, it must take in more energy than that. For example, to make 1 g (dry weight) of root, a plant typically expends the energy equivalent of 1.5 g of carbon. Some tissues cost more, others less. The point at which income exceeds expenditure is called the compensation point, also shown in Figure 2. That, too, varies by plant species. Some plants can exist in shade so deep (say, on the forest floor, under dense tree growth) that only 1–2% of the incoming sunlight reaches them. Other species cannot turn a profit unless they catch much more than that.

PLANT STRATEGIES

Overcoming Overheating

Plants have several ways to avoid overheating. One approach is to use water to carry away heat, in a process called transpiration (as we see again in **Module 3: Water**). Also, leaf shape itself can play a role. First, every leaf (like every other surface, including your skin) has a boundary layer of air that moves slowly and slows heat loss (especially by slowing water loss). (When can that be an advantage?) This layer may be very thin, just a fraction of a millimeter, but relative to the leaf's thickness it is significant. Air movement around the leaf breaks up the boundary layer to some degree, but the larger the leaf area, the more resistant the boundary layer.

Three common solutions to overheating are smaller leaves, more complex leaf shapes, and leaves angled away from the sun. Reduced leaf size, however, also reduces photosynthetic area. Making the leaf shape more complex—by giving it teeth or lobes or by breaking each leaf into leaflets—reduces the distance from any part of the leaf surface to an edge. That makes the leaf more accessible to wind currents and speeds heat flow from the leaf by breaking up the boundary layer. Turning the leaf so it catches sunlight at an angle also cuts down on overheating. (How much tilt would reduce the light striking a leaf by about half? Refer to Exploration 3a in **Chapter 1** for help with the calculations.)

Overcoming Light Overload

Remember, overcoming light overload is a problem of avoiding waste, that is, light that hits the leaf but cannot be used. Two strategies work together to solve this problem: (1) make more and smaller leaves and (2) spread your leaves horizontally or, if you cannot spread horizontally because your neighbors interfere, arrange your leaves in layers.

Smaller leaves reduce overheating, but to maximize surface area, you must multiply the little surfaces. (Remember **Chapter 5** in **Unit 2** on mice, moose, and surface area–volume ratios?) That lets the lower leaves catch the light passing between the upper leaves. If you have (evolutionarily) reduced the area of each leaf by changing leaf size or shape, then you must increase the number of leaves.

TURNING AN ENERGY PROFIT

A leaf will not survive if it does not catch enough light to compensate for respiration. That means a leaf must either avoid self-shading or make the best use of low-light conditions. So, if a plant's strategy includes having many leaves arranged in layers, it must also have ways for the lower leaves to survive.

A plant can limit how much shade each leaf casts on lower layers by separating the layers enough. One researcher has suggested that if a leaf is separated from an upper neighbor by a distance equal to seven times the diameter of that shading leaf, the shadow will be reduced to a level that allows the lower leaf to reach its compensation point. That is because the shadow "thins out" over distance—it is darkest just below the leaf. In dense growth, a leaf will be shaded by many other leaves, but light is available from directions other than straight overhead. (Why is this so? Where is the light coming from?) In very sunny conditions, leaf layers can be packed more closely than in shady conditions.

In shadier conditions, where only leaves on the outer layers may get sufficient light or even occasionally be saturated with light, the plant's strategy is not to arrange the leaves in layers. Lower leaves or leaves closer to the trunk may not get enough light to reach their compensation point. If a plant grows in such a way that a leaf is shaded too much (i.e., the leaf never makes an energy profit), the plant sheds the leaf (a phenomenon called self-pruning).

Trees with their crowns in light and their lower branches in shade have an additional strategy: they grow different leaves to suit the different light conditions. For example, sassafras trees grow sun leaves that tend to be lobed while the shade leaves are plain ovals or with small, few lobes. In most cases, however, the differences are harder to see.

Exploration 2
A PLANT'S YEAR IN YOUR PART OF THE WORLD

What factors or variables are features of the growing conditions in your area? In <u>Reading 2</u>, we saw that growth (or lack of it) is the most common plant response to environmental conditions. With what kinds of conditions must plants in your area cope to complete their life-cycles (or a year's portion of their life-cycles)?

Materials
- **Notebooks**
- **Poster board or newsprint** for poster

- **Markers**
- **Reference materials on weather** (e.g., <u>The Weather Almanac</u>, a world almanac, weather records from your area)

Procedure

1. **The variables brainstorm.**
   You know what plants need, at least in terms of energy. As a class, list some climatic variables that might affect a plant's energy capture over the course of a year.

2. **Dividing the work.**
   Once the class has identified four to eight variables, break into groups, one group per variable plus one group for plant-growth cycles (phenology).

3. **Finding the data.**
   You can find relevant information in almanacs and newspapers and from local weather stations, airport weather stations, and similar sources. If you cannot find data for every month, fill in the blanks with probable numbers until you are able to locate actual data. We recommend that you seek data averaged over several years (many sources include 30-year averages).

4. **A one-year cycle of your group's variable.**
   Produce a graph or other display of the change in your variable, month by month. For example, a temperature-versus-time graph for the Boston area would look like Figure 3. What does that graph mean, in words? Be ready to explain it to others.

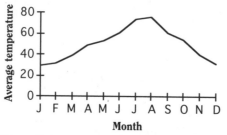

Figure 3. Average annual temperatures for the Boston area.

5. **Predictions based on your findings.**
   As a group, discuss and write down your answers to the following questions, in preparation for step 6, in which all the groups contribute to a composite "portrait" of your area.

   What do you predict the other groups found for their variables?

   What connections or relationships do you expect to find between their variables and yours?

   In particular, make predictions about the year as experienced by plants: when would be the best time for plant growth? The unfavorable times? Why would one time be better or worse than another, based on your data?

   How about animals? What are they doing during the annual cycle you have constructed? What challenges do they face?

6. **The whole picture: Class discussion.**

    Now the class comes back together. Each group contributes its data on a composite chart or on parallel charts, so you can see all the variables side by side. This makes a picture of the conditions that a plant in your area encounters over the course of a year.

    The group describing the year's plant growth should add its data last, overlaying the biological events on the physical ones that all the other groups contributed.

    Consider the composite picture. Are there unfavorable times for plant growth in your area? If so, can you identify them in terms of the annual cycles you have graphed? Conversely, are there identifiable times of most plant growth? If so, when? Why?

Exploration 3
PLANT FORMS: PATTERNS AND DIFFERENCES

Marigolds and maples, lilies and lilacs, cacti and casuarinas—how do they differ in form? Why? In its lifetime, a plant will take on a shape and size that reflects its growing conditions. Plants of the same species can be so strongly affected by their environment that two individuals will appear to belong to different species. Yet some things remain constant, such as flower shape and the arrangement of leaves on the twig. The interplay between the response of a plant to its environment and the limits imposed by family genetic background creates patterns of similarity in plant communities around the world.

Here we group and classify plants by their life forms using plants you know, plants on your field site, and plants you examine during class. This work with plant shapes raises important ecological issues, which we also consider.

Materials
- **Field notes** from Exploration 1
- **Notebooks**
- **Sample plants**
- **Reference materials**

Procedure

1. **Sort the plant forms.**

    As a team, consider and describe the differences among the plants you know. What makes one plant or kind of plant different from another? Use plants you know, including those from your field site, sample materials from class, and the five plants in Figure 4. Group them into whatever categories seem useful.

    Think about plants you have seen in your neighborhood, in the grocery store, in your home, in illustrations. Refer to plants growing in the laboratory or classroom.

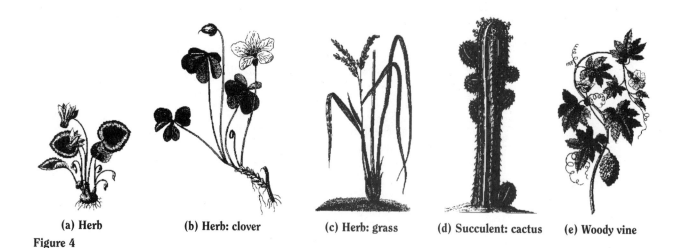

(a) Herb   (b) Herb: clover   (c) Herb: grass   (d) Succulent: cactus   (e) Woody vine

Figure 4

2. **Establish first groupings.**

   Discuss why you grouped plants the way you did in step 1. Do not hesitate to change any grouping or the "group membership" of a plant. If your team cannot reach agreement on something, keep track of alternative groupings and the reasons for them.

   Write down the groupings and the reasoning behind each one in your notebooks.

3. **Revisit the field data.**

   How do your classifications in steps 1 and 2 relate to the classification you developed on your field trip? Would you change the groupings you made on that field trip or any groupings you have made today to include all the plant types you have considered? Why?

4. **Test and revise your groupings.**

   Once you have some possible groupings or categories of plants, consider the following questions. They include criteria botanists use to make groupings and might stimulate your thinking about your groupings. Feel free to use reference materials to answer questions about the plants you are working with.

   In what tissue type does each plant put new growth? When during the seasons does it produce that tissue?

   What are the essential tasks in an organism's life-cycle? What are some typical life-cycles for plants? (Focus on flowering plants and conifers for now, excluding ferns, mosses, and other "lower" plants.)

   Do plants in some of your categories seem to be associated with particular kinds of habitats? If so, which? What possible explanations can you give? How might you test your conjectures?

READING 3
RAUNKIAER'S CLASSIFICATION SYSTEM

Look at Figure 5. Each habitat is from a different biological region. What is the first thing that strikes your eye? The vegetation? The plant shapes, their relative size, their abundance—all these are part of the region's "ID," the characteristics by which it differs visually from other places.

In Exploration 3, you developed a grouping that makes sense in light of your data from your field trip and from class. How have other people gone about developing plant groupings? Here we describe how one ecologist put together climatic data and plant-form data to describe important aspects of a region's ecology.

BACKGROUND

Raunkiaer, a Danish botanist working in the first third of this century, developed a system to describe plant communities on both small and large scales by describing the proportion of plants of each grouping, that is, various life forms. He built his grouping system by looking at climate and the way plants allocate their resources to different kinds of tissues and at how those two factors might interact.

BIOREGIONS

We can correlate naturally occurring plant groupings, called bioregions or biomes, with temperature and precipitation. For example, in areas with high mean annual temperatures (say, above 25°C), depending on precipitation levels, we find desert (mean annual precipitation < 50 cm), seasonal tropical forests (rainfall between about 150 and 250 cm per year), or tropical evergreen rainforest (rainfall > 300 cm per year).

A PLANT'S POINT OF VIEW

Raunkiaer looked at climate and plant groupings from a plant's point of view. He started by considering annual variation in the two physical variables most important to plant life: temperature and precipitation. He asked when were the times of maximum availability of precipitation. He produced graphs (of the sort you produced for your area) for many regions of the world for which he had information also about the plant communities. Compare Raunkiaer's diagrams for Denmark (Figure 6[a]), Sumatra (6[b]), Batavia (now Djakarta, the capital of Indonesia) (6[c]), Sweers Island, off the north coast of Australia (6[d]), and Nagasaki, Japan (6[e]). Note in each case the places where the temperature (indicated by solid lines) reaches maximum and minimum values, where precipitation (indicated by dotted lines) is most and least, and where the two cycles coincide.

Compare these profiles with the Whittaker diagram in Figure 7. Raunkiaer considered that, from a plant's point of view, a period of low precipitation is unfavorable, as are freezing temperatures; a combination of freezing or high temperature with a scarcity of water is the most unfavorable.

Figure 5

Figure 5, continued

329

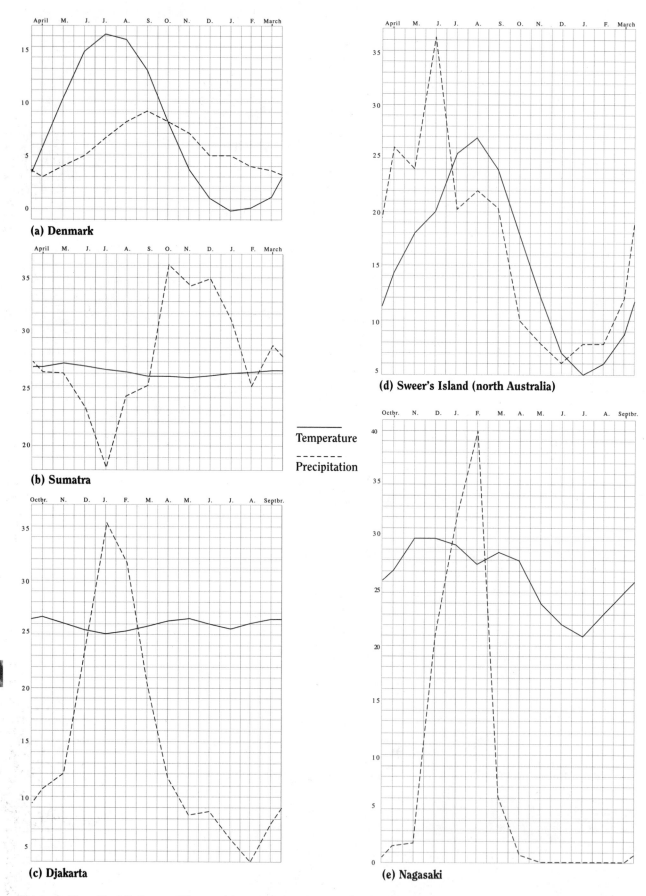

Figure 6. (From <u>The Life Forms of Plants and Statistical Plant Geography</u> by Raunkiaer, © 1934. Reprinted by permission of Oxford University Press, Oxford, UK)

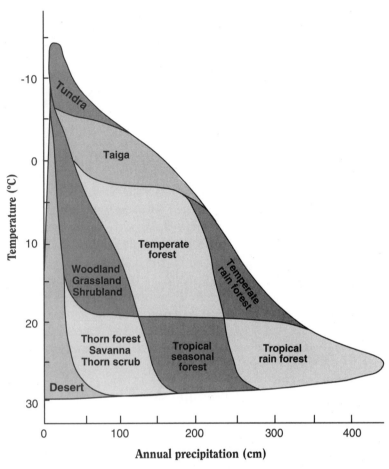

Figure 7. A Whittaker diagram. The relationship between precipitation and temperature and how it influences plant community types. (From <u>Communities and Ecosystems</u> by Whittaker, © 1975. Reprinted by permission of Prentice-Hall, Inc., Upper Saddle River, NJ)

PLANT TYPES OR FORMS

Plants have various methods for coping with the unfavorable conditions that occur regularly in their locale. These methods may include dropping leaves, producing "antifreeze," or even the whole adult plant dying, with the population surviving as dormant seeds. Raunkiaer classified plants according to the way they protected the next year's growth and (a related characteristic) what parts of the plant survived through the unfavorable periods of the year. Each of these types of plant add biomass at the roots but differ widely in how they add biomass above ground. Raunkiaer's system has been elaborated greatly, reflecting the vast variation in the plant kingdom, but the basic categories can be reduced to the following four.

Tall Woody Plants

Trees, tall shrubs, and woody vines are woody plants that have their buds well above the ground, with new biomass added as leaves and as growth in the woody parts. Raunkiaer called these plants "phanerophytes," from the Greek for "obvious plants."

Low Woody Plants

Low shrubs and other low woody plants have their buds above the ground but lower than 25 cm. That is low enough to be covered by snow. This cut-off height is somewhat arbitrary, but it reflects the different micro-climate near the ground. A rose bush, forsythia, raspberry, and honeysuckle are good examples of this kind of plant. They add some biomass in their woody sections, but most biomass is added in single-year, nonwoody growth, especially leaves and flowers. Raunkiaer called these plants "chamaephytes," from the Greek for "plants on the ground."

Perennial Herbs

Perennial herbs are nonwoody plants that live for more than a year and have buds at or below the surface of the ground. This excludes most woody plants (although some botanists include some dwarf shrubs in this category) and includes most wildflowers and grasses that live for 2 or more years. Most of these plants flower and set fruit several times in their lives. Their above-ground biomass dies at the end of the year, and the root and next year's buds lie in or near the ground, often protected by the dying or dead leafy tissue. Raunkiaer called these plants, together with other plants that have their buds wholly underground, "cryptophytes," for "hidden plants."

Annual Herbs

Annual herbs are nonwoody plants that get through the unfavorable time of the year as a seed; adult plants live less than a year. These plants start as seeds from one or more years ago. In one growing season, they complete their life-cycle: develop a root and shoot system, flower, and disperse seeds. Raunkiaer called these "therophytes," or "summer plants." (We also use this category to include "others," such as water plants.)

Figure 8 shows some typical plants of each category.

QUESTIONS

In preparation for class, think about these questions. Write down your thoughts and bring your notes to the class.

How does the classification your group devised relate to Raunkiaer's scheme? That is, what differences do you see? Does either scheme have too few or too many categories to describe the vegetation you know? In that case, which categories should be split into more or lumped together?

Think about the spectrum of plant forms for a ballfield and a shady park at some latitude. Where is the bulk of the carbon being stored in plants at each of those two settings? What would be the most important categories of plant forms in each kind of place? What do you mean by "important"?

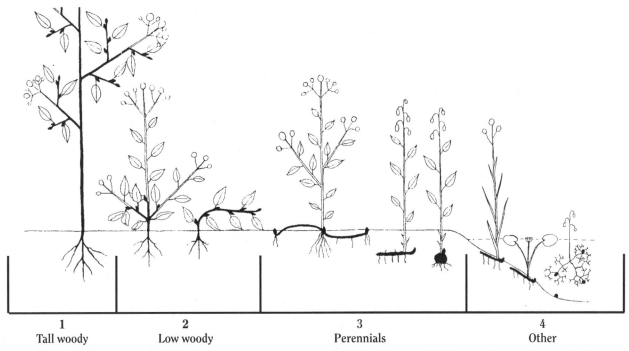

1	2	3	4
Tall woody	Low woody	Perennials	Other

Figure 8. (From The Life Forms of Plants and Statistical Plant Geography by Raunkiaer, © 1934. Reprinted by permission of Oxford University Press, Oxford, UK)

Exploration 4
PLANT LIFE FORMS AROUND THE WORLD

We can apply Raunkiaer's plant form classification to describe ecological systems of many kinds. In this Exploration, we use Raunkiaer's system and your own to "diagnose" the kind of ecosystem represented by your study site. You may decide that your classification is more useful than Raunkiaer's for your field site, or you may decide to blend the two systems. The goal is to develop a tool that describes the site and the plants you observed, in a meaningful, reliable way.

Materials
- **This worksheet**
- **World atlas**
- **Poster paper or newsprint**
- **Markers**

Procedure

1. **Choose a location.**
   Data for seven places are included in Table 1. The total number of plant species is recorded under the name of each site, in the leftmost column. The numbers in the body of the table are the percent of species from that total in each category. (Because of rounding, the percentages in a row do not always add up to 100.) The "Other" column includes water plants, succulents, and epiphytes. Divide the class into seven groups; each group should take one place and prepare a brief presentation.

Table 1

Plant Classifications in Seven Different Locations

LOCATION	PERCENTAGE OF PLANT CLASSIFICATIONS				
	TALL WOODY PLANTS	LOW WOODY PLANTS	PERENNIAL HERBS	ANNUAL HERBS	OTHER
Seychelles (258 species)	33	30	15	16	6 (epiphytes and succulents)
Ellesmere Island (107 species)	—	23.5	65.5	—	3 (water plants)
Altamaha, Ga. (717 species)	12	15	59	8	6.5 (mostly water plants)
Death Valley (294 species)	—	28	20	42	8 (3% succulent, the rest water plants)
Tripoli (369 species)	—	17	28	51	2 (water plants)
Denmark (1,084 species)	4	6	61	18	11 (water plants)
Stuttgart, Germany (862 species)	6	6	64	17	7 (water plants)

2. **Where in the world?**

In an atlas or on a globe, look up where your group's place is located. Note latitude and longitude, distance from the nearest large body of water, and information about elevation above sea level.

3. **Picture it.**

Construct a graph or other visual presentation, as you did for your own study area. What would each place look like? In general terms, where is plant biomass getting stored? What are the principal forms in which plant biomass is stored? What implications do your conclusions have for the animals that live in those areas? What kind of a place is each (e.g., desert, forest, tundra)?

4. **Present it.**

The groups take turns describing their location and answering the questions in step 3.

5. **Summary: Plants on the globe.**

As a class, consider the relationship between the physical (abiotic) characteristics of a site and plant growth. Include total number of species as well as the percentage of each growth-form type. Where do plants of each type tend to occur? Where do they not occur? What might be some reasons for that?

(If you have a world atlas that shows vegetation information or a similar reference, you might test your conclusions with a game. Choose a spot on the earth at random, guess what the vegetation is like, then look it up.)

ENERGY ALLOCATION IN PLANTS

CHAPTER THREE

OVERVIEW

Are plants like mosquitoes, moose, frogs, fishes, bears, bees, or bacteria? Yes and no. Yes—all those organisms have to solve the same problems: survive and maintain their metabolism, develop, grow, reproduce. No—only plants get their energy from the sun. So a plant's energy use budget might look slightly different. And because they cannot move, plants respond to many external factors by growing in different directions, different amounts, and putting energy into different tissue (more into storage tissue, less into leaves). Plus often it is unclear just where one plant begins and another ends. Can you tell where one mosquito begins and ends?

CASE STUDY
WHAT IS AN INDIVIDUAL?

It is not easy to say what an individual plant is. Our notion of plants is shaped largely by the "domesticated" plants we see—marigolds in pots, squash planted in rows in a garden, or bunches of individual beets in the produce section of the grocery store.

From a biological point of view (and certainly from an ecological point of view), that is far from being the "normal" situation. When we look at a forest of hundreds of tree trunks or a field with millions of stalks of grass and stems of clover, we actually may be seeing just a few genetic individuals. Moreover, when we look at a potted plant on the windowsill, in many ways we actually are looking at a population of organisms, which both cooperate and compete for space and may differ from each other in shape, size, color, and physiology.

Figure 1

MODULES: HOW THEY WORK

Plant ecologists have come to see plants as "modular organisms" that grow by multiplying some basic, simple unit over and over. (Remember Exploration 1 in **Chapter 1**? Your plant modules are modeled more directly on current ecological thinking than you may have realized.) These units act like a population of individuals, and the shape of the total plant is a result of the interplay of the semi-independent modules. A plant unit can be an internode (a length of stem), plus a node (where leaves emerge), plus the attached leaves. The units may branch; each draws from the stream of water coming from the roots, but it is first come, first served. (See Figure 1.) Each leaf must photosynthesize enough carbohydrates to maintain its health and growth and that of the rapidly dividing cells at its tip. The modules may compete for light, as you have seen in earlier Explorations. The farther from a leaf you go, the less connection there is with that leaf—"extra" photosynthate may get transported to other modules or to the common root system, but only after local needs have been satisfied.

REPRODUCTION

Any module has the potential to reproduce. Furthermore, genetic mutations can occur in different modules at different times and with different results, so each module may differ from all the others on the plant (although it is not known how common such local mutations are). That means that different branches of a tree or shrub may be different genetically.

In addition to typical sexual reproduction (e.g., by seeds resulting from pollination of one flower by another), plants often reproduce asexually by various types of cloning. A common pattern is for a tree to send up shoots, new "trunks" from its roots. Although at first the "mother" and the "offspring" are physically connected, the new tree grows its own root and shoot systems under the conditions it finds where it arose, and the connection between the trees eventually decays. New trees give rise to their own clones. Thus, when we see a hillside grove of poplar trees, we very likely are looking at dozens of genetic replicates of one (or a few) original settlers that started from seed but "moved" about the hill by sending up new trunks higher or lower on the slope, where conditions were slightly better (or worse) than where the colony started.

MODULARITY AND ENERGY ALLOCATION

Now we can see some connections with topics we addressed in earlier Explorations. The modules of a plant both cooperate and compete. As plants accumulate energy from photosynthesis and water and mineral nutrients from the soil, the resources can be incorporated into plant tissue of various kinds. If light is low, the plant may allocate more energy to stem tissue or leaf tissue. That is what happens when a potted plant becomes "leggy," growing a long stem with no flowers—it is reaching for the light, "foraging" for energy. If light is abundant, the plant may grow tough sun leaves designed to take advantage of the abundance of light. If water or nutrients are hard to come by, more photosynthate may be incorporated into root tissue than shoot tissue, and the roots "forage" through the soil.

If temperature and light conditions are right, one or more modules may be triggered to reproduce, and the developing flowers and fruits draw resources from all through the plant. If, on the other hand, one branch is shaded, its leaves may not be able to turn a profit and the leaves die. Eventually, the branch is lost—a process foresters call "self-pruning."

MODULES AS A WAY OF "MOVING AROUND"

This modular approach, with modules both cooperating and competing, gives organisms like plants a way to respond to changing energy and nutrient conditions. Such response is critical for plants, since they cannot "move away" when conditions become less favorable in their locale.

The modular approach is not limited to plants. Colonial animals like corals and salps behave in a similar way. It has been argued that the individual members of a colony of social insects can be seen as replicable modules of a population that functions in some ways as a composite individual.

What experiments might you use to explore how different plant species exploit the modular system under different conditions? Look at any growing plant. What repeating modules, if any, do you see?

Exploration 1
ALLOCATION TO ROOT AND SHOOT

We have been working with simplified models of plants and focusing on the plant and its light environment. Plants, both individuals and species, respond to characteristics of the light environment in which they grow with a variety of shapes and structures. How do your model plants compare with some real plants?

As we have seen, all plants need to solve the same general problems. But they live in quite different places and might solve these problems in quite different ways. Those solutions are reflected in plants' bodies and express both genetic and nongenetic factors. Individuals within a species vary (remember the finches in **Module 1**?), and their environments can vary. Let's compare some plants for shape, size, and body variation and what that might mean, ecologically.

Materials
- **Notebook**
- **Plants**
- **Hand lenses** or other magnifiers (10x, at least)

Procedure
1. **Observe a vegetable individual.**
   Gently free the plant from its growing medium. Lay it out on the table. For

the next series of questions, handle your specimen carefully, so it does not break apart! As you look at the plant, sketch and label the specimen and write in your notebook answers to the following questions:

What functions do the different parts of the plant perform?

What proportion of the plant's body do you estimate performs each of those functions? (Do not be afraid to take measurements!)

How might you find out how much energy the plant has invested in each part of its body?

2. **Variation in plant organs.**
What is the arrangement of the leaves on the stem? How do the leaves relate to each other? Is there more than one layer of leaves? Branching? In life, would the leaves shade each other? If so, under what conditions?

What is the typical shape of the leaves of the plant?

Look at the surface of the leaves and the stems. How smooth are they? If they are not smooth, how would you describe the surfaces? Are there differences between the surfaces of different parts of the plant?

Now look at the surfaces of the plant's parts with a hand lens. What can you see that you could not see before?

Sketch the plant on a separate sheet of paper. Show the arrangement and general shape of the leaves and the pattern of roots that you see.

3. **How big a solar collector?**
Estimate the total upper surface of the leaves on the plant. That is, estimate the area of each leaf and add up the areas of all the leaves. For our purposes, a good estimate can be made simply by multiplying the length of the leaf by the width at the widest point. Now calculate the ratio between this leaf area and the area of ground it might shade, as you did in **Chapter 1**.

4. **Comparing plants.**
How does your plant differ from that of the group next to you? What differences in plant lifestyle or environmental conditions might account for the differences?

5. **Brainstorm about experiments.**
What are some ways you might test your answers to the previous questions? In the next few Explorations, we will use some tools for exploring these and other aspects of the ecology of plant growth.

6. **Preparing for Exploration 2.**

In the next Exploration, we use carbonometry and calorimetry to estimate the energy allocation in different portions of individual plants. In preparation for that, each group chooses and weighs 5 individual plants, and dries them. Dry them as your teacher directs.

READING 1
MAKING A LIVING—PLANT LIFE-HISTORY STRATEGIES

What is a "life-history strategy?" An organism's "life history" is the manner and timing of the major events in its life: birth, growth, reproduction, and death. The ways in which those major events happen, how frequently, and under what conditions are important determiners of the organism's success. And the acquisition and allocation of energy often are important in how and even whether an organism's life is completed.

HUMAN LIFE HISTORY

The human life history seems reasonably easy. Since we are humans, that way of doing things seems "natural." We are born helpless, in litters of one or two, rarely more. To reach reproductive maturity, at age 12 to 14, we need a large amount of parental care. That care may be provided by a variety of social groupings embedded in an extended social fabric. In the teenage years or a little later, humans seek a mate and can begin bearing young. Total reproductive output ranges from zero to perhaps a dozen offspring. The survival of the young is limited by available resources and by the skill of parental care, in addition to random factors, such as disease or accidental injury.

TWO EXTREMES

Humans are a good example of one kind of life history. We can describe it as follows: a long life, which enables a long and large parental investment in each offspring, increasing the likelihood of the survival of each offspring born.

Other organisms follow a different approach. Take something that appears to be at the opposite extreme. A small mammal like a mouse or a bandicoot may have a short life span (perhaps 2 years), but in that time it may give birth to dozens of offspring in frequent large litters. The parental investment in each offspring is lower, in terms of both time and materials (tissue for each newborn and milk thereafter), and each offspring reaches self-sufficiency and reproductive maturity after a few weeks.

A life-history strategy thus represents a set of trade-offs, balancing when and how much you invest of energy and time, in your own growth and survival and that of your offspring. Very often, an organism with large body size or long life span (why might those two occur together?) also has a few large offspring. Small organisms with short life spans may have many small offspring, each representing a very small investment of energy.

The semi-log graph below summarizes general trends in life-history strategies. Line a shows little mortality among individuals until late in life (e.g., large mammals). Line b shows a constant death rate at any age throughout life, and line c shows high infant mortality (e.g., many insects and plants).

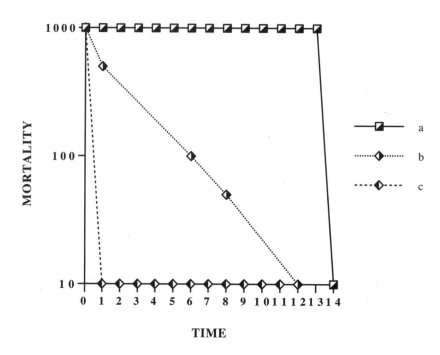

PLANT LIFE-HISTORY STRATEGIES

Plants are a fascinating group of organisms in which to study life-history strategies because they have such a great variety. First is the matter of "birth." A seed can germinate on the parent plant itself (as with mangroves), or it can fall and sprout right away, as with many tropical fruits, such as citrus. Or the seeds may need to be passed through the gut of an animal (which thins the seed coat enough for the root and shoot to escape). It may need to spend a certain amount of time in cold weather (while the seed finishes ripening or until growing conditions are likely to improve), or the seed may lie in the soil for years or even decades, awaiting a trigger of some other kind to start growing (e.g., when a forest fire exposes bare soil, the sudden higher light levels may stimulate seeds to grow).

WHAT IS A SEED?

But how does the seed get produced? Some plants produce their seed by cross-pollination: either by wind or with the help of an animal, pollen from one plant reaches the female flowers of another. Some plants can produce seed by self-pollination: pollen moving from male to female flower parts on the same plant or even within the same flower. Some plants do not require pollination at all and produce seed without it or reproduce by cloning. Even more confusing, the same plant may be capable of all those forms of reproduction, perhaps more, such as sprouts from an underground stem or from roots that send up shoots, or branches that grow roots and then separate from the parent tree. The varieties seem endless.

FREQUENCY OF SEED PRODUCTION

How many seeds? How often? Some perennial plants produce a few seeds every year over long lives. Some perennials, though, are trees, which can produce year after year large quantities—millions—of seeds, which may be small, dry, and relatively cheap, energetically speaking (e.g., willow and birch seeds), or large and costly to produce (acorns), or wrapped in a costly fruit whose value is its attractiveness to animals that will disperse the seeds (e.g., apples and berries).

Some species live a short time and flower only once (annuals). Others may flower once but only when the plant gets to a certain size (biennials or "short-lived perennials"). Or a species may live a very long time indeed and flower only once, such as the agave, or "century plant," of the American deserts, which grows to great size over the course of decades and flowers and fruits only once, after which it dies.

INTERNALLY CONSISTENT STRATEGIES

Each reproductive strategy is part of an integrated whole with other aspects of the plant's growth and life—just as with animals, in which size, diet, thermoregulatory mode, and so on, are integrated. If a plant is going to live only a year and then flower, fruit, and die, the plant would not be selected to invest in woody supporting tissue—indeed, that would siphon off critical resources needed to invest in the fruits and seeds. An annual plant may spend up to 50% of all the energy it gathers on its reproductive parts.

That means, though, that the plant will not be adapted to grow high above its competitors for light. And that means the plant might have been selected either for early, fast growth (before other plants in its community are able to overtop it) or to specialize in growing in places where light competition is naturally low, such as roadsides or newly plowed fields or gardens.

If the plant will be living and reproducing for decades or centuries, however, it needs other ways in which to compete with other plant species and individuals for light and nutrients and to be able to withstand all the variations in weather that will occur over that long time. Thus, it may invest a lot of energy in a woody stem to lift it high (trees), or an extensive root system to forage for water (grasses), or in developing a lower compensation point, so it can subsist on lower levels of light (many woodland species). It might develop storage organs, such as bulbs or tubers, to survive a bad year of drought or cold and be able to send up new growth in a better time.

Remember from **Module 1** the three requirements for natural selection and that finches have no choice about natural selection. Either an individual does or does not survive under particular conditions and because of its particular genetic characteristics. Thus, being "successful" means to gather as much energy and other resources as possible and to produce as many viable offspring as possible, given your life span. In every case, a species survives that produces the same number of offspring to replace the number of individuals that die each generation. If a species produces more viable offspring than that, its population will grow; if it produces fewer offspring, the population may be headed for extinction.

Exploration 2

ENERGY AND CARBON CONTENT OF PLANT ORGANS

How much energy does a plant allocate to the organs of its body—the root, shoot, leaf, flower, and seed (which we measured in Exploration 1)? Let's use the techniques of calorimetry and carbonometry to estimate the amount and proportion of carbon individual plants have invested on average, in each kind of organ.

Materials
- **Plants** from Exploration 1, weighed wet and then dried
- **Scissors**
- **Technique: Calorimetry**
- **Technique: Carbonometry**
- **Scales** (that measure to 0.1 or 0.01 g)

Procedure

1. **Make a prediction.**
   What percent might you expect the root and the shoot systems each to be of the total weight? Write down your expectation and use it as an initial hypothesis against which to compare your findings.

2. **Prepare for measurements: The specimen and the data table.**
   Select five specimens at random. Separate the roots, leaves, stems, and fruits (if any) from each specimen. For now, keep them separate for each plant. Set up a data table in your notebook to record the mass of each organ and its caloric and carbon content. Your data table might have the specimen numbers in the left column and the plant parts as separate columns.

3. **Individual weights and percentages.**
   If it has not already been done, weigh the roots, the leaves, the shoot, and the reproductive materials from each individual plant. Calculate the proportion that each part forms of the whole for each plant.

4. **Calculate averages.**
   Calculate the mean (average) proportion of each plant part for all five specimens combined, that is, what is the average proportion of root for your sample? The average proportion of leaves? The average proportion of stem?

   How much variation is there in your sample, that is, how much does each individual differ from the mean values? What is the median value? Does the mean or the median tell you more about your sample? Discuss this with your group and perhaps the class.

5. **Predict energy values.**

   Remembering that carbohydrate and protein both contain about 4 kcal of energy per gram, estimate the amount of energy allocated to each kind of plant tissue in each plant in your sample. Use the weights you took in step 2, and assume that the plant is 100% carbohydrate and protein. What is the average for each plant part for your sample? How about the root (the below-ground portion) versus the shoot (the above-ground portion)?

6. **Test your prediction.**

   Using the calorimetry procedure, test your predictions. Remember that some heat is lost in the procedure, so the results might be 10–20% below the standard published values for energy content.

7. **Test for carbon content (optional).**

   For one (individual) plant, use the carbonometry procedure to calculate the amount of carbon contained in one kind of tissue. Compare your results with the calorimetry results. What would you predict would be the proportions of carbon in the other parts of the plant?

8. **Summarize your results.**

   How do the plants in your samples differ from those in other teams' samples? What might explain the differences, if any? Under what conditions might a plant vary the proportion of investment in each portion of its body? What experiments might you perform to test your ideas?

READING 2
COSTS OF REPRODUCTION

By now we know that, in animals at least, reproduction is costly. Organisms have only a limited amount of energy available to them, and they must use some of it—much of it—to stay alive (metabolism). Some of that energy is spent in the gathering of supplies—energy and nutrients. In addition, animals spend varying amounts of energy on establishing a place to live and (after reaching maturity) finding a mate.

The costs to animals of reproduction is addressed in **Unit 2**, **Chapters 3** and **4**. Here, we look at the costs of reproduction in plants. As part of this topic, let's explore how to tell a plant's state of health.

As we have noted, many plant responses to environmental factors can be measured in terms of the plant's growth. How much does its stem lengthen or thicken in a standard time period? How many leaves does it produce in each season, or how large are the leaves? How long before it comes to flower? How many flowers and then how many fruits does it produce this season? How do this year's growth measures compare with last year's?

EXPERIMENTAL DATA

We would expect that the cost of a plant's reproduction might show up in such measures of performance, but it rarely has been demonstrated experimentally. One good study of the pink lady's-slipper orchid (*Cypripedium acaule*) over several years provides strong evidence that reproduction does in fact have a measurable cost, so that the plant has to make trade-offs among many possible energy expenditures.

Pink Lady's Slipper

The lady's slipper is a simple plant on which to make measurements— most plants produce one or two large, oval leaves each year, at ground level. The leaves die in the fall, and new ones are produced each spring. The plants live for decades (at least); older plants, with larger root stocks, tend to put out larger leaves or even two leaves, plus another new plant springing from the same stock.

The lady's slipper is pollinated by bumblebees (*Bombus*), which enter the flower seeking nectar. They discover that the advertisement was misleading and that there is only one way out. They have to squeeze past the stigma (the tip of the female organ) and then the flower's male organ, which smears pollen on the bee's furry back. When the bee soon visits another lady's slipper, the first flower's pollen is wiped onto the female part of flower #2, and the bee then picks up flower #2's pollen.

In New England, there is one problem with this system—relatively few flowers are visited by bees. In one part of Massachusetts, for example, only about 10% of the flowers fruit each year. Yet if a researcher pollinates flowers by hand, practically every one will bear fruit. This provides a good setting to try an experiment: the ecologist can pollinate the same plants year after year and watch what happens to the plants that reproduce often.

How does their growth compare year after year? How does it compare to the growth of unpollinated plants of a similar size?

In a 10-year study of this sort, the results were striking. At first, there seemed to be no differences between researcher-pollinated plants and other individuals. But as the years went by and the hand-pollinated plants repeatedly set seed, their new leaves each spring were smaller and smaller. This was even clearer when those plants experienced some stress, such as drought or fire—they literally did not have the energy to grow new leaves. Furthermore, plants that fruited every year became less and less likely to flower the following year and were more likely to succumb to disease and other causes of death. The "control" plants, which were pollinated only occasionally by bees, showed no significant change in frequency of flowering, and many of them increased the size and number of their leaves.

Like any organism, a plant has only a limited amount of resources to allocate among metabolism, tissue growth, and reproduction. Although ecologists often say that reproduction is the "point" of an organism's existence, in fact it is in balance with all other life processes.

ABOVE-GROUND BIOMASS
MEASURING PRODUCTIVITY

OVERVIEW

Since so many organisms eat plants, why are there any plants left? In the Serengeti, herbivores eat at least 6×10^{12} kcal per year of plant biomass. Yet the Serengeti still has plants. Why? What does this tell us about energy flow?

We consider that question, how to calculate the plant biomass in an area, and why eating plants is more energy efficient than eating herbivores.

CASE STUDY
PLANTS AS PREY: WHY IS THE WORLD STILL GREEN?

Oceans aside, the world is covered with vegetation. Most places have at least a covering of grasses; a very large portion of the land is covered by forest, from the sub-Arctic regions in the northern hemisphere to the tropical rain and seasonal forests around the globe.

All these plants produce new tissue at a great rate every year, representing a vast pool of potential energy and nutrients for eaters of plants. Yet studies of many ecosystems suggest that most of that potential (between 50% and 99%) goes unused by herbivores—detritivores and decomposers get most of it. Why do the herbivores not take a bigger share?

A related question is what determines what an herbivore can eat? By weight, number, and number of species, the most important herbivores are insects. It is clear from brief field observations (or examination of their mouth parts) that insects have specialized and subdivided the plant world (the potential "menu")—there are chewers on leaves and eaters of wood. There are insects that specialize in seeds, on nectar and pollen from flowers,

346

and on sap. There are even species that specialize in plants that are poisonous to most other animals.

The answers to those two questions lie in an evolutionary relationship between some herbivores and plant-prey that has been going on since the time of the dinosaurs. The advantage shifts back and forth between eaters and eaten as characteristics of one produce selective pressure on the other. Given how important plants are to life, this is a crucial story of evolutionary biology.

PLANTS ARE TOUGH

Plants are hard to eat. That is not surprising when we think of a tree. Much of a tree is wood, support material that is designed to be tough and low-maintenance metabolically. Those same properties also make it low in energy and nutrition content. Few organisms can digest wood; those that "eat" wood, such as termites, get nutrition from it only by means of a symbiosis with bacteria that are doing the real work of nutrient extraction. Even grass leaves, the principal food for grazers like cattle and wildebeest, are hard for most animals to digest (Reading 1 in **Unit 2**, **Chapter 8**). Remember also that animals for whom leaves are a staple food have specially adapted digestive systems and rely on bacteria as indispensable partners in the work.

PLANTS ARE PROTECTED

Aside from the toughness of lignins and other plant structural tissues, a major reason that plant eaters do not make a bigger dent is that plants are not helpless. In fact, some scientists have described the relation between plants and their predators in terms of an evolutionary "arms race" over tens of millions of years.

Plant defenses take many forms, from mechanical to chemical. Plant species tend to be specialized to fend off a certain class of predator; thus, herbivores tend to be specialists as well, able to cope with some kinds of plants or parts of plants and not others.

Mechanical Defenses

Perhaps the most obvious kinds of defenses are mechanical barriers, such as thorns and prickles, as are found on rosebushes, blackberries, and hawthorns. They are certainly a deterrent to large mammals that might damage the plants—people, deer, and similar creatures.

On the other hand, insects traveling on a rosebush can just walk around the thorns—they are at the wrong scale to be affected. Some plants have very fine hairs, sometimes seeming even woolly, that impede insects' walking, tangle their feet, or bar them from reaching the leaf or stem tissues. Other plants just make their tender parts less tender—many grasses and horsetails concentrate silicon crystals in their tissues, which makes them indigestible or even irritating to grazers, even large mammals like zebras or gazelles, who then try to eat younger leaves in which the defenses have not matured.

Chemical Defenses

Mechanical barriers can be removed or avoided by the persistent plant eater. Many plant species have a second, more subtle line of defense: chemical deterrents. The great majority of our medicines are plant derivatives. (You probably have heard that one reason to prevent the extinction of more plant species is because of the undoubted medical discoveries waiting to be made.)

Plants do not produce chemicals for our benefit: they are poisons, antipredator devices. Plants allocate some of their energy to the construction of carbon- or nitrogen-based compounds that attack the digestive system, metabolism, or nervous system of some class of predators. Other species produce thick, white latex sap, which gums up the mouth parts of insect herbivores and incidentally plugs holes caused by the attacker. Sometimes this gummy stuff has chemical compounds mixed in—one entomologist has imagined that the experience of eating such a plant must be like having your mouth filled with glue spiced with cayenne pepper.

ONE HERBIVORE RESPONSE: PREFER THE TOXICS!

Some organisms have evolved a tolerance for the particular defense of a plant and even specialize on plants with specific defensive compounds. For instance, certain moths are not bothered by the mustard oils of the cabbage family, which can be lethal to other insects. The tobacco hornworm moth and its relatives can tolerate the nicotine produced as a defense by some species of the plant family that includes potatoes, tomatoes, petunias, and tobacco. In fact, not only can the hornworm tolerate this diet, it will not thrive if the nicotine "dose" is too low.

BORROWING THE DEFENSIVE CHEMICALS

Taking things one step further, some insects not only specialize in eating plants with particular chemicals in them, their digestive system sifts out the defensive chemical and uses it as a defense in turn. One of the most famous examples is the monarch butterfly of North America. This insect, remarkable for its transcontinental migrations, lays its eggs on milkweed, a plant whose sticky sap is laced with potent cardiac poisons. The caterpillars incorporate the poisons into their own tissues and thereby become distasteful, even harmful, to birds that eat them. Furthermore, the caterpillar's "cargo" of defensive chemicals is retained through metamorphosis, so that the adult monarch, brightly colored in orange and black, also is quite distasteful.

HUMANS AND PLANT DEFENSES

How is it that humans can eat things like rhubarb, tomato, broccoli, and other plants from families that are well protected against herbivores? Human cultures have adopted two strategies. First, we cook or process our foods before we eat them. That makes some tough tissues more digestible and destroys some poisonous compounds—boiling, roasting, grinding, and fermenting are among the ways we "predigest" the foods that we otherwise could not use.

A second strategy is artificial selection, a principal tool of agriculture. In every population of plants defended by poisonous or mechanical means, there are individuals that are less defended and whose weaker defenses are a result of genetics rather than of growing conditions. Over centuries of trial and error, farmers in every culture have selected the most palatable or useful varieties of the plants they cultivate and continually bred them for desirable characteristics—less chemical defense, seeds that are easier to harvest, more tender leaves. Such artificial selection of plants and animals has been a prime data source for evolutionary biologists since Darwin started it all in 1859.

Exploration 1
OLD MacGREGOR'S FARM

Here, we invite you to engage in a "thought experiment" about ecosystem implications of different amounts of plant productivity. Although we set the stage on a farm, consider the implications of such variations in productivity for all kinds of ecosystems. Some simple arithmetic will lead to rather interesting conclusions.

"Biomass" means the material in living organisms, recently dead organisms, or their parts (such as fallen leaves or feathers). Since organic molecules contain energy in their bonds, the amount of biomass in an ecosystem tells us about the amount of energy available to that system.

Because plants are the organisms that capture light energy and make it available to other organisms, variations in plant productivity (the amount of plant tissue formed over a given period of time) have important energy implications for ecosystems.

As we have seen in other Explorations in this Chapter, plants can vary where they put their energy. Depending on conditions, a plant might put more into leaves, roots, stems, or fruit. Each of these kinds of tissue is usable by some other organisms, so changes in allocation can have important effects on species that depend on those tissues. Having looked at how individual plants allocate their carbon and energy to various tissues, we can think about carbon and energy on a larger scale.

Materials
- Notebooks
- Pencils
- Calculators
- Your imagination

Procedure
1. **Productivity: What is it?**
Be sure your group has a common understanding of the concept of productivity and its importance to ecosystems. Write down the ideas on which you all agree.

2. **Productivity of a farm: The cows.**

It takes 25 kg of grain to raise 0.5 kg of cow. Farmer MacGregor raises 10 cows each year to a weight of 500 kg each. How much grain is that?

3. **Cow food: Grain and wheat.**

A plant fixes carbon all through the growing season. Of the biomass added, the fruit (in this case, the grain) represents only 10%. So how much total grain plant growth do those 10 cows require for their year's growth?

4. **How much land?**

In a typical year, 1 m^2 of grain-planted land in Freedonia can produce 1 kg of plant matter. How many square meters are needed to feed MacGregor's herd for 1 year?

5. **A perturbation: A drought.**

There has been a drought this year, so plant growth has been reduced by 20%. What effect will that have on MacGregor's cattle?

6. **The SunScheme.**

Agriculture is the principal source of income in Freedonia. A group of underemployed scientists has decided to enhance agriculture by putting a huge mirror into orbit around the earth. It will, they say, reflect sunlight onto the dark side of the earth and thus increase plant productivity by doubling the hours of light available. MacGregor is tempted by the SunScheme—she would like to produce an additional cow each year. Is the SunScheme plausible? Would you base your family farm on it? Why? What else might happen? What else might you want to know?

7.   Class discussion.

The situation in this Exploration is hypothetical, but think about how it relates to "real" ecosystems. Draw some conclusions, and remember both **Unit 2, Chapter 10** and the questions posed in **Unit 2, Chapter 3** about what is a real ecosystem.

First in your group, and then as a class, consider and discuss these questions:

What leads to variations in primary productivity? What differences do such variations make to an ecosystem in the current growing season? What about in the following year?

READING
HOW DO YOU WEIGH A TREE?

In **Chapter 3**, when you were calculating energy and carbon content for plants you had grown in the lab, you were assessing biomass in a simple system that allowed you to measure whole plants. In the field, that is rarely possible, because the bulk of biomass on land is in trees. Their primary production can be measured indirectly, however. In <u>Exploration 2</u>, we use one of several common techniques to estimate above-ground biomass of plants too large to harvest and weigh.

Plants store fixed carbon in the tissues that make up their form: trunks, branches, leaves, bark, roots, and flowers. Much of that energy is no longer available to the plant that produced it, but it can provide food for other organisms in the ecosystem. Therefore, knowing how much carbon and energy are stored in plant parts is essential for understanding other ecological issues like global carbon cycling. It also is useful for predicting the number and kinds of heterotrophic organisms that will live in an ecosystem and for estimating the productivity of an ecosystem. The amount of carbon stored in the forest is also of interest to foresters, who are interested in the volume of wood in the forest that can be converted into lumber.

BIOMASS AND PRODUCTION

Now, what processes control the rate at which carbon is accumulated? To begin, we consider productivity. The productivity of an ecosystem is measured as the rate at which carbon is fixed by green plants. Several terms that ecologists have defined will help in a discussion about productivity within ecosystems.

The rate at which green plants fix carbon is called **gross primary productivity** (GPP). This is a difficult number to estimate because of the carbon plants use for metabolic respiration and maintenance. This is the plant's **R** term.

If we subtract from GPP the respiratory requirements of plants, we are left with carbon the plant uses for producing tissue (biomass). This portion of GPP is called **net primary productivity** (NPP). The following equation summarizes the relationship between the three terms:

$$\textbf{GPP} - \textbf{respiration} \text{ (maintenance)} = \textbf{NPP}$$

Estimating NPP then means accounting for the rate at which biomass is added to a green plant. Remember (from **Chapter 2**, Exploration 2) that this varies with time of year and by plant part (leaf, fruit, stem, etc.). Each component can be measured or estimated for a particular ecosystem, but many of the estimates are time-consuming and tedious. When you weighed the bean plants and their parts, you could work with whole individuals. It is hard to do that with trees (although it has been done).

FROM ONE TREE TO A FOREST

Luckily, the trunk of a tree is close in shape to a regular geometric shape, the cone. By using the formula for calculating the volume of a cone, we can do a Fermi-type calculation. Assuming that the tree trunk is a cone and that it contains the largest portion of a tree's biomass, we can estimate the biomass of a tree, and then of a forest full of trees.

THE FIELD WORK: PREPARATION

Here is a summary of the procedures you will follow at your field site and later when you analyze your field data. (Details are in Exploration 2 and Exploration 3.)

In the Field

Choose an area for establishing a plot in the forest.

Stake four corners of a square plot, 10 m on a side.

Mark all trees in the plot with sequential numbers using chalk or paper and thumbtacks.

Measure the circumference of each tree in centimeters at 1.4 m above the ground. Record the circumferences in a data table.

Estimate the height of each tree in the plot. Record the heights in centimeters in a data table.

Back in the Classroom

Use the height and diameter data to calculate the mass of each tree you measured.

Sum the biomass on your plot, then scale up to larger areas, even a forest.

Compare the estimates based on your sample with those of other groups.

Summarize and write up your data. Pose some possible research questions.

Now please read all of Explorations 2 and 3 before you go out into the field. Exploration 3 includes a worked-out example of the calculations of a tree's biomass, in case you want to refer to it when you do your own.

Exploration 2
ESTIMATING ABOVE-GROUND BIOMASS IN THE FIELD

Remember those bison we were considering in **Unit 2, Chapter 8** (Exploration 1)—how (and whether) we could tell how much energy was in the grass they ate, so we knew how much land we needed for 500 animals? We answered one-third of our question there, using calorimetry to discover the energy content of grass. Here we use a technique to answer the other two-thirds of the question: how much plant biomass (such as grass) is there on the land we are considering and how much might a buffalo need? Nifty, no?

This fieldwork has three key parts: establishing the study site; marking the trees; and measuring their diameters and estimating their heights.

Materials
- **30-m tape measure**
- **5-m cloth measuring tape**, in cm
- **Meter stick**
- **Tent stakes** or other markers
- **Compass** (optional)

Safety

> **WARNING**
> If you are allergic to any plants or insect bites or stings, take precautions as necessary. IF YOU ARE ALLERGIC TO BEE STINGS, BE SURE TO BRING A BEE-STING KIT WITH YOU.

> **WARNING**
> When you do fieldwork, always work in pairs at least and use the buddy system.

Procedure

1. **Establishing study plots.**
   Find an area typical for the forest with a dozen or so trees in close proximity to one another. Do not pick the densest patch of trees, but avoid open areas where trees are absent. In your notebook, describe your site with reference to roads, signs, or other landmarks so you and others can find it again. If possible, refer to the landmarks both by compass bearings from one corner of the study site and by distance (even if just paced off).

   Mark off an area roughly 10 m on a side, thus enclosing an area of 100 m².

2. **Numbering trees.**
   Number the trees on your site. Use chalk or paper labels tacked to trunks and make the numbers large and thick enough to be seen from 30 m (about 20 cm high).

3. **Circumference measurements.**

When you look at a tree trunk, notice that the diameter of the trunk changes from the base to the top. The fact that the tree trunk ends at a point allows us to use the cone as an approximation of trunk shape.

Stand facing the tree you want to measure and wrap a string around the tree 1.4 m from the ground. Hold the string where the end meets it and measure the length of the section of string. Do this measurement for all the trees within the plot and record the circumferences in your notebook.

Using the correct place to estimate the diameter of the base is important for accuracy and standardization. Ecologists usually measure the diameter of trees at 1.4 m above the ground. Although this is a somewhat arbitrary place to make the measure, it ensures standardization. The measurement of diameter at this height often is referred to simply as "diameter at breast height" (DBH). Before we go on, find out how high up on your body 1.4 m falls. For most students, it will be near your chest, but for some it will be closer to their waists and for others their eyes. The important thing is standardization—that the measurements are taken at the same height on each tree. And since the measurements are all taken at the same height above the ground, we can compare our measurements to those taken at DBH on any tree from any place, measured by any researcher.

4. **Estimating heights.**

   Here is a simple way to estimate tree height in the field.

   a. Select the tree to measure.

   b. One student sights the top of the tree at 45° relative to the ground, using a protractor or clinometer as directed by your teacher.

   c. Having established a 45° angle with the top of the tree, another student measures the distance, in centimeters, from the base of the tree to the first student's feet.

   d. To that number, add the height from the ground to the first student's eyes. Assuming that the tree is at a right angle to the ground, the number of centimeters from the tree to the first student's feet plus the student's height, in centimeters, equals the height of that tree, in centimeters. See Figure 1.

   e. Repeat the procedure until you have measured all the trees on the plot. Record your estimates of tree heights in the data table.

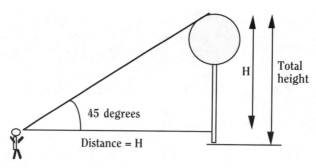

Figure 1. Total tree height = H + height of observer.

Exploration 3
ABOVE-GROUND BIOMASS: THE DATA AND THE CALCULATIONS

Using the data you collected in the field, we can now calculate biomass for each tree individually and for all the trees in each plot. Using some approximations, what might be the biomass of different-size forests? Where might our approximations be off? Can we make them better?

Materials
- Calculators
- Field data from **Exploration 2**
- Notebooks

Procedure

1. **Diameter.**
   Convert the tree circumferences into diameters. Remember that diameter is equal to circumference divided by π ($d = c/\pi$), where $\pi = 3.14$.

2. **Volume.**
   Use the height and diameter data to calculate the volume of each tree. Approximate the volume of a tree trunk by using the equation for the volume of a cone (a tall and skinny cone!):

   $$h\pi r^2 / 3$$

   where

   h = the estimated height of the cone (tree), in cm
   r = the radius (or 1/2 the diameter, $d/2$), in cm
   $\pi = 3.14$

   Following is a worked-through example.

   Calculate the biomass for a hypothetical tree, with a circumference of 100.5 cm and an estimated height of 1,800 cm.

   The first step is to calculate the diameter:

   d = circumference / π
   d = 100.5 cm / 3.14
   d = 31.99 cm, or rounded to the nearest tenth, 32.0 cm

Now use the diameter (32 cm) in the equation for the volume of a cone (modeling a tree trunk): $h\pi r^2 / 3$

where

h = estimated height of the tree, in this case, 1,800 cm

r = radius of the tree trunk (half the diameter, d / 2), in this case, 16 cm

π = 3.14

Thus, in this example:

volume of tree trunk = {3.14 × (16 cm)² × 1,800 cm} / 3
volume of tree trunk = 1,447,603.2 cm³ / 3
volume of tree trunk = 482,534.4 cm³

3. **Use heights and circumferences to calculate the biomass of each tree.**
To calculate biomass, we need all the calculations done so far, plus one more. We want to convert the volume of each tree trunk to a weight. We do that by considering the density of wood, that is, the weight per unit volume. While this may seem circular, considering weight and volume together allows us to get more information than by considering either alone. (It is another kind of renaming example.) Although density varies by tree species, age, and where in the tree the wood is formed, we are using an average value of density, one used by researchers for this kind of approximation.

A reasonable average density value for wood is 0.5 g/cm³. Using that value, convert the volume of each tree to biomass.

4. **Biomass of all trees in your plot.**
Now that you have an approximate biomass for each individual in your study plot, add all those values to obtain the tree biomass for your entire 10-m × 10-m plot.

5. **How much wood in the forest? Scaling up your sample.**
Because trees tend to be large, folks who think about tree biomass tend to think in terms of areas larger than our study sites. After all, there are not many trees in a plot the size of ours—100 m²—compared to a whole forest. A standard area for considering forests is a hectare (ha), a square that measures 100 m on a side. But researchers often measure tree biomass in several small plots, such as ours, within the hectare and average those biomass values. Then they multiply the average biomass value they obtained for the smaller plots by the number of those smaller plots in a hectare. By how much have they multiplied their biomass average? In other words, how many 10-m × 10-m plots are in 1 ha?

6. **Whole-class data and a whole hectare.**
Each group reports to the class about the results from their plots and their prediction about the biomass of a hectare, based on their sample.

How similar are the estimates of biomass per hectare reached by each group? How similar are the plots used in your sample in terms of number and size of trees or biomass? (If you want to explore that topic further, you might be interested in the **Technique: Describing and Comparing Communities.**)

Suppose you average the biomass values of all the plots and use that value to extrapolate to the whole hectare. Do you think that might be more realistic? Reconsider also points raised in <u>Reading 2: Averages</u> from **Chapter 3**.

If we extrapolate to 1 ha by using the biomass value from a different small plot, how different is the total biomass value for the whole hectare? Which small plot gives a more accurate picture of the whole hectare? How can we tell?

7. **Sampling issues.**

These are important issues about sampling and data collecting. How representative is a small part (one 10-m × 10-m plot) of a bigger part (one 100-m × 100-m plot). And how representative is that bigger part of an even bigger part, such as the whole forest or area? How many small plots do we need to sample to get a good picture of the bigger plot or of the forest? There <u>are</u> answers to those questions, but not quick answers. They include things like scale (such as, how small can the small plot be compared to the bigger plot) and the amount of similarity between small plots (the more similar they are, the fewer you need to examine to extrapolate to a bigger plot). If you are interested in thinking more about these issues, see the **Technique: Introduction to Research**.

8. **Write a group report.**

Now that you have seen all the reports from the various field groups, summarize your study as a group. The summary should include your initial observations in the field, the methods and materials you used, the results (including the data table), and your conclusions about the exercise. Include some thoughts about sampling. Be sure also to discuss things you might do differently or places where your data might be shaky.

For example, maybe for the first few trees you measured, you realize that, because you were unfamiliar with the techniques, you were less accurate than on later trees. There is no "shame" in shaky data—the shame is in pretending that they are not shaky. In fact, sometimes data are <u>too</u> shaky to include with other data and should be left out. In our case, we can re-measure the tree by going back to the study plot. If that is not possible, however, you have to work around those shaky data—by measuring biomass in some other plots or by noting that your data are incomplete.

In this Exploration, we estimated only trunk biomass. Yet there are many other portions of the forest where fixed carbon is stored. What other components of the forest store carbon? Given what we know about estimating biomass in tree trunks, how might we estimate biomass contained in other components of the forest?

Conclude your report with three to five questions on which your group would like to do more field research. The list might include questions about the allocation of biomass among various species in the forest, the makeup of the forest community, the herbaceous plants or shrubs, the biomass of animals in the forest—whatever ecological questions came up in your fieldwork, your data analysis, or your discussions afterward.

GLOBAL CARBON

GLOBAL CARBON

UNIT 4 OVERVIEW

GLOBAL CARBON

We use the term "global carbon" here literally to indicate the globe-wide carbon cycle and global warming, as well as metaphorically to indicate the "cosmic" nature of the full cycle. Throughout this Module, we have explored the links between carbon and energy at many levels, from bonds and molecules, from individuals, species, and populations through food chains and simple food webs to communities. In this Unit, we integrate all those levels to consider the global picture of atmospheric change, which depends on all those lower levels, including plant growth, microbial respiration, the balanced energy use equation, and your own energy use.

Recall that carbon (like other nutrients) cycles through the system as it participates in chemical transactions of various kinds. Carbon from the biosphere (by way of respiration and combustion) and from the seas and rocks mixes in the atmosphere. Some of it is absorbed into the waters of the earth, while a crucial amount is taken up by photosynthesis. But sooner or later carbon ends up as CO_2 (the most dynamic component of the cycle) in the atmosphere.

Thus, the atmosphere is a crossroads for carbon, passed around as CO_2. It is nearly impossible to monitor precisely processes at the global level, so we sample what and as we can (e.g., the makeup of air). We then build a story with those results, plus all the other data across the various levels we study.

To complete the story, we return to an individual organism's carbon budget. That allows us to close the circle from individual to global aspects of the carbon and energy cycle and to see how we humans "count" in the grand debate about the climate's future.

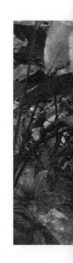

THE GLOBAL CARBON CYCLE

CHAPTER ONE

OVERVIEW

In the other Units of this Module, we have seen carbon cycling and energy flowing at various levels through individuals, food chains, populations, and ecosystems. Here we focus on the carbon cycle at the global level. We see how all those levels are interconnected: how carbon-and-energy capture and use by organisms across lesser, local levels add up to play a big part in the global picture.

CASE STUDY

THE GLOBAL WARMING DEBATE: ASKING THE RIGHT QUESTIONS

In June 1992, delegates from 178 nations gathered in Rio de Janeiro, Brazil, for the United Nations' Earth Summit, officially called the U.N. Conference on the Environment and Development (UNCED).

During that conference, the delegates debated many issues. Among them was a proposal that the U.S. government opposed: that the nations of the world adopt a plan to stabilize emissions of carbon dioxide, perhaps at the level expected for the year 2000. That plan included limits on the amount of CO_2 that could be emitted by the burning of fossil fuels and on the amount of forest that could be cut down each year.

The earth summit was a cover story around the world. Many commentators asked, "What is wrong with President Bush that he doesn't see the urgent need for these steps?" Others asked, "Why should we let the ecoextremists push us into measures we don't need? These matters should be left up to each nation to decide."

THE TEAMS AND THEIR POSITIONS

Your class will divide into three groups, each group taking one position of that proposal. Each team then will divide into subteams. Your task is to prepare a presentation to the class, arguing for your position. To prepare, use the Background Reading in this Case Study (which provides evidence for all points of view), plus any other information you can gather from magazines, books, or newspapers.

Team A (U.S. Position)

What was the United States' position on the issue? What scientific reasons might be advanced for that position? Were there other reasons as well? What unanswered questions do you have after your reading—missing evidence, reasons based on guesses, and so forth?

Team B (Other Delegates' Positions)

What were the scientific arguments in favor of the proposed treaty? Were other reasons advanced as well? What unanswered questions do you have after your reading—missing evidence, reasons based on guesses, and so forth?

Team C (Representing Nonhuman Species)

You represent the nonhuman organisms of the world. Imagine what Teams A and B may argue—how is your point of view different? What questions would you want the human decision makers to ask? How strong is the evidence for one side or the other? If you could have only three questions answered in order to plan your long-term survival, what would those questions be?

Each team should consider what aspects of energy capture and allocation and plant and animal energy use might come into play in this debate. During the discussion, your teacher will make a list of questions that people ask. You will make use of these questions in your study of the global carbon cycle.

BACKGROUND READING

In 1988, in testimony before Congress, James Hanson, the head of NASA's Institute for Space Studies, painted a scary picture of the next century.

It is 2050. Plentiful rains bring lush growth to the southern Sahara, eroding memories of the terrible droughts and famines of the twentieth century. Maine and Minnesota enjoy Georgia-style weather, with hot summers and mild winters. Large areas of the Arctic tundra are warm enough for long enough in the summers that the upper layers of permafrost are melting, and the spruce forests are creeping north into the barrens. The decomposers finally have access to some of the dead plant matter locked in the arctic "freezer." Instead of 10–15 days per year over 90°F, places like Boston and New York have 20–25 such days, and the weather farther south (like in Washington, DC, Texas, southern California) is hotter than it used to be, too.

Increased CO_2 in the atmosphere has enhanced plant growth in some species, so they grow taller faster in the spring; in other species, the seeds are bigger, but with a tougher seed coat. Some flower earlier in the spring; others delay their flowering for a month. In some plant species there is no observable change. The species-by-species changes (or lack of changes) wreak havoc with the forests and farms of the earth.

Meanwhile, the Midwest's crops are parched and baked in the long, dry summers. Lake Michigan is drying up, and Chicago is no longer a coastal city. Twenty-five years of low rainfall and high temperatures have wiped out most of the grain farms in the region, and North America's breadbasket has moved north into south-central Canada. Similar changes have taken place in Ukraine, once the richest farmland in Europe, but now dry grassland.

While the midlands of the continents are seeing drastic changes in rainfall and temperature, the coasts are being swallowed by the rising sea. Half of Boston and large parts of New York City are under water, or protected from flooding by a new system of dams and dikes. Two-thirds of Bangladesh is now tidal delta, and the same is true of Louisiana. The lowlands are devastated each summer by hurricanes of unparalleled power.

All this is being driven by a global temperature increase of only about 4°C. Some places have many more hot days (over 90°F), but most places have summers a little hotter, but winters a lot warmer.

CO_2: A Greenhouse Gas

What does this have to do with carbon in the ecosphere? We have seen that carbon (as CO_2) is taken up by plants in photosynthesis, passed from plants to animals and microbes as organisms take their food, grow, die, and decay. Respiration at every stage releases carbon dioxide to the atmosphere. We know that the vast bulk of carbon in biomass is in plant tissues, a lot of it woody, in the stems and roots of trees in forests around the world. (Animals are a much smaller part of the picture, but anything that affects plant growth affects animals, too.)

The connection with Hanson's nightmare is this: CO_2 is a "greenhouse gas." All the ingredients in the atmosphere are warmed by the solar energy they have absorbed, and radiate some of the heat. CO_2, methane, water vapor, and the chlorofluorocarbons (CFCs) that are destroying the ozone layer are all good at catching and radiating heat. Thus, although CO_2 is a small proportion of the atmosphere (0.035%), it can have a large effect. CO_2 and other gases act as a "blanket" for the earth, keeping temperatures within the range that supports life. The planet Venus has a very high proportion of CO_2 in its atmosphere, and it is vastly hotter than the earth. You would think, therefore, that there can be too much of a good thing.

Human Effects

But plants and animals have been circulating CO_2 for eons. What is going on? The culprit, Hanson says, is human activity. Deforestation and fuel emissions put so much carbon into the atmosphere that the earth's average annual temperature will climb sharply over the next half-century. We need to take drastic measures now to prevent that from happening.

Wait a minute, though—"temperature will climb"? Has anything actually happened? Hanson was talking in 1988, when the northern hemisphere had a terrible summer, but since then things have not been so bad. Was Hanson's warning a false alarm?

At the Rio Earth Summit, representatives of the U.S. government argued that the evidence for global warming was too weak and that there was too little reliable information to take drastic action. President Bush argued that the recommended proposal that nations set a limit on CO_2 emissions would penalize industry by requiring expensive changes in the way power is generated and goods manufactured. The higher costs would be passed on to consumers. The official U.S. position was that we need more facts before we act.

Data from Models

Most of the predictions that Hanson and others have made about the future climate actually are based on computer models of the atmosphere and the climate. A model is a simplified description of a system (a climate, traffic patterns, a town water supply) that allows you to see relations or make predictions about what will happen under various conditions. Atmospheric scientists have developed complex models of the global climate and use them to explore how climate and weather might change under various conditions over the next few decades. It is those general circulation models (GCMs) that lie behind the scary global warming scenarios. Although the models are not complete, they are carefully constructed, and test runs (using them to "predict" weather and climate that have already happened) show that they seem to give good results.

Model Components

When you build a model of this sort, you must build into it as many facts as possible. The climate models include information about weather patterns, the processes by which clouds are formed, the way that gases such as CO_2 and methane mix in the atmosphere, and many other factors. One firm finding is that there is more CO_2 in the atmosphere than there used to be 100 years ago. It is also possible to calculate how much heat will be retained by air composed of different proportions of gases.

We also know that because the earth's atmosphere contains small amounts of CO_2 and water vapor, the earth holds enough solar energy to keep the temperature at levels that allow life to exist. Mars is cold partly because its atmospheric blanket has no such elements; Venus is as hot as it is because of the high proportion of CO_2 and other "greenhouse gases" in its atmosphere. The atmospheric models are based on things we know about the way the world works.

Actual Temperature Data

Influencing the models are actual weather data. The 1980s saw a series of years with record-high average temperatures worldwide—in fact, the five hottest years on record fell within the years 1980–1988. More heat records were set in 1994 and 1995. This very unlikely set of events may be more than a coincidence.

The term "record-high average global temperature" does not mean that every single place on earth was hotter during a particular year. In fact, some places had record colds, others normal averages. That misleads some writers and politicians to ridicule the warnings of global warming, because the United States had cool years during the record-high years. Reckoning with data from around the earth, though, those years were hot; the skeptics forget that the U.S. has only about 2% of the earth's surface area. (Remember, we keep running into this issue of assessing data: especially averages, what they mean, and how they can be misleading.)

On the Other Hand. . .

There is some real reason to be skeptical, though. We know how hard it is to predict the weather for one city even a few days in advance. Why should we believe predictions about the whole globe for years into the future?

There is much about climate that we just do not understand. There have been variations in the average global temperature in the past, long before fossil fuel emissions could have played a role and long before there were enough humans to have any impact at all. Maybe the warm years in the 1980s were just the result of natural variation. Only in the past few years have we begun to understand the full implications of the El Niño pattern. An "El Niño" is a cyclic weather event that brings extra-warm years, unusual ocean circulations, and extra-strong typhoons to the south Pacific and affects the weather in the northern hemisphere in ways not well understood as yet. (Recall the drastic effects of El Niño in 1986 on the Galapagos finches?)

Who knows what else may suddenly make sense, when we have been watching long enough? After all, our weather records stretch back hardly a century. Perhaps it does not make sense that human activities could have an effect on the global scale that is predicted. After all, the atmosphere is huge, and CO_2 is only 0.035% of the total—350 parts in a million. If humans add a little more, what difference could it make?

Yet, What If. . . ?

What if the predicted changes do happen, though? We know that CO_2 is a plant "fertilizer"—perhaps the extra CO_2 will stimulate more plant growth, and the plants will take up the excess from the atmosphere.

Warmer temperatures are good for plant growth, too (as well as for winter heating bills). Plant and animal species have been under selection by changes in the climate before; why or how is the current situation different? Are the climate changes more rapid? Less rapid? Or like any others that have occurred before? Perhaps some plants and animals will adapt to these changes also (like the Galapagos finches).

Exploration 1
WHAT IS A SYSTEM?

We have discussed systems in various ways: an organism, a classroom, an ecosystem—all are systems. Indeed, once you get the hang of thinking in terms of systems, you will see systems everywhere you look: a flock of birds, a forest, a pond, your family.

Here, you and a partner will build a working physical model of a system and explore its behavior. Instead of carbon or energy, we have water flowing through the system (water is much easier to follow). As you design, build, and rebuild your model, think about how changes you make in your system can affect the way the water moves through it.

Materials
- **Paper or plastic cups**
- **Clear plastic straws** or **clear plastic tubing**
- **Hole-punching implements** (thumbtack, pushpin, awl, pencil)
- **Water**
- **Food coloring** (optional)
- **Flow restrictors** (e.g., aluminum foil, paper clips)
- **Measuring devices** (graduated cylinders or measuring cups)
- **Timing device** (a stopwatch or a watch or clock with a second hand)

Procedure
1. **Cup-straw systems.**
To make a hole in a cup, use a thumbtack, a pushpin, or an awl to make a single small hole. Enlarge the hole to almost the diameter of a straw by twisting a sharpened pencil in the hole (a tapered ballpoint pen also works well). Practice making holes in a single cup until you can make a hole that will seal around a straw and not leak. Then connect two or more cups with straws.

Safety

> **WARNING**
> Be careful not to push too hard when punching holes into the cups—you may jab yourself.

2. **Get to know the materials.**
You and your partner may want to experiment with a simple system, per-

haps just two cups and one straw. Explore the properties of your simple system—how fast does one container empty into another? Can you decrease the rate of flow between the containers? Can you increase the rate of flow between containers? How does the rate of flow affect the length of time that water stays in the upper container (from which the water is flowing)?

3. **Choose system goals.**

Once you are familiar with the materials, you are ready to build your experimental system. Compare these two design goals and choose one:

a. Build a system in which the final container in the system (the one where most of the water ends up) fills at a rate of at least 1 liter (1,000 ml) per minute.

b. Build a system in which the final container in the system (the one where most of the water ends up) fills at a rate slower than 0.25 liter (250 ml) per minute.

4. **Build your system.**

Build your system. Consider how you might improve it, then build two final versions.

5. **For further thought.**

Discuss the following questions with your partner:

Can you build a system in which the water keeps flowing from container to container, cycling back to the original container and then out again on its original path? Be ready to explain how or why not. Do you need additional equipment?

What is it that gets water flowing in the system? How did you build that into your design?

Exploration 2
SYSTEMS EVERYWHERE

You and your partner have spent some time designing, building, and studying a model system. Now apply your understanding of systems. Copy the following table into your notebook and fill it in. Then think of three (or more) systems and add them to the table.

SYSTEM	WHAT FLOWS IN THE SYSTEM?	POOLS	PATHWAYS
1. Water supply	Water	Storage tanks	Pipes
2. School	Students	Classes	Corridors
3. Circulatory system			
4. Economy			
5. Digestive system			
6. Traffic			
7.			
8.			
9.			

Exploration 3
THE CARBON BUDGET OF A SMALL SYSTEM

We have explored basic characteristics of systems, using water as the material. Now let's return to carbon, in the context of a nonecological model system.

We are approaching a picture of the global carbon cycle. But we are not yet ready to come back to the global level—missing are some pieces of the puzzle having to do with time and the processes of change. This Exploration helps us think about the parts of a particular, small carbon cycle—a house, which from foundation to roof contains carbon in many forms, forms that change through many different processes.

Procedure

1. **The task.**
On Murdock Street in the city of Somerville, Massachusetts (latitude about 42°N, near Boston), there is a one-family house built in 1893. It is a wooden house, with wooden shingles on the side and asphalt shingles on the roof. It is not heated by electricity or by any solar-collection system. Such houses typically stand for no more than about 200 years. (How do houses "end their lives"?) A family of four, the Johnsons, currently lives in the house. The children are 7 and 12 years old. They have one pet, a cat (Norman). Over the course of time, all the organic contents (living or formerly living) of the house will be broken down, and the carbon will end up in the form of CO_2.

Construct a model of the carbon budget of this house over the course of its lifetime. In this case, the "model" describes the places where carbon is stored in some form, the ways it leaves the house or moves from one location to another, and the rate at which those changes happen.

2. **Questions to consider.**
What elements of the house contain carbon compounds from organic

sources? (You do not need to know the chemical formula for each form.) In what ways do the different forms of carbon compounds get converted to CO_2? What parts of the house system cycle daily? Yearly? At longer intervals? What carbon compounds do not complete their cycle within the house system? It turns out that the amount of some forms of organic carbon and the rate of cycling of those forms are higher now (1996) than they were 5 years ago (1991). What might account for those differences? What is the boundary between the carbon cycle of the house and the carbon cycles outside the house? Is the house a closed or an open system? What is the relation between the energy budget and the carbon budget of the house? Is there energy flow by paths other than the carbon cycle?

3. **Comparing system pictures.**

You might want to describe your picture of the house's carbon cycle in pictures or diagrams, as well as in word answers to the questions in step 2. When your model—your description of how your system works—is complete, compare your notes with those of other groups.

4. **Class discussion.**

As you discuss different systems, consider what assumptions have been made about the following:

Where can you find carbon in the house? What are the quantities of carbon in each pool? What kinds of changes does each kind of material go through? How long does each material last in its present form?

Exploration 4
YOUR CARBON CONTENT

In your notebook, write your answers to the following thought experiment.

You are in a room-size dessicator, an industrial freeze-dryer of the sort some museums use to make "stuffed" animals. Specimens made this way look particularly life-like and are also light and easy to carry around. Why do you think they are much lighter than the original animal?

If an adult raccoon weighs 16.3 kg at death and 4.9 kg after six months in the freeze-dryer, how much water was dried out of the body, in kilograms?

What percent of the raccoon's original body weight remains?

The remaining weight is called the dry weight; the original weight of the animal is its wet weight. (When used alone, the word "weight" usually refers to wet weight, but ecologists and biologists often use dry weights in their work. When they do, they usually specify dry weight.) About 50% of dry weight is carbon. How many kilograms of the raccoon are carbon?

By now you have a formula for calculating the percent dry weight of carbon—what is it? Actually, you may also have found a shortcut to calculate percent carbon directly from wet weight—what might that be? Using your formula, calculate your own and your organism's carbon content.

	WET WEIGHT (KG)	DRY WEIGHT (KG)	C (KG)
You			
Organism			

For comparison, how much carbon is contained in all the humans in the world? A rough average wet weight for humans is about 50 kg. It is estimated that by the year 2000, the world population will be 5.9×10^9 people. How much carbon is that?

The carbon in organisms is part of the pools, or stores, of carbon that exist in the world. To keep track of all the carbon in the world, we need to know how much is in all the pools and how fast it moves, or "flows," into and out of those pools.

Given what you already know about carbon, why might we want to keep track of it?

Exploration 5a

GLOBAL CARBON CYCLE: THE ATMOSPHERE

In the global-warming debate, an important assumption on all sides is that the earth functions as a system. In a system, the parts are interconnected. Thus, change in one part affects other parts, even if the effects are not visible. We assume as well that subparts of the earth system also are systems: particular cycles or ecosystems are networks within themselves, as well as parts of the whole.

The global carbon cycle can be thought of as a system; by now, we think right away of its possible pools and pathways. What are they, and how do they interrelate? How might change on the global level affect your locality and vice versa?

Here one of three teams considers just such questions at the global level, or "top down." (Exploration 6 looks at how our energy budgets relate to the global picture, that is, "bottom up.")

Materials
- Table 1
- Graph paper
- Notebooks

Procedure

1. **Graphing the data.**

   The atmosphere is a crossroads for several elements of the carbon cycle. It is also the pool of the system whose carbon content is the easiest to measure.

   Table 1 lists monthly readings of CO_2 levels for 3 years, taken from observations at a research station on Mauna Loa. The readings are taken to be representative of a global average. They are in parts per million (thus, the January 1964 number means that out of a million parts of air 319.41 parts are CO_2).

   Please graph the data.

2. **Interpreting the data.**

   Try to explain the shape of your graph. Consider any other questions you have. If there are peaks on the graph, what might explain them? What might explain any troughs?

   Why would these data be taken on a place like Mauna Loa (as opposed to, say, Lima, Peru, or Cincinnati, Ohio)? What conditions are important for the data to be representative of world CO_2 levels?

   On the basis of these data, what might you predict will be the average level of CO_2 in 30 years?

3. **Presentation and class discussion.**

   Share your graph with the class. Discuss your findings and what they might mean. Include the questions raised in step 2. How do they add to the picture (including data from the other two teams)?

Table 1 ## Atmospheric Concentrations of Carbon Dioxide

| | CO_2 CONCENTRATIONS (PPM) | | |
	1964	1965	1966
Jan	319.41	319.27	320.46
Feb	No data	320.28	321.43
Mar	No data	320.73	322.22
Apr	No data	321.97	323.54
May	322.06	322.00	323.91
Jun	321.73	321.71	323.59
Jul	320.27	321.05	322.26
Aug	318.54	318.71	320.21
Sep	316.54	317.65	318.48
Oct	316.71	317.14	317.94
Nov	317.53	318.71	319.63
Dec	318.55	319.25	320.87
Annual average	319.04	319.87	321.21

Exploration 5b
GLOBAL CARBON CYCLE: CARBON POOLS

In the global-warming debate, an important assumption on all sides is that <u>the earth functions as a system</u>. In a system, the parts are interconnected. Thus, change in one part affects other parts, even if the effects are not visible.

We assume as well that subparts of the earth system also are systems: particular cycles or ecosystems are networks within themselves, as well as parts of the whole.

The global carbon cycle can be thought of as a system; by now, we think right away of its possible pools and pathways. What are they, and how do they interrelate? How might change on the global level affect your locality and vice versa?

Here the second of three teams considers just such questions at the global level, or "top down." (Exploration 6 looks at how our energy budgets relate to the global picture, that is, "bottom up.")

Materials
- **Table 2 and Table 3**
- **Graph paper**

Procedure

1. **Background: Sources of carbon.**
    Carbon is cycling in different forms throughout the ecosphere. The major pools are the oceanic, the atmospheric, the biological (biosphere), and the geological (lithosphere). We already know something about the biological pool: on land, it exchanges carbon in the form of CO_2 primarily with the atmosphere.

    The geological pool includes the deposits of fossil fuels (coal and petroleum) and also rocks formed from ancient oceans. Limestones and chalks, for example, contain a lot of calcium carbonate from the shells of marine organisms and other carbon compounds formed from the combination of dissolved CO_2 with other elements in the water and deposited on the sea floor in ages past.

    The processes that produced the geological pool are still at work. Carbon dioxide is dissolved in seawater, and though some escapes, some is fixed by photosynthesis (by algae and phytoplankton), and much is taken in and used by mollusks and other creatures in their shells. When those organisms die, the carbon is released in decay or deposited in the oceanic "bank"—the sediments that in future years will become rock.

2. **The data.**
    Table 2 contains information about the major pools of carbon. Table 3 presents the annual rates of exchange between various pools of carbon. Note that the amounts are in metric tons, or tonnes (not avoirdupois, or U.S., tons). A metric ton is equivalent to 1,000 kg.

Use the data in the tables to design a chart that pictures the major pools and shows which pools are exchanging carbon. Prepare a report to the rest of the class, answering the following questions, in addition to others you may have:

Which pools exchange very little carbon on a yearly basis?

Which pools exchange a significant portion of their carbon (as CO_2) on an annual basis?

On the basis of these data, what do you predict about the size of the atmospheric pool of CO_2 30 years from now?

Table 2   ## Size of CO_2 Pools

WHERE	HOW MUCH (METRIC TONS)
Atmosphere	720 billion
Oceans	38,000 billion
Biosphere	600 billion
Earth (rocks and fossil fuels)	40,000 billion

Table 3   ## Annual CO_2 Exchanges

EXCHANGE	AMOUNT PER YEAR (METRIC TONS)
Oceans to atmosphere	105 billion
Into atmosphere from earth's interior	0.1 billion
Biosphere (including soils) to atmosphere	120 billion
Into new sediments	0.1 billion
Atmosphere to biosphere	120 billion
Atmosphere to oceans	107 billion

3.   **Class discussion of results.**
Present your group's results to the class and discuss what they might mean. How do they add to the picture (including data from the other two teams)? Compare your predictions about the size of the atmospheric pool of CO_2 30 years from now.

Exploration 5c

GLOBAL CARBON CYCLE: HUMAN FACTORS

In the global-warming debate, an important assumption on all sides is that the earth functions as a system. In a system, the parts are interconnected. Thus, change in one part affects other parts, even if the effects are not visible.

We assume as well that subparts of the earth system also are systems: particular cycles or ecosystems are networks within themselves, as well as parts of the whole.

The global carbon cycle can be thought of as a system; by now, we think right away of its possible pools and pathways. What are they, and how do they interrelate? How might change on the global level affect your locality and vice versa?

Here the third of three teams considers just such questions, at the global level, or "top down." (Exploration 6 looks at how our energy budgets relate to the global picture, that is, "bottom up.")

Materials

- **Map (Figure 1)** and **data graphs (Figures 2–7)**
- **Graph paper**
- **Calculators** (optional)

Procedure

1. **Background.**

   Until now, in all the units of this curriculum, we have treated humans *(Homo sapiens)* as one species among millions. You used yourself and your species as model organisms on several occasions, for example, when thinking about what goes into an animal's energy budget.

   In fact, though, we know that humans are not typical animals. One way in which we differ from other animals is the way we make use of resources and also the way we alter the landscape and even the air with our activities. What does all this have to do with carbon and energy?

   The graphs in Figures 2–7 from the Oak Ridge National Energy Laboratory show CO_2 emissions for the earth, region by region. Together, those regions cover the entire earth.

   Notice that measurements are in metric tons, or tonnes (not U.S. tons). A metric ton is equivalent to 1,000 kg, or 10^6 g.

2. **Examine the graphs.**

   As you look at the graphs, what questions come to mind? Compare the graphs, looking for differences and similarities.

3. **Calculating and interpreting the data.**

   Calculate the global emissions for the most recent year for which data exist. Predict what global emissions will be in 30 years and also what emissions will be in three of the regions. Why do you predict what you do? Do you expect that the size of the atmospheric pool of CO_2 (the amount of CO_2 in the atmosphere) will rise, fall, or hold steady over this period of time?

4. **Reporting to the class.**

   Tell the rest of the class about your investigation. Discuss anything you have noticed about the data. Be sure to include the final figure from step 3 and your predictions. How do your results add to the picture (including data from the other two teams)? Compare your predictions about the size of the atmospheric pool of CO_2 30 years from now.

   The map in Figure 1 shows the regions of the earth that correspond to the graphs of CO_2 emssions in Figures 2 through 7.

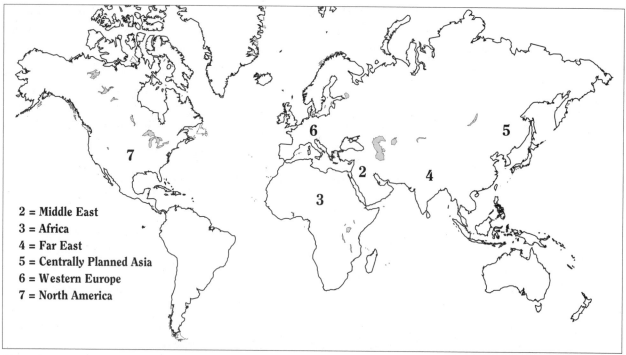

Figure 1

The Middle East, as represented in Figure 2, comprises sixteen nations that may contribute a large fraction of the world's oil but through their own energy consumption produce only 3% of global CO_2 emissions from fossil fuels and cement. The three major fuel consumers in the Middle East discharge 62% of the region's CO_2: Saudi Arabia, 47.4 million tons of carbon; Iran, 45.3 million tons of carbon; and Turkey, 34.4 million tons of carbon. Gas flaring has been a major source of regional emissions. For a few years during the early 1970s, before the technology was available for gas use and reinjection, flaring accounted for almost half the total CO_2 emissions. Growth has been nearly continuous since 1950, although it started from a very low base. Per-capita emissions underwent rapid growth until 1973 but have changed little since then.

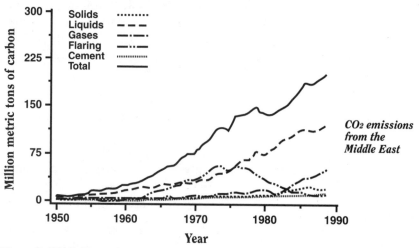

Figure 2. Middle East

Africa is a region with CO_2 emissions that are low in both absolute and per-capita terms (Figure 3). Total emissions have increased by a factor of 7 since 1950, and have been increasing at a linear rate of about 5 million tons of carbon per year since 1963. Per-capita emissions in 1989 were 2.4 times those of 1950 but are still only 5.5% of the comparable value for North America. Solid and liquid fuels contribute about equally, with gas fuels adding only 8%. To the extent that we can rely on gas-flaring data, 1986 was the first year in which gas use exceeded gas flaring. Regional emissions from fossil fuels and cement are dominated by a small number of nations, with South Africa accounting for 43% of the continental total, and another 37% of the CO_2 coming from Egypt, Nigeria, Algeria, and Libya combined. Only these countries on the continent have annual CO_2 emissions over 1.0 ton per year: Libya (2.4), South Africa (2.2), and Gabon (1.9). Many African nations have per-capita emissions below 0.1 ton of carbon per person per year.

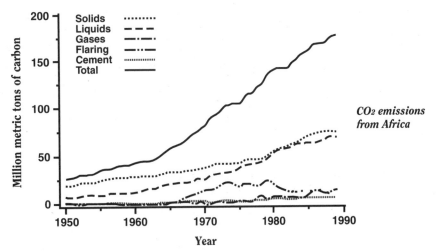

Figure 3. Africa

Emissions of CO_2 from the Far East were 14 times greater in 1989 than in 1950, the culmination of 39 years of growth, averaging 6.7% per year (Figure 4). This reflects the growth that has taken place not only in countries like India and the Republic of Korea but also in Indonesia, Taiwan, Thailand, Pakistan, Malaysia, the Philippines, and other smaller nations. India and Korea are responsible for 60% of the region's CO_2 emissions, with the above-mentioned six countries contributing another 33%. Per-capita emissions in the region are as low as 0.01 ton of carbon per person per year in Bhutan and Nepal, as high as 4.7 in Brunei and 3.6 in Singapore, but more typically in the range 0.15 to 0.8 ton of carbon per person per year. That total emissions have increased by a factor of 14 while per-capita emissions have increased by a factor of 5 shows that population growth has been an important factor in the Far East. Coal is the major source of CO_2 in the region, but 85% of the coal is used in India and Korea while 58% of the emissions from liquid fuels is from countries other than India and Korea. Unlike those for some countries, emissions from the Far East show no break in slope in the middle of the late 1970s.

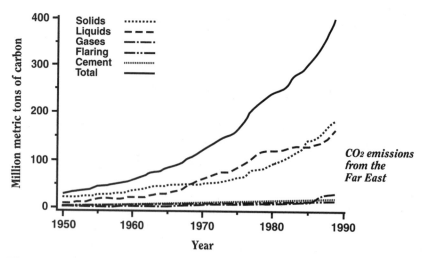

Figure 4. Far East

The region of Centrally Planned Asia (CPA) includes Vietnam, North Korea, and Mongolia, but regional statistics are dominated by the People's Republic of China (Figure 5). China currently contributes 92.5% of the region's population and 93% of regional total CO_2 emissions. In 1950, China produced over 98% of the region's CO_2 emissions from fossil fuel burning. Growth in CO_2 emissions has been virtually continuous since 1950, as the CPA contribution rose from 1.3% of the world total in 1950 to 11.7% in 1989. There has been more than a doubling of CO_2 emissions since 1973, when growth in many western nations essentially ceased.

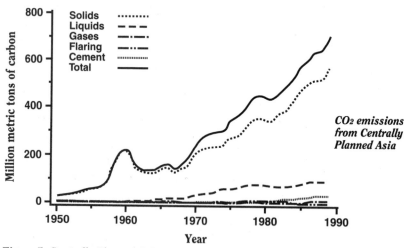

Figure 5. Centrally Planned Asia

Like other groups of developed nations, Western Europe experienced increasing CO_2 emissions up until 1973, with a sharp break in slope at 1973 for both total emission and emissions from liquid fuels (Figure 6). Unlike emissions in other developed regions, emissions in Western Europe since 1973 have not shown a tendency toward resuming. Both total and per-capita emissions remain below the peaks established in 1973 and 1979. The region comprises twenty-three political entities, five of which (Federal Republic of Germany, United Kingdom, Italy, France, and Spain) are among the top twenty national CO_2 emitters. Those five nations contribute 73% of total regional CO_2 emissions. Per-capita emissions range from a high of 6.8

tons of carbon per person per year in Luxembourg to values below 1.0 ton of carbon per year in Gibraltar. For most countries, the value lies between 1.5 and 3.0 tons of carbon per year. Gas fuels have become increasingly important since about 1970 and now contribute 16% of total CO_2 emissions.

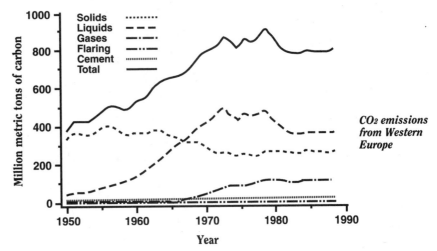

Figure 6. Western Europe

North America, as used in Figure 7, consists of the United States and Canada. Because over 91% of current CO_2 emissions from the region are from the United States, the 39-year time series closely resembles that for the United States. In addition, the patterns of change for the two countries have been similar in gross features, although they differ in detail because of political and resource differences. In contrast with CO_2 emissions from other regions, the striking features are a relatively uniform growth rate from 1950 to 1973 (2.9% per year) and an essentially constant rate of emissions since 1973, albeit with a slight upward trend since 1983. Because of more rapid growth elsewhere, emissions from North America have shrunk from 45.1% of the global total in 1950 to 24.4% in 1989. Per-capita emissions have been consistently high and well above those for any other region, 20 times the per-capita emissions from the Far East.

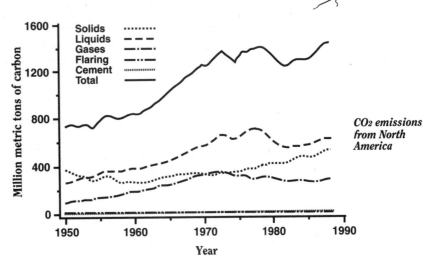

Figure 7. North America

Exploration 5d

"TRUTHING" YOUR PREDICTIONS

Each of the three groups—for the Atmosphere (Exploration 5a), Carbon Pools (Exploration 5b), and Human Factors (Exploration 5c)—ended its research by making a prediction about the future of the amount of atmospheric CO_2.

The Atmosphere group worked with some numbers from Mauna Loa. Those numbers were a sample of 3 years from the whole data set. That restricted set of data was provided so the group could focus on the dynamics revealed in the annual cycle. In fact, though, the Mauna Loa data look like Keeling's curve in Figure 8, which is generally considered a good estimate of global atmospheric concentration of CO_2. Keeling's data also has been confirmed by briefer but still reliable studies done in some other sites.

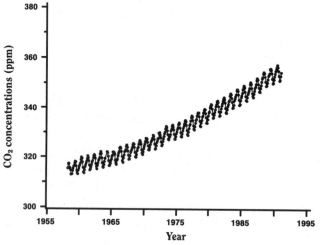

Figure 8. Keeling curve

Procedure

1. **Team questions.**

   Each of the three groups made a prediction about how the atmospheric pool of CO_2 would change over the next few years. What is the difference between your team's prediction and the prediction you would make on the basis of the Keeling curve in Figure 8? Based on that graph, what would you predict the CO_2 level might be in 2030? Why do you think the trend is the way it is?

2. **Class wrap-up.**

   What implications might your new prediction have for climate and for plant and animal life in the future, based on all you have read and done in the carbon curriculum so far?

READING
HUMAN ENERGY USES: BIOLOGICAL

Now we go back to *Homo sapiens* as a sample organism—with one difference. The human species has developed a lifestyle that requires intensive tool use. Since the last Ice Age, people in many parts of the world have developed extraordinarily complex tools that require industries to make them, economic systems to move them about, and many kinds of activity—metabolic and otherwise—to put them to use. You can see that these tools cost energy to make, energy to transport, energy to use, and even energy to destroy or recycle. How does that relate to the global carbon cycle?

YOUR ENERGY BUDGET

Recall for a moment the energy budget you created in **Unit 2**, **Chapter 2**. To create your budget, you kept track of all the foods you ate and all the activities you performed during a 24-hour period. To complete the budget you calculated your total energy intake and expenditure, using information about the caloric contents of foods and the caloric requirements of various activities.

When you created your energy budget, were you able to account for <u>all</u> the energy that you spent during those 24 hours? Here you consider a number of energy uses that you did not include in your original budget and how those energy uses affect the global carbon cycle.

CHWA AND SABRINA

To help you understand your own patterns of energy use, we will begin by comparing the lifestyles of Chwa, the daughter of a !Kung San family from the Dobe area of the Kalahari desert in southern Africa, and Sabrina, whose family lives in Miami, Florida. (The character "!" in the name !Kung represents a "click" sound and is like the cluck used to urge on a horse, pronounced at the same time as the "k.") As you can imagine, their family life, their lifestyles, and their energy uses are very different. As we discuss Sabrina's lifestyle, keep your own lifestyle in mind. We explore the relation between these lifestyle differences and the global carbon cycle.

Chwa's Lifestyle

Both young women are 16. Like many teenagers, Chwa spends time doing chores with her mother and siblings. Unlike most teenagers you may know, however, her chores are directly linked to feeding and caring for the family. The !Kung are a hunter-gatherer people who make their living by doing just that: hunting local game (including some of those animal species we already know from the Serengeti, especially wildebeest and hartebeest) and gathering wild plant foods. The men hunt large game, while the women gather small animals and plant foods and prepare the food. The women's work also includes carrying water and collecting and carrying wood.

Depending on the season and what fruits are ripe or which waterhole is full, Chwa may walk up to 25 km a day, but her average is about 6 km a day. She knows how to feed and care for herself using the natural world around her. She has never been to school and cannot read or write, though her people have a rich oral literature of stories, myths, and natural history.

Sabrina's Lifestyle

Sabrina, on the other hand, is a typical U.S. teenager who goes to school (by bus) and is responsible for a few household chores, including keeping neat the room she shares with her sister. She is on a basketball team, and summers she works to save money for college. She eats pizza, hamburgers, and sometimes vegetarian food.

The Two Compared

Let us briefly consider the energy budgets of these two young women. As you may recall, body size and body weight play an important role in overall energy use; larger (heavier) people generally spend more energy doing a given task than smaller people. Chwa is about 142 cm tall (4'8") and 42 kg; Sabrina is 163 cm (5'4") and 46 kg. Thus, the two are roughly the same size and weight, with Sabrina being a little larger.

How do these two teenagers spend the energy they absorb from their food each day?

Exploration 6

HUMAN ENERGY USES: CHWA AND SABRINA

Let's compare the daily energy budgets of Chwa and Sabrina, at least the portions of their budgets that are fueled by the food they eat. Look at your own energy budget from **Unit 2**, **Chapter 2** to remind yourself of the activities that went into your food intake and energy expenditure.

Materials

• **An atlas**

Procedure

1. **Comparing Chwa and Sabrina.**
Consider the approximate energy expenditure budgets of our two young women.

	TOTAL ENERGY USE	BMR	ACTIVITY
Chwa	2,240 kcal	1,100 kcal	1,140 kcal
Sabrina	2,430 kcal	1,230 kcal	1,200 kcal

Compare the two sets of data. What do you notice?

Let's return to our original questions from the Reading. Are the energy uses of these two young women, based on our calculations, much different? Given what you know about the global carbon cycle, are the young women likely to have different effects on carbon cycling or, indeed, much effect at all? Why or why not? What have we left out?

2. Two lifestyles.

Is our picture of energy use for each teenager complete? Here is a hint, in case you are stuck. What are the two major ways in which energy is released from carbon compounds? Have we considered both?

3. More data and comparison.

Chwa lives in a grass hut that she helped assemble and that her family may use for only a few months, depending on whether the camp of thirty or so people, including her near relatives, moves. She has never been in a motorized vehicle and walks wherever she goes. The !Kung men use nets, bows and arrows, spears, snares, and clubs for hunting. Other tools include knives, digging sticks, canteens, and various sacks, slings and carryalls, plus stones to crack and grind nuts. The !Kung make all their tools of local materials. The canteens are ostrich egg shells or antelope stomachs, the carryalls and much clothing are from their prey hides, and the spears, knives, and axes consist of natural wood and scrap metal from European leavings that the !Kung beat into shape with clubs and sharpen on stone. (One especially fine knife blade was made from a railroad spike—the nearest railroad was 500 km away!)

From trading posts, the !Kung acquire a bit of fabric, three-legged cooking pots (these are a recent addition to the culture, but now every family has one), and sometimes a fire drill kit. They burn wood for cooking, for warmth, and for sociability. Every household keeps a fire smoldering 24 hours a day and stokes it up for cooking and for evening warmth and sleeping. Infrequently they also use fire to soften the metal from which they shape their tools. Food is shared equally within the group, and any leftovers go to the dogs.

Sabrina lives in an apartment complex built of steel, brick, and concrete. She spends her days in school, and her food comes from the grocery store, wrapped, processed, and even ready-made. She gets around by bus, car, and subway, and her family has a CD player, computer, TV, and VCR. Sabrina makes some of her clothes from fabric she buys (not from skins of anything hunted for her). She wears running shoes, stenciled shirts, acid-washed jeans, and clothes in various artificial fabrics like rayon, acrylic, and polyester. Leftover food and packaging become garbage and are carried away by trash collectors.

4. Other questions.

What other things can you name that Sabrina might use or do that Chwa does not?

Use the atlas to locate the homes of each young woman by latitude and longitude. How might the locations affect their lives? What if Sabrina lived in Juneau, Alaska?

A BRIEF REFRESHER: RESPIRATION AND BMR

In past Chapters, we broke energy expenditures into two major categories: **P**roduction (of new tissues) and **R**espiration. Let's review the **R**espiration term now.

Remember basal metabolic rate (BMR), the energy it costs just to be alive—for example, just to sit quietly in a warm room without moving? BMR is the bottom line, the minimum cellular activity possible for a living organism. When scientists calculate an animal's or a person's BMR, they make sure the study subject is inactive, not digesting, pregnant, or agitated, and is in a comfortably warm environment. Basically, BMR is the amount of energy we use when we are doing nothing but being metabolically alive. BMR is fairly constant for two animals of the same size and same species. Thus, it is fairly constant for same-age, same-size humans around the world.

On top of this minimum expenditure, our **R**espiration term includes the cost of any additional activity. As we may recall from our energy budget, different activities require different amounts of energy. Some, such as running fast, may require 10–20 times as much energy per minute as does BMR. Thus, more active people generally spend more energy than less active people of the same size. Note that, in light of the conditions under which BMR is measured, a wide variety of things are considered to be activities.

The range of activities on which we spend energy includes obvious ones such as running, walking, and scratching our heads. In addition, the process of digesting raises the rate at which we use energy, and even experiencing strong emotions can affect our rate of energy use. (Think about it—don't a pounding heart, red face, and clenched jaw require energy?)

Probably the most important of these not-so-obvious activities is regulating our body temperature. When we are in an environment that is too cold or too hot, we can spend a considerable amount of energy regulating our body temperature (thermoregulating). As we know, when we are in a cold environment, our bodies start to shiver. This muscular activity requires energy and releases heat as a byproduct, keeping us warm.

When we are in a hot environment, we sweat, we may breathe faster, and our heart rate may go up—all processes that require energy. Thus, people in cold and hot environments spend more energy thermoregulating than do people in moderate environments (assuming we are comparing people of similar size and activity rates). Thus, we can say that energy spent on respiration has two major components:

Respiration = BMR + activity (including thermoregulation)

Exploration 7a
AN ENERGY-USE LOG

In the Reading, you considered the ways in which two young women with vastly different lifestyles spend their food energy. You also began dealing with ways in which people use nonfood energy—energy from burning wood, coal, gasoline, oil, natural gas, and electrical energy. In this activity, your class thinks of the ways in which people with different lifestyles spend their nonfood energy.

"Lifestyle" includes many things in addition to those mentioned in the Reading, and getting a handle on their energy costs can be quite complex. Here, you list all the activities you perform that are fueled by sources other than the food you eat. Remember, for now we are leaving the topics of energy in foods and energy expenditures you make with your physical activities; we are concentrating on nonfood uses of energy.

To get started, imagine that you take the bus home from school, walk three blocks to your house, and arrive eager to relax. On this particular afternoon, relaxing consists of cooking and eating a grilled cheese sandwich (of course, washing the dishes afterward) and listening to music on your stereo until dinner.

As you and your classmates discuss the ways you use energy on a typical afternoon, the teacher or one of the students may be noting on the board the kinds of energy use. In any case, make sure to note the kinds of energy use that are mentioned, plus any others you can think of, in preparation for Exploration 7b.

After you and your classmates have brainstormed about the kinds of nonbiological energy use, use the list as the basis of an energy-use log that you will keep between now and the next class meeting.

Procedure

1. **Your task.**

Record your nonfood energy use for a 24-hour period on the data sheets your teacher hands out. This log will be much like the one you created for your physical activity log in **Unit 2**, **Chapter 2**, but here you will list only your nonfood uses of energy, not activities (such as running or dancing) that are fueled by the food you eat. Once again, pay attention to "background activities" and energy-spending activities that others might perform for your benefit (such as when someone cooks you dinner).

NOTE: Data on rates of energy expenditure (kilocalories per minute) for different activities will be provided by your teacher. Those data will allow you to calculate total energy spent. In other words, fill only the first two columns when recording your data.

ANOTHER NOTE: If you can, look at utility bills (electricity, natural gas, oil) to find out how much commercial energy your family uses. Look for units such as kilowatt-hours of electricity use, gallons of home heating oil, and therms, cubic feet, or BTUs of natural gas. Your teacher can help you convert these units into kilocalories in class.

2. **Note time spent.**

Note how long you spend on each activity—estimates are OK if they are not too wild. It will simplify things if you record activities in 10- or 15-minute units of time and round off if the amount of time is close to the unit you chose. So you might call 8 or 12 minutes of TV a 10-minute estimate.

If you have much shorter bursts of some activity, such as switching lights on and off or using the microwave or hair dryer, record those individually. (What will happen to your data if you round off several 2-minute activities to 10 minutes each?) Later, when you analyze the data, add shorter times together for the total appliance use time. For example, if you spent a little over a minute making nachos in the microwave, and you did that seven times, you might record "using microwave" seven times, then add that up for a total of 8 minutes of microwave oven use.

3. **Record everything.**
Keep track of every activity—driving, taking a bus, using <u>any</u> appliance, being in a heated or cooled room. Note both the types of activity (radio, hair dryer, car travel) and the length of time for each. You often will have to estimate the time spent. Such estimates may mean that on some points your data will not be completely precise, but probably accurate enough not to change the final conclusions.

4. **Bring your data to class.**
Bring your data to class to calculate your energy use for your sample day.

Exploration 7b
CALCULATING YOUR TOTAL ENERGY USE FOR 24 HOURS

Now calculate how many kilocalories you used per day for each activity and your total energy use in a 24-hour period.

Materials
- **Your energy-use log**
- **Table 4**

Procedure

1. **Convert each energy use to kilocalories.**
For each activity entered in your energy-use log, multiply the number of minutes that you spent on the activity by the amount of nonfood energy it requires per minute, listed in Table 4. The energy-use values for the appliances listed in the table are only approximate; not all refrigerators use 4.6 kcal/min, but the figures are a reasonable guide for your calculations.

Example
If you used a microwave for 5 minutes, your total nonfood energy expenditure for that activity would be:

$$5 \text{ min} \times 21 \text{ kcal/min} = 105 \text{ kcal}$$

When you have finished calculating the energy spent on each activity, sum your total energy use.

Table 4   **Energy Uses**

APPLIANCE	ENERGY USED (KCAL/MIN)	APPROXIMATE USE PER DAY (MINUTES)	TOTAL ENERGY USE PER DAY
Air conditioner	22		
Clock	0.30		
Clothes dryer	69		
Coffeemaker	13		
Deep-fat fryer	21		
Dishwasher	17		
Electric light (60 W)	0.86		
Window fan	2.9		
Blender	5.5		
Freezer	6.3		
Disposal	6.4		
Hair dryer	5.5		
Iron	29		
Microwave	21		
Radio	1.0		
Stereo	1.6		
Refrigerator	8.8		
Electric stove	170		
Television	2.9		
Toaster	16		
Trash compactor	5.7		
Vacuum cleaner	9.0		
Washing machine	7.3		

2.   **Compare your energy use with Chwa's.**

If you are like most U.S. citizens, you probably used a lot of nonfood energy during the 24 hours in which you recorded your activities. How about Chwa—how much nonfood energy might she use during any given 24 hours? To help you think about her energy use, look back at the section in the Reading that describes her lifestyle. Also, look over your own energy uses from your log—might Chwa have performed any comparable activities? If so, what are they, and what types of nonfood energy does she have available to her? Try to estimate how many kilocalories of nonfood energy she might spend in 24 hours and compare her energy use with yours. Table 5 lists the energy contents for various types of nonfood energy sources.

Table 5 **Energy Content of Various Fuels**

FUEL	ENERGY CONTENT
Coal	6.9×10^6 cal/kg
Oil	10.2×10^6 cal/kg
Gasoline	10.5×10^6 cal/kg
Wood	3.3×10^6 cal/kg

3. **Calculate your commercial energy use.**

   If you were able to get commercial energy-use totals (from electricity, natural gas, or heating oil bills) for your family, calculate your family's total daily energy use. The information in Table 6 will help you convert the energy data from the utility companies into kilocalories. Once you have your family's total monthly energy use (most bills are monthly), divide by the number of days covered by the bill to get your family's daily use. Then divide the family daily use by the number of people in your family to calculate your portion of the total use.

Table 6 **CO_2 Emissions from Various Energy Sources**

ENERGY SOURCE	AMOUNT OF CO_2 EMISSION
Fuel oil	12 kg/gal
Natural gas	5.5 kg/therm
Coal	2,256 kg/ton
Gasoline	11 kg/gal
Electricity from coal	1.1 kg/kWh
Electricity from oil	1.0 kg/kWh
Electricity from natural gas	0.6 kg/kWh

Now, once you have calculated your daily energy use from your family's monthly data, compare the result with the total from your log. How do the two numbers compare? Are you surprised at how similar or different they are? If they are different, how might you explain those differences?

4. **Summing up.**

   Now here is the $64 question: assume that your energy use is representative of your family's. Assume also that Chwa's is representative of her family's. Assume one more thing: her family is the same size as yours.

   What is the impact of your family on the environment in terms of CO_2 emissions? What impact does Chwa's family have?

Use Tables 5 and 6 to help you convert kilocalories of electricity per kilogram of fuel burned at the generating plant, and then gallons of fuel to kilograms of CO_2 emitted. You also may want to refer to Table 4.

Thus, running an air conditioner for 1 hour would take 373 cal/sec × 3,600 sec/hr = 1,342,800 cal. If this is produced by the complete combustion of coal, then it would take 1.3×10^6 cal / 6.9×10^6 cal/kg = ± 0.2 kg coal. (We assume that the coal is completely burned and that the energy is completely transferred to the air conditioner. Neither of these is actually true, so we would need more coal to get the job done!)

5. **Class discussion.**

Are Chwa and Sabrina similar in their <u>biological</u> energy uses? How about their other energy uses?

TECHNIQUES

CONTENTS

TECHNIQUE
INTRODUCTION TO RESEARCH

This Technique discusses aspects of scientific reasoning and the scientific process. It aims to provide a brief overview of the elements of careful science practice and procedure, such as solid experimental design, that you will need to keep in mind if you undertake research that you intend to share, especially with scientists. Careful methods and clear reporting of your assumptions, methods, and results are the essence of scientific research.

It is important to recognize that there is a difference between doing interesting activities, even "discovery-oriented" activities, and engaging in scientific research, that will be instructive to you and of value to other researchers in the field. This Technique is more about the latter. You are likely to have a good feel for where both you and your students are along the continuum represented by those two points. Although you will learn a lot no matter where you begin, your experience may be more satisfying sooner if you try for an approximate match between your class's familiarity with science process and their first activities. True research is readily within the reach of any science class, so do not shy away from it even if you or your class has no experience with research.

KINDS OF SCIENCE

Science can be descriptive or experimental, depending on what is already known about the specific topic under study. If little is known, basic data or information must be gathered: describe what you can see. For instance, one exploration in this curriculum is a field trip to describe the vegetation on your study site. Such data can be compared across sites at a given time, to gauge differences due to geographic location. They can also be compared across time at given sites, to gauge changes due to influences such as pollution or global warming. Such observations of phenomena subject to the influence of climatic or ecosystem changes can make you notice new developments or unusual events. Those observations, in turn, can serve as the basis of a thorough scientific investigation.

Alternatively, when enough descriptive data exist to suggest a cause-and-effect relationship between two phenomena or events, we can test, by carrying out experiments, whether there actually is causality or just coincidence. Do increased concentrations of carbon dioxide (CO_2) actually make plants grow faster, all else being equal? Or is the apparent relationship a coincidence? Perhaps increased CO_2 concentrations and plant growth are related, but only indirectly: CO_2 causes atmospheric heat retention (global warming), and the resulting rise in temperature may cause some plant species to grow more rapidly. Your conjectures about such relationships can be tested experimentally: you can try growing different plant species at different combinations of CO_2 concentrations and temperatures.

The investigations in this curriculum take the form of descriptive science, experimental science, or both. In this Technique, we consider both somewhat formally—not because we want to be rigid, but because some formality or standardization makes things easier to discuss and consider. For example, to talk about testing hypotheses, we need to say what we are including and excluding for consideration. So, let us examine the full chronology of a scientific study: the steps involved and how to carry them out. We explore here the design of a hypothetical research project that includes the use of some of the curriculum activities, as well as other work of your own.

THE SCIENTIFIC PROCESS

The scientific process can be thought of as having roughly three steps, each of which has three parts. Although these divisions are somewhat arbitrary, they do correspond to functional divisions and help less experienced researchers keep track of their progress through the scientific process. The "three threes" are summarized here.

Learn: Step 1
1. Observe and describe the phenomenon.
2. Ask questions and make comparisons.
3. Perform a literature search and organize an overview of the topic.

Test quantitatively: Step 2
1. Develop a tentative causal explanation: what seems to cause the phenomenon?
2. Design experiment(s) to test the tentative causal explanation.
3. Carry out the experiment(s).

Analyze and interpret: Step 3
1. Tabulate and analyze the experimental results.
2. Interpret the results narrowly and broadly.
3. Disseminate the results via publication and/or presentation.

In the remainder of this Technique we consider these steps in some depth from the perspective of science process and science reasoning. Each activity or procedure in the body of this curriculum provides some parts of or materials for the first two steps, with participating students and teachers providing the rest. The third step—analyzing and interpreting data—comes primarily from participants, since it is based on the data they collect. However, we consider major issues affecting data analysis and interpretation.

Learning and Background: Step 1

Observing, Asking Questions, Investigating

Very often, you come to a research question because you observe something that seems out of the ordinary, or you make a connection between facts or processes that you had not connected before.

For example, let's say we realize something about our environment: that the sky is not blue and that the air smells funny.

One thing these observations have in common is that they are comparisons—which actually means we are noticing things twice. We assume on the basis of past observation that the sky is a certain color, and now we notice it no longer is that color. When we say, "The air smells funny," we have noticed (perhaps unconsciously) how air once smelled, and now we are noticing that it smells different. (In fact, "different" is more accurate than "funny," so let's use that word from now on.)

Some people are more observant, that is, they make such comparisons more readily, than others. But everyone can improve his or her observation skills, and such skills are valuable: being a good scientist requires good observation skills, both conscious and unconscious.

Being a good scientist also requires articulating those observations—both the initial, often unconscious observation and the second, conscious one. Learners may identify more clearly with this process if it is cast in the form of solving a mystery. "The air smells different" is an observation; so is "The dog did not bark while someone robbed the house." In each case, we have an expectation of what should happen: the air should smell a certain way (it previously smelled a certain way); a dog should bark if someone robs the house. These expectations or assumptions may be unconscious, at least at first. Part of being a good detective—or a good scientist—is becoming aware of such expectations and assumptions, so we can think about and build on them.

Part of this process and of observation is curiosity—wondering, asking questions. Probably in a shorter time than it takes to read the preceding paragraph, an observer would have progressed from observation to question:

Why is the sky not blue?

Why does the air smell different?

Why did the dog not bark?

Some questions—such as "Why is the sky blue?"—can be readily answered by using appropriate reference materials (asking people, reading, etc.) that is, part or all of the answer is already known. (Part of the fun of doing research is studying things that other people also are studying or know about and getting to talk with them about it. By doing research, we join a community and its conversations, which can be pretty exciting. But more about that later.) Other questions are more complicated, such as, "Why does the air smell different?" That complication can mean several things. Perhaps there is no single answer—the air smells different for several reasons. Perhaps no one knows the answer. Either no one has ever answered that question, or we have not been able to find the answer wherever we looked. Or it may be that the question is unanswerable, either absolutely (we cannot prove that we are experiencing reality rather than a vivid hallucination) or relatively (the technology is not available to understand fully the inner structure of the atom).

We can consider any of those because science is a way of investigating questions.

ASSUMPTIONS AND EXPECTATIONS

In asking these questions, we also continue to articulate assumptions or expectations. A conversation with yourself about air might go like this:

"Why should the air smell a certain way?"

Because it has smelled that way until now.

"What does it actually mean that air smells or has an odor? What is air, anyway!?"

By looking up "air" in a basic reference book, we discover that it is a colorless, odorless, tasteless mix of gases that makes up the earth's atmosphere.

"Aha!" we say. "So air should not even have an odor . . . ," and we read more.

Air is 78% nitrogen, 21% oxygen, and small amounts of argon, carbon dioxide, helium, and other gases. It also carries gases produced by combustion and respiration, particles of physical matter, water, and other things.

"So, when air has an odor, as when we smell smoke, presumably it is carrying something that imparts that odor." Such a dialogue or articulation gives us a lead, a line of reasoning to pursue, with a set of appropriate questions to ask.

"Since combustion (burning in an engine or an oven, for example) and metabolic combustion both add things to the air, are there new sources of either nearby? A new restaurant or factory, increased traffic, or a fire? Where? Or have wind patterns changed, bringing us products of combustion we have not previously received?"

Similar reasoning applies to our burglary mystery. Why do we expect that a dog will bark when someone is robbing a house? Because we assume that the robber is a stranger and the dog barks at strangers. Or because the dog barks at everyone. Each of these statements has interesting implications. Perhaps the robber was not a stranger. Or perhaps the dog was not present—either physically not present or drugged and thus unable to bark. Again, this gives us a lead. "Was the dog present? How do we know? Who sold the homeowner the dog? Could that person have been the robber? What about other people known to the dog?" And so on.

In the case of the burglary, investigation probably would involve more asking people questions and less going to the literature. But in the research likely through this curriculum, investigation probably will involve more literature search.

READING THE LITERATURE

The so-called primary literature is a major forum for scientific conversations. And, as in any conversation, these written "conversations" show that different authors or sources usually say different things. Sometimes they say radically different—even opposite—things. That presents a challenge to the reader, perhaps especially to learners making use of primary sources. First, it is important for them to remember that the fact that something is in print is no guarantee that it is true. That applies even to the scientific literature. Everyone makes mistakes, mistakes that include misprints, misquotes, misunderstanding, and misinformation. Often, differences in the scientific literature stem from disagreements—over definitions, data, what the facts are, or how to interpret those data or facts. Sometimes such differences reflect the rapidly changing state of scientific knowledge—what was previously the "truth" or state of the art is now seen quite differently, perhaps because of some discovery or a new technique that allows new discoveries. This is particularly true in the sciences, where information often can be provisional. Sometimes disagreements are resolved in a dramatic way. Famous examples in which researchers revolutionized their fields by flouting tradition and the accumulated knowledge of their age include William Harvey demonstrating the circulation of blood; Charles Darwin putting forth his theory of adaptation by natural selection; Marie Curie discovering radium; and Barbara McClintock discovering jumping genes. Often in such instances, the relevant journals and literature show strong "before" and "after" differences. After Magellan sailed around the world, few people still believed it to be flat.

Sometimes, though, the period of discussion (even animosity) in the literature can go on for years. In one case that raged for years, the so-called "nature/nurture debate," members of the two extremes attempted to ascribe all or most human behavior to, respectively, genetics or upbringing/environment. The controversy has fizzled out, since by now it is apparent that both genetics and upbringing are involved in most human behavior. Sometimes, as in the case of McClintock's jumping genes, a finding is too divergent from the current state of "knowledge" and is scarcely acknowledged or not accepted for publication. It simply is dismissed, until the weight of evidence from various sources convinces people of the truth of the initial observations. (It took about 30 years for jumping genes to be accepted in the field of genetics—then the work won McClintock a Nobel prize.)

It may seem scarcely believable that scientists can argue over "facts"; surely, either a thing is true or it is not. Fortunately—or unfortunately—theory, state of the art, context, and interpretation play a huge part in our understanding of "truth." Some things are demonstrably true: if you drop this book, it will fall to the floor. However, many (most?) phenomena are subject to context or interpretation. Let's consider how a particular "truth" has changed over time. For some 40,000 years, humans (if they thought about it at all) probably thought the sun moved around the earth. That is, they saw the sun "rise" in the east and "set" in the west, an observation consistent with the explanation that the sun rotated around a fixed earth. Several times in the past few thousand years, different peoples had the ideas and developed instruments necessary to gather data on other celestial bodies. Those data convinced the observers both that the earth is not stationary and that the earth revolves around the sun. However, it was less easy to convince other people. In a particularly well-documented example of confrontation between new and old "truths," in seventeenth-century Europe, Galileo and then-Pope Urban VIII had words over "the truth" about the motion of the earth and the stability of the sun. Those "words" ended with Galileo's being put under house arrest and excommunicated from the Roman Catholic church, so, at least for the moment, the old "truth" held sway. But by now, few people still believe what Pope Urban believed, and the new "truth" has become _the_ truth.

In many and perhaps most such scientific disputes or debates, there is not an immediate or cataclysmic resolution. Debate may continue for long periods, with people contributing ideas and data for both perspectives. Because this curriculum includes doing original research, most of the research topics presented are not resolved. That means a survey of the literature will turn up differing perspectives.

How, then, does a reader differentiate among those perspectives? Practically, start by grouping the literature. For any topic actively under study, there are usually two or more camps or schools of thought with major differences. (There are probably also minor differences, but concentrate on the big ones, at least to begin.) What are the differences? What evidence or reasoning does each group bring in support of its ideas? Does the evidence or reasoning actually support what it claims to support? Are there underlying assumptions that influence those interpretations, but that are themselves not substantiated? Does any of the evidence contradict other evidence, either from the same or from a different camp? Are there flaws in the logic or reasoning? Overall, submit the ideas to rigorous scrutiny. See whether they meet the same criteria we use to develop our own research.

After examining the various positions, we can come to one of three conclusions. One camp seems to us more likely to be correct; one seems likely not to be correct; or there are not enough data to decide which camp is correct.

Fortunately, in each of those cases, our general response is the same, namely, to design a research project incorporating our assessments of the schools of thought. If we agree with a perspective, we build on and extend it. If we disagree, we substantiate the disagreement. This can be direct, through restudy of the things with which we disagree, or indirect, by designing a study that avoids the points of disagreement. In the third case, the case of too few data, we design research to collect more data.

There are several kinds of scientific literature (Table 1). The most scholarly, the type containing formal conversations among scientists, is the primary literature. Here, scientists report their findings directly, and the intended audience is other scientists. Articles are reviewed by other scientists for value, accuracy, logic, and scientific and statistical validity before they are published. That is not the case for secondary and tertiary literature. Those literatures tend to be based on the work of a number of people, are written for a broader, nontechnical audience, and do not routinely get reviewed by scientists. <u>Science</u> and <u>Nature</u> are two widely available primary science journals. <u>Scientific American</u>, <u>The American Scientist</u>, and <u>Natural History</u> are good secondary literature. For the sake of convenience, we group all others in the tertiary category, although there are differences between the Sunday <u>New York Times Science Supplement</u> and <u>Prevention Magazine</u>. But the point is that scientists "talk" to one another in the primary literature, and being part of that conversation requires reading and, ultimately, publishing in that literature.

Table 1 **Types of Scientific Literature**

Type	Examples	Contents
Primary	Scientific journals, meeting proceedings	Direct observations and experimental findings
Secondary	Popular scientific magazines, books	Discussion and synthesis
Tertiary	Newspapers, newsweeklies, popular magazines, some books	Limited reporting and discussion

At some point, however, merely seeing and reading are not enough. The next step is to turn some of our questions into hypotheses, that is, potential or tentative causal explanations for what we have observed, and to find a way to test those explanations experimentally.

TURNING QUESTIONS INTO A RESEARCH PROJECT: STEP 2

A hypothesis is more than a question. It is a testable statement, that is, a potentially answerable question as opposed to an inherently unanswerable one. A hypothesis includes the initial question and whatever information and reasoning can plausibly answer the question. For example, "Why does the air smell different?" is a question. But "We suggest that the air smells different because the new factory upwind of us is releasing 'stuff' into the air" is a hypothesis. It includes the question, information resulting from your reading and asking about air, and some reasoning, and it is testable.

Once we have developed a hypothesis, we must examine it for underlying assumptions and also develop a null and alternate hypotheses.

KEY INGREDIENTS OF A RESEARCH STUDY

Our starting point for a research project or study is the comparison of two observations and seeking an explanation for the observations. Designing a study and experiments just means putting our observations and potential explanations into the framework typically used by scientists. Although such formalization may seem off-putting, in fact, it is very handy. By standardizing the approach to research, scientists can more readily understand each other's work. By identifying component parts of a study, such standardization helps ensure that no components get left out. It is really just a tool, as a recipe is a tool. To bake bread, the key ingredients are flour, a leavening agent, some liquid, and a source of heat. Anything else is up to the baker. In comparing recipes, an experienced breadmaker immediately looks at the key ingredients and discounts "bread" that lacks any one of them. Similarly, there are key ingredients to a scientific study, and an experienced researcher looks for them in reading someone else's work.

We have already said that our observations and potential explanations are "key ingredients," and we have formally defined a potential explanation as a hypothesis. Let us fit all our key ingredients into our scientific framework. Figure 1 shows the progression over time of a research project. It parallels the scientific and common (vernacular) terms for various stages and describes what happens in each stage.

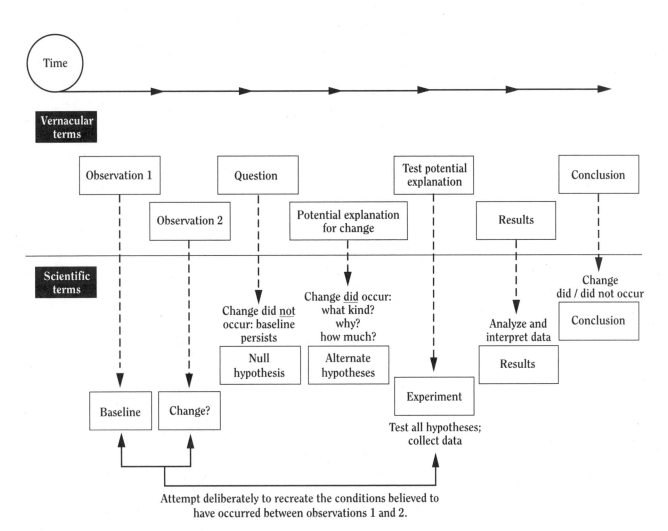

Figure 1. Research: The parallels between the vernacular and scientific descriptions of each stage or key ingredients.

NULL AND ALTERNATE HYPOTHESES

The whole process of assessing or testing for change from the baseline is research. (By "baseline," we mean the status quo, the neutral or normal situation. Sometimes, we must start by describing or defining the status quo. That can be a whole study by itself, likely of the more descriptive type.) The change from the baseline can be deliberate, as in an experiment, or unintended. Our hypotheses specify the factors that might be causing change from baseline, the direction of the change, and, perhaps, the amount of change. The null hypothesis, which is just another name for our original observation, means that there is no change from the baseline. The convention of stating a null hypothesis is one way to try to increase open-mindedness in research. It is the scientific way of saying, "innocent until proven guilty."

The other hypotheses are called alternate hypotheses. They are simply the set of possible explanations for change from the baseline, if change occurs. Hypotheses usually are ranked by how likely each is to explain the potential change under study. (When scientists use the word "hypothesis" without modifying it, they mean their first-ranked, alternate hypothesis. We follow the same convention.) Sometimes, unfortunately, hypotheses also are ranked by the preference of the researcher.

No particular outcome to a study should be preferred, and no particular hypothesis should be preferred. All data must be considered and evaluated, without regard for whether it supports the anticipated conclusions.

UNDERLYING ASSUMPTIONS

As thorough scientists, we cannot stop with null and alternate hypotheses. We also must "push" each hypothesis to find its loopholes, what actually substantiates it, and where it falls short. Making the bases of hypotheses explicit is a challenge, since such bases, expectations, and assumptions often are not conscious in the mind of the researcher. Remember our burglary example? Remember that the dog did not bark? We simply can accept that fact and pass over it. Or we can force ourselves to puzzle about it, to ask why we think the dog should have barked. As we saw, answering that question, making explicit our assumptions about why a dog should bark during a burglary, led to several promising lines of inquiry.

The dog was not present.
The dog was present but did not bark.
The dog was present but did not bark because the robber was not a stranger.
The dog was present but did not bark because it was unconscious, so the robber could have been a stranger.
Would the dog have eaten a drug-laced tidbit from a stranger?

And so on. Each of those explicit statements can be addressed with evidence (data) of a more or less accurate nature. Based on the evidence and its reliability, some of the "statements" can be eliminated. But without the systematic listing and thinking through of each statement and what it implies, how easy it would be to miss something.

The same making explicit of assumptions, expectations, and implications is necessary in a research project.

For instance, with respect to global warming, the null hypothesis is that no systematic warming change is occurring in global temperatures owing to anthropogenic (human-based) factors. That sets up the framework within which the research and data are examined. What is the baseline with respect to global warming, that is, what are "normal" global temperatures? How have they been recorded? Why do we think that temperatures have changed? Has change been gradual or sudden? In the case of gradual change, how much change is statistically significant, that is, more than the chance variations seen in all phenomena? How much change is relevant, that is, affects biological phenomena such as plant growth or physical phenomena such as the melting of icecaps?

Having this framework within which to set global warming is useful in several ways: It clarifies our baseline and comparisons with (hypothesized) deviations from the baseline; it forces us to be explicit and precise about expectations, assumptions, and definitions; it simplifies the job of working out the logic of our explanations.

DESIGNING AN EXPERIMENT

Dissecting out the component parts of a research project makes it much easier to design an experiment. An experiment is the specific procedure by which we test hypotheses. Although it is only one stage in the research process, a true experiment cannot be carried out in the absence of the preceding stages. (That probably is why scientists often use the words "research" and "experiment" interchangeably.)

An experiment reproduces, in a controlled environment, the conditions hypothesized to be responsible for the difference between observations 1 and 2. If we have four possible explanations (alternate hypotheses) for that change, we must test each one separately. Since that is a good deal of work, it is important to rank the hypotheses by likelihood.

An Example

Global warming is beyond the scope of any laboratory experiment, although it can be modeled. Instead, let us consider a slightly more focused topic, namely, ozone. Ozone is a pungent gas with two roles in the environment. Stratospheric ozone absorbs some of the sun's ultraviolet radiation and thus helps protect the earth from its damaging effects. It is also being depleted due to release of chlorofluorocarbons into the atmosphere. However, ground level (also called atmospheric) ozone is increasing. It is produced in a series of chemical reactions involving byproducts of combustion (e.g., car exhaust) and sunlight and is noxious to various forms of life, including humans. How noxious? To which forms of life? How long does ozone stay in the atmosphere? Do combustion engines produce most of its major precursors? What is the quantitative relationship between combustion and ozone production, that is, how much exhaust yields how much ozone? Clearly, much more information is essential to understand the phenomenon and to manage it wisely.

Although there are partial answers to some of the questions we just posed, the information is spotty in many respects. And as an issue, any one of its effects is well beyond the scope of any single group of researchers. However, there also are many component parts that can be addressed fruitfully. For instance, ozone can damage plants, including crops such as corn, soybeans, wheat, and clover. In combination with acid rain, ozone may be responsible for widespread forest decline in parts of the globe subject to air pollution. But we have no systematic information on which plants are damaged, how damage relates to the amount of ozone exposure, or what effects such damage can have in a wild-plant community. So original research might involve documenting specific effects of ozone on local plants. Such data would be a real contribution to the science and understanding of ozone and its effects by helping to untangle some of those effects.

Let us proceed through the stages for designing an experiment. Let our hypothesis be that fewer individual plants belonging to five species of local annual grasses will survive to maturity in an ozone-rich than in an ozone-poor environment. Note that "ozone-poor" represents our baseline, or observation 1, and "ozone-rich," observation 2.

Controlling Variables

To ensure that we are testing only for effects of ozone, we must have a controlled environment. That means we must be certain that conditions for the two sets of plants are identical except for the factor on which the experiment is based, the amount of ozone they receive. The plants must be in same-size pots, with same-mix soil; they must be watered equally often and at the same times of day; they must receive the same amount of light, from the same compass direction, at the same time of day; they must be planted at the same time and in the same way; and the results must be noted at the same times and using standardized criteria. Without such efforts to control the environment, it would be impossible to know whether results were due to the effects of ozone or to the effect(s) of whatever else was also going on. For instance, if the ozone-rich plants were kept at a cooler temperature than the others, we could not say whether differences between the two sets of plants were due to the lower temperature or the higher ozone concentration.

Natural Experiments

We can also take advantage of "natural" experiments. For example, we might capitalize on the ozone produced on a huge highway by planting the plants requiring ozone-rich treatment under the ozone "cloud" produced by that road. (Such a cloud is not necessarily easy to find, since ozone may not be produced at the road or may drift some distance.) Using such a natural setup has the advantage that we do not need to add the ozone to the high-ozone treatment. It has the potential drawback that we can less easily control other factors. Are the low and high ozone sites sufficiently similar with respect to slope, exposure, drainage, soil, wind, other pollutants produced near the road, and so forth, that they are comparable?

Sometimes an experiment does not take into account (control for) all the relevant factors, because not all the factors are known. However, that itself can be a source of learning. It is also another reason for being objective and fair about data collection and analysis. If our results seem "wrong," that is, do not support any of our hypotheses, they may in fact point to something unexpected and even more interesting. For example, the effects of light on the pituitary gland were discovered because a scientist (Nalbandov) studying chicken reproduction developed the habit of working late in the laboratory. He would come back after dinner for another stint at his desk, which was in the same room as some of the chickens, and since it was dark, he would turn on the lights. Chickens in that room bred on a wholly unanticipated cycle, quite different from the cycle of the rest of the animals. Fortunately, he was a good observer. He realized that the difference was that the chickens kept near his desk experienced longer "days" due to the artificial light he used in the evenings. So he developed a set of experiments directly to test his new hypothesis. He was correct, and thus opened up a whole new area in physiology and reproduction. A popular expression sums up this opportunistic and highly fruitful approach to research: "If you get handed lemons, make lemonade."

By now it should be clear that the actual collecting of data is likely the simplest part of an experiment. It is the thinking through of assumptions, expectations, and hypotheses, the experimental design, controlling for all but the test variable, and considerations of sampling that require so much effort.

TESTABILITY OF HYPOTHESES

Some hypotheses cannot be tested directly. Perhaps they are too complex, asked in the wrong way, or are impossible to test, or perhaps they involve factors that it is unethical to test. Examples might be how the earth's gravitational field would vary if we put several moons into orbit around it, or testing whether human language is innate by raising children in isolation on an island to see whether they speak. Complex issues often can be investigated by the construction of models. Issues of science and research ethics tend to be of two sorts. Is the research actually science, that is, does it follow scientific methods, as we are outlining them here? Second, even if it is science by that standard, does the outcome justify the costs? Can the procedures or experiments in conscience be carried out? This latter question is more complex than the former, and the answer is likely to vary with the ethos of the time. Now there is concern among consumers about the ethics or appropriateness of using live animals to test cosmetics; 15 years ago this was a nonissue, about which consumers showed little awareness and even less concern.

An example about which most people would agree is the study in humans of brain function and its recovery. This could be studied directly as it is studied in other animals—by selectively destroying target areas in a human brain, observing the consequences, and attempting to restore normal function through systematic testing of assorted treatments. But we do not do that. Although such research would provide knowledge to benefit people who have suffered brain damage, how can we justify deliberately damaging some humans in order to help others? We cannot, and so such research proceeds indirectly, by assessing brain damage and its attempted restoration in people injured accidentally. Other, less obvious examples include the use of animals in research. Can forensic medicine justify studying the effects on live monkeys of gunshot wounds sustained from different distances? Why not assess the damage to dead animals or to sides of pork and beef and spare live animals? Deliberately to damage a live animal is a grave thing. It should be considered as part of research only when the likely benefits resulting from that damage decidedly outweigh the costs.

Examples of nonscience would include astrology, which does not proceed via scientific methods. Note that people claim various endeavors to be science, even using names like "Scientology." But just because an activity is called science, is carried out by people calling themselves scientists, or even occurs in a laboratory does not make it science.

Although we are about to consider aspects of sampling and experimental design, perhaps it is useful to recap briefly where we are in our overall scheme of "research." We have considered much of the first two sets of our "three threes," as illustrated in Table 2. By this reckoning, we are about to embark on stage 5.

SAMPLING

When we design an experiment or any quantitative procedure, it is important to have a match among the components. For example, how does the time frame of the experiment correspond to the time frame of the phenomenon? Does the number of observations correspond to the magnitude or frequency of the phenomenon? Is the sample representative of the whole, statistically and actually?

Sample Units and Intervals

The units in which human age is expressed make a good illustration of the match between time frames. The unit used—weeks, months, or years—is roughly proportional to the age of the person being considered. Adult life span typically involves decades of years and is universally sampled and expressed in years. Counting birthdays in seconds or even weeks, at 3.2×10^6 and 52 per year, respectively, is impractical. A 20-year-old would be 6.3×10^8 seconds or 1,040 weeks old! But ages of children often are given in years plus parts of years (e.g., 5½), while for infants, months or (briefly) even days are used.

Thus, the unit of time we typically use is proportional to or representative of the total age of the person. The same reasoning applies to sampling: when taking or expressing any measure, it must be representative of the total entity being sampled.

In our discussion of age and units, however, we set ages for the individuals in our examples and worked backward toward appropriate units, that is, we considered adults, youths, and children, and what would be the most appropriate unit of age for each. In real data collection, we do not necessarily know the equivalent of "age" or whether what we are studying is an adult, a youth, or a child. But it is important to know enough about the phenomenon under study to make an intelligent guess at the equivalent of "age" or its range and thus to choose an appropriate unit of measurement. Indeed, a preliminary or descriptive study often is necessary to discover

Table 2   **Overall Research Scheme**

Step 1. Learn

1. Observe and describe.
2. Ask questions and make comparisons.
3. Perform comprehensive literature search of the topic.
    a. Critically read the literature.
    b. Organize an overview of the topic.

Step 2. Test quantitatively (experimental science)

4. Formulate tentative causal explanations (hypotheses) and null and alternate hypotheses.
    a. Articulate the assumptions underlying each hypothesis.
    b. Check that the hypotheses account for all the information available.
    c. Check that the hypotheses are distinct.
5. Test the explanations experimentally or by modeling.
    a. Design experiment(s), controlling for all but the test variable.
    b. Consider sample size for statistical and scientific validity.
    c. Consider time interval between samples for validity.
    d. Consider method(s) of data analysis for ease of use and statistical validity.
6. Collect data.

OR

Step 2. Describe quantitatively (descriptive science)

4. Establish quantitative comparisons, formulate tentative causal explanations.
5. Carry out comparison.
    a. Evaluate the phenomena or items being compared.
    b. Consider sample size (as above).
    c. Consider time interval (as above).
    d. Consider methods of data comparison (as above).
6. Collect data.

Step 3. Analyze and interpret

7. Analyze data, that is, assess experimental results for statistical significance.
8. Organize and interpret results narrowly (quantitatively in the context of the experiment) and broadly (qualitatively in the context of the "big picture").
    a. Assess results for scientific validity.
    b. Compare results obtained to those expected by the null/alternate hypotheses.
    c. Reevaluate hypotheses and reexamine their underlying assumptions.
    d. List questions answered, unresolved questions, and new questions raised.
    e. Draw conclusions.
9. Convey results to other people by preparing results for publication or other dissemination.

things like the "age" equivalent, so we can carry out more quantitative hypothesis testing.

Suppose we were actually sampling human age and that we wished to compare the survivorship of urban dwellers in New Haven, Connecticut, and Calcutta, India. Would we get the information we wanted simply by censusing the population of each city? Not really—what about immigration, emigration, and the birth rate? We could count individual people in some part(s) of each city and re-count them later, asking how many are there, how many have left, how many have died. But when is "later"? How much "later"?

The answer depends partly on which hypothesis is being tested or which question is being asked. Are we suggesting that there is a causal, short-term relationship between a particular month and increased mortality? For instance, does Ramadan, the month-long holy fast, increase mortality among older Muslims for whom all-day fasting is too taxing? Does mortality increase around the Christmas holidays due to drunk driving? Does intense summer heat increase infant mortality or aggression and killings among young street toughs? Alternatively, are we suggesting that longer-term causal influences are involved—nutrition, health care, social support systems? Are lifestyles in the two countries sufficiently similar (or dissimilar) that long-term mortality rates are similar (or dissimilar)? Clearly, if the question is more short-term, the interval between samples, between the "now" and "later" counts of individuals, must be shorter; if the question is about life expectancy, the interval between samples can be longer. Suppose we hypothesize that life expectancy is higher in Calcutta because the social support systems are better there—most of the social support organizations are run by religious orders and thus are ethically rather than politically motivated.

Another aspect of this between-sample interval must also be clarified. Even if we decide that life expectancy is our focus of study, we must specify whose life expectancy—that of infants, children, adults, or all ages of people as a whole? Again, scale, or the fit between sample interval and phenomenon, applies. If we are studying adult survivorship, a 6-month or yearly intersample interval is appropriate. But for infants less than 1 year old, monthly or bimonthly sampling would give more useful information and therefore be more appropriate. Let us select for study the population of children 3 years or younger. We have established that the specific topic (life expectancy), the age group or population of interest (3 years or younger), and the phenomenon (survivorship) are critical aspects of choosing the appropriate sample units and intervals. In addition to units and intervals, we will now consider sample size or number and sample significance or validity, scientific and statistical. Still other aspects to consider are reliability, sources of error, coherence, and relevance. (For an outstanding and comprehensive discussion of sampling, data collection, and experimental design, see Moore 1991.)

Sample Size and Validity

There are two issues to sample size: how representative is our sample of the population as a whole, and how large a sample do we need? To some degree, these issues are inversely related—the more representative our sample is of the whole population, the fewer items from it (up to a point) we need to measure or sample. Or the less representative our sample, the more items we need to sample. In terms of our life expectancy example, that means which children will we follow or sample and how, and how many children do we need to sample and for how long?

To answer those questions, we must refer to our original hypothesis or question and to some statistical considerations. What do we really want to know? How narrow or broad is the basic question: how much do we want to extrapolate from the answer? How broad or narrow is our study population? Does it include all the under-3-year-olds or just the one named Solh? If we ask, "What is the longevity of the single person of 3 years or younger named Solh?" we need measure only that child's life span. But an observation based on so small a "population" cannot be generalized. Since a single child is not representative of all children, data on that child is not representative, is not a valid sample, of the population of children under 3. This "sample" gives us information only about the single person we measured. If we want to know about the longevity of a population, we must define the population and choose a representative sample, just as we defined the phenomenon—age—and chose representative units.

The Study Population

Although we chose our study population as children 3 years or younger, we must be more specific about which children we will include. If our interest is in comparing social services in the two cultures, are certain children more likely to use such services? Do we wish to know survivorship among children in each culture as a function of whether they use these services? Or do we wish to know survivorship of children given that they use those services? How are we defining "use"? It may be that the services are very good once children get to them, but few children do get to them. Since we are interested in "use" in the broadest sense, let's more accurately define our population as all children under 3 or whose family socioeconomic status (income, family composition, and background) makes them likely to use public social services. Note that by focusing the question to this extent, we already have narrowed the ways in which we can extrapolate from our results. They are likely to be of limited utility in understanding longevity of same-age children from other socioeconomic backgrounds or longevity of other-age children from any background. That is not necessarily bad—it is an inevitable consequence of being precise (focused) and objective. And it has the advantage of allowing greater understanding of the specific phenomenon and the causality or causalities involved. Indeed, one reason that thorough research is relatively time-consuming is this inverse relationship between generalizability and precision. To generalize precisely requires the accumulation of a number of focused studies.

Now we can illustrate the possible relationships between a population and samples, using bull's-eyes (from Moore 1991, pp. 24f). If a sample is representative of a population, the sample can stand for the population. That means the results we obtain from sampling are not different from the results we would get if we actually measured all members of our population.

(In fact, some statistical tests and concepts are evaluated by collecting data on whole populations and then comparing those data with data from samples or subsets of the same populations.) For our sample to be representative, our sampling methods must be unbiased and random, our sample must be large enough, and our target population must be clearly defined. In this illustration, the defined population is the eye of the bull's-eye, and each dot represents a sample. A sample usually is described with respect to the population it should represent and with respect to other samples of the same population and made the same way. If a group of samples differs from the population in a consistent way, those samples are biased. If a group of samples differs from the population and they also differ from each other, they are considered to be unbiased or to have low bias. Finally, if the samples in a group are like one another, whether or not they resemble the population, they are considered to show high precision or to be highly precise. The process of sampling can give four possible combinations of these properties—let's look at the properties and the outcomes in Figure 2.

The outcome in Figure 2a is that samples are highly repeatable. That is, they are very similar to one another and precise. However, they are off the target population (the center of the bull's-eye) and off in a particular direction or with a particular bias. That means we have a reliable (repeatable or replicable) sampling procedure, but the sample differs from the population in a consistent way.

A second possible outcome is that the samples are scattershot across the bull's-eye (Figure 2b). That means they are unbiased—they do not fall in any particular direction—but they also are not repeatable; each is rather different from the others.

Another possibility is that the samples are scattershot but in a particular direction (Figure 2c). That is, our samples are scattered so our method is not reliable or repeatable, and our samples are biased.

The ideal outcome is shown in Figure 2d. The samples are unbiased and highly precise or repeatable; they center on the population and are thus representative of it.

Validity and Bias

Now that we have accurately defined our population, we must determine how to sample it in a representative or valid way. That means we must

a. High bias,
high precision

b. Low bias,
low precision

c. High bias,
low precision

d. Low bias,
high precision

Figure 2

sample wisely and be sure our sample is large enough. Suppose we want to know how many blue marbles are in a multicolored population of 200 marbles? To sample the marbles randomly, we pour them all into a bag, shake well, and, without looking, scoop out two dozen marbles. Unlike most things we are likely to sample, the marbles are approximately alike in size, shape, and weight; they differ only in color. They also do not move, and by confining them in a small area, we make our sampling even easier. Most things are not so easy to sample randomly; the evenly-shaken-marbles-in-a-bag are our ideal. How does this translate into our previous example?

People are not going to be in a single place. That means, for instance, that we cannot restrict our sampling to telephone interviews, to a single neighborhood, or to written questionnaires (unless we actually <u>know</u> that all our population families have telephones, live in that neighborhood, and can read). Since it is most unlikely that all three of these conditions (as well as others we have not even mentioned) are true, we must devise techniques that will sample children of all families in our population, including those who do not meet one or another of these conditions.

For a valid sample, one that is representative of its population, adequate sample size can be determined relatively easily. There are excellent guidelines for setting sample size (see Moore 1991, Sokal and Rohlf 1981). Remember that sample size depends on the things we have considered here, on the phenomenon being studied, on which statistical tests will be used, (to some degree) on what is typical in the field involved, and sometimes on purely practical considerations (such as how rarely the phenomenon occurs). For our example, we need to consider the number of children sampled relative to all children in that class. If we sample only five children per city, although the total population of children 3 years in age or under is 20,000 in New Haven and 80,000 in Calcutta, our sample is too small to represent its class accurately for either city. Another way of saying this is that the sample is not valid or significant. (The words "significant" and "significance" have technical meaning in statistics: the assignment of a specific probability or likelihood of occurrence. Unfortunately, in the vernacular they simply mean that something is important or meaningful. It is best to avoid the word unless you are using it with reference to specific statistical probabilities.) We must increase our sample size. To how much? How many children must we sample?

Increasing the size of the sample increases how accurately it reflects the population, but only if sampling is random and unbiased and if the population is much larger than the sample. If both these conditions hold, a sample of 1,500 will give a highly precise representation of the population. However, this size sample is impractical for most of the laboratory experiments considered in this curriculum. Moreover, initial sample size also must be larger than what is ultimately desired, because things always go wrong: people move, some data are suspect (a child's birthday may be misremembered or misreported), and so on. For our survivorship example, if all conditions are met and we take into account that Things Will Go Wrong, an initial random sample of 2,000 should be adequate to give a final sample of 1,500.

Difficulties also can arise if we doubt whether the sample is representative, or if we do not sample randomly. In both cases, increasing the sample size can improve its likelihood of representativeness. Be aware of the problem, be prepared to question your results, and consult a statistics book.

Significance

Once we have collected our data, how can we tell whether our sample (and the conclusion we draw from it) is indeed valid and representative of our population? Statistics, a systematic, math-based way of getting information from data, includes various tests that were devised to answer just that question. An appropriate statistical test or tests can tell us whether our sample is on target or off, as in the outcomes we illustrated with the bull's-eyes. We mentioned that in statistics "significance" has a more precise and narrower meaning than it does in common usage. Commonly, the word means that something is important—it has a remarkably high or low frequency, size, cost, weight, whatever. Statistically, significance refers to the probability or chance that a sample differs from its population, based on whichever statistical test was used.

Different kinds of data and experiments require different statistical tests. To find which are most appropriate for a given experiment, consider the test(s) mentioned in scientific works you have read on the subject. Then use an introductory statistics book to learn more about those tests, the data you will be collecting, and how to match data to a statistical test. See also References, especially Moore 1991.

GOOD DATA: OTHER ISSUES

Whether any data we collect are sound depends on everything we have considered so far, as well as a few other things: the coherence, relevance, and reliability of the data and sources of error. Authors often discuss these issues as part of data analysis, that is, after data have been collected and as a way of interpreting the data, especially if the results are not as expected. However, by considering those issues before data collection and as part of designing our experiment, we can avoid some common pitfalls. That seems preferable to considering and understanding pitfalls when it is too late to avoid them.

Reliability and Sources of Error

Reliability has statistical and other aspects. We considered the statistical aspect in the section Validity and Bias: is a sample a true representation of the population? Other sources of error not related to sampling include Things That Go Wrong , which we also mentioned earlier, including missing data, response errors (misreporting or misremembering), processing errors (typographical and other errors such as computer bugs), effects of the sampling method, and instrument inaccuracy or failure.

Coherence

Coherence refers to whether the data hang together; relevance refers to whether data actually pertain to the subject being studied. Do data hang together logically—are appropriate comparisons being made? In the life expectancy example, are we comparing survivorship between people of different socioeconomic status? Even if we collect exactly the same kind of data, if they are from people who differ in basic ways, we will not be able to say much about influences on survivorship in the two cities, since we will be unable to distinguish between city effects and socioeconomic effects. Inappropriate comparisons can be made in the actual experimental design (as just suggested) or in the interpretation of results. Thus, someone may report temperatures from a site in the midwestern prairies over the past 80 years. The data are sound and the analyses appropriate. But say the author attempts to interpret those analyses by direct comparison with analyses of data recorded in a major urban site that had a tenfold increase in population during the same period. What insights about global warming can come from comparing two such different sites?

A frequent miscomparison is seen in some ecology literature. A phenomenon is reported for a plant or animal species, say, that a given plant species grows as well under ozone levels three times the normal concentration as at normal concentrations. The paper then lists other plant species that also tolerate ozone. From a list like that, which contains no further information about the species, we cannot tell whether it is appropriate or inappropriate to compare them. Were all the plant species raised under the same conditions: same temperature, humidity, photoperiod, and so on? Do they all use the same photosynthetic pathway? How are the plant species related—are they all in the same family or genus? What does it <u>mean</u> that the plants are ozone tolerant? How can we make sense of that information? How can we understand it? Without appropriate comparisons, we have information but not understanding.

Relevance

Relevance has obvious and less obvious meanings in the context of research. The first meaning includes whether the data apply to the topic. For instance, while collecting survivorship data, we may deliberately or incidentally collect data on other aspects of life in New Haven and Calcutta, such as personal habits, family ties, or uses of money. Although those data might be interesting, they cannot be used directly to test our hypothesis. They have no direct relevance to it, no matter how nicely we organize or analyze them.

However, such data can contribute in other ways to our understanding of the topic. In fact, this illustrates a more subtle aspect of relevance—having a feel for the topic and learning everything about it in order to have as complete a picture as possible in which to interpret the data. For instance, we may learn that one of our study cultures condones selective neglect and even infanticide of female infants. Clearly, that will affect the survivorship data, probably for both sexes: girls may be neglected, boys spoiled.

Once you have discussed and agreed on the specific question or hypothesis, the population being sampled and how to sample it, the unit of measurement, approximate sample interval, approximate sample size, desired generalizability of results, and which statistical tests to use, you are ready to set up and carry out experiments and collect data.

ANALYZE AND INTERPRET: STEP 3

Rather than replicate examples and discussions of actual data analysis that can be found elsewhere (see References), we will skip on briefly to consider interpretation and reporting of results.

The biggest part of interpretation is this: what do the results mean? What do they tell us about the test phenomenon? How do they increase our understanding, not just what facts do they contribute? Facts alone are uninteresting and trivial; it is the implications of those facts, the bigger picture to which they contribute. Suppose Nalbandov's chickens had bred on an idiosyncratic cycle? He could have rushed the facts into print or stopped to learn more and try to understand those facts. What did that new breeding cycle imply? How was it controlled? How could Nalbandov find out? And so on. Sometimes interpretation requires thinking about your results; sometimes it requires more research, because you do not have enough information to find a pattern or understanding.

Finally, how about reporting results? Up to this point, your role in our scientific conversation has been that of a good listener, that is, a reader. But now that you have results, you may wish to participate more actively, by sending or actually talking to scientists about your results, by attending conferences, by presenting your results at a conference, by writing up and publishing your results.

There are many ways to get your results out; we mention only a few. You may be working more or less closely with other schools, with scientists from a university, with a government organization such as the EPA, with a nongovernment organization such as the Audubon Society, or with a local body such as your local waterways management committee. How you proceed depends on the nature of your arrangement with those persons or groups. For instance, say a scientist offers you use of some equipment or space in a laboratory. In exchange, that person may expect to incorporate your data into his or her next paper, with or without formal acknowledgment of your efforts. Or, he or she may expect to publish with you as co-author, or that you will publish independently but with acknowledgment of the support you received. Still other possibilities might be that you are adding data to an ongoing, long-term study, so your work will be included in the whole. Or you may have observations and records of some phenomenon you want to make available to others, so you publish them as such.

There are also several kinds of scientific publications, each corresponding to a type of study. From least to most sophisticated they might be ranged something like this:

- A **note** presents an observation and may raise a question. An example is reporting that baleen whales were seen ingesting sea birds as well as their target food of krill when they lunge up through and out of the ocean. Although brief, a note must include the frequency of occurrence and over what period of time; the names of the species involved; where the incident(s) were seen; and why they are of interest. This example is of interest because no one thinks of baleen whales as eating sea birds or of the seabirds, some of which stay near the whales to catch fish the whales disturb, as possibly paying a price for their proximity to the whales.

- A longer descriptive **paper** is based on more than a few observations and considers the matter it reports in more depth.

- A full-blown **test of a hypothesis** must include all the parts of a research study outlined in this chapter.

- A **theoretical paper** might have no data at all, or none of the author's collecting, but makes a point on theoretical grounds.

It is important to choose an appropriate journal for each type of study and for the topic of the study. One way to find the appropriate journal for your study is to determine where studies similar to yours have been published.

References

Bashaw, W. L. 1969. Mathematics for Statistics. New York: John Wiley & Sons.
A good refresher or reference book for basics such as exponents, logs, ratios, fractions.

Hairston, Nelson G., Sr. 1989. Ecological Experiments—Purpose, Design, and Execution. New York: Cambridge University Press.
Logistics, techniques, etc.

Huff, Darrell. 1982. Lying with Statistics. New York: W. W. Norton & Co.
A slim book which gets people thinking about precision and quantitative relationships with an approach which combines accuracy and amusing examples.

Keller, Evelyn Fox. 1985. Reflections on Gender and Science. New Haven: Yale University Press.
Chapter 8 is a more concise treatment than Kuhn of "truth" and how it grows.

Kuhn, Thomas S. 1970. The Structure of Scientific Revolutions. Chicago: University of Chicago Press.
Interesting, slightly windy discussion of some "truths" in the field of physics and how they have changed over time.

Lehner, Philip N. 1979. Handbook of Ethological Methods. New York: Garland STPM Press.
Includes logistics, techniques, technologies, and some discussion of data analysis as well.

Moore, David S. 1991. Statistics: Concepts and Controversies. 3rd ed. New York: W. H. Freeman and Co.

———. 1991. Instructor's Guide. New York: W. H. Freeman and Co.
Outstanding discussion of sampling and procedures. Less comprehensive than Sokal and Rohlf but more detailed for what it covers and directed at the intelligent non-academic reader.

Sokal, Robert R., and F. James Rohlf. 1981. Biometry. 2nd ed. New York: W. H. Freeman and Co.
This is the bible of statistical methods and reasoning. It can be overwhelming at first look, but is quite readable and an outstanding reference book.

TECHNIQUE
ANIMAL BEHAVIOR

The general public believes that all of the common aspects of nature are already well known. Nothing could be further from the truth in the field of bird behavior. This was one of the biggest surprises to me when I started writing this book. . . . Even with the birds that have been well studied, such as the Song Sparrow, Red-Winged Blackbird and Mallard, there are still far more mysteries than answers . . . In fact, in most cases there has not been enough observation to know for sure what is individual behavior and what is the general behavior of the species.

—Donald Stokes, <u>Bird Behavior</u>, Vol. 1

What Donald Stokes says about bird behavior is also true for all other groups of animals. Careful observation of almost any animal over time will produce interesting and perhaps significant information and insight. The key is to prepare for your observations, to record them in a useful way, to think about them, and to use them to answer questions.

Animals do a lot of their moving around in response to other animals, so it is important to do some planning before you go out to take data. This technique suggests how you can plan for any project that involves watching animal behavior. You might practice by watching a pet, a brother, a sister, a parent, a friend, or kids on the playground.

BEFORE COLLECTING DATA: OBSERVATIONS AND QUESTIONS

As with any research, before you collect data, start by deciding what you are looking for. That does not mean to ignore everything not on your list; it does mean you can choose methods and equipment that will help you take the data you need and then make additional (or simultaneous ones) observations.

List some questions about your research. You may need to start with the simplest question: does the animal occur in the study area? If so, do you know how to recognize it? Are there other animals of its type in the area that might be confused with it? For example, someone interested in sparrows needs to know how to tell one kind from another, preferably by song as well as by appearance. If the animal is hard to see because it hides most of the time, you may have to look for signs—tracks, scat, leftovers from meals, burrows or nests, and similar traces.

If you know your animal is present, you are ready to ask some ecological questions. It is not hard to come up with good questions, but some good questions are hard to collect data on! You may have such questions in mind. If not, think about the animal's lifestyle and life-cycle, and think of questions about each kind of activity or life stage. For example, suppose you want to work on an insect, and you are considering the common cricket *(Grylla humilis)*. Your question list might include any of the following.

Interactions with other animals and with plants: do you always find the cricket in the company of another kind of animal or plant? Does it have a home territory or range?

Environmental constraints: where does the cricket occur? For example, must it be near water? Does it live on its food (i.e., is the cricket a leaf eater)?

Describe its life stages: early juvenile, late juvenile, reproductive adult, postreproductive.

Describe its life activities: foraging, defense, courtship and reproduction, social relations.

Once you have an idea of your interest, you can think about how to go about investigating it.

BECOME FAMILIAR WITH THE ANIMAL

<u>Start slowly</u>. If you are not familiar with the animal, you may want some sessions in which you just observe it, take notes, and think about what you see.

How do individuals of the species differ from one another? That includes appearance (color, markings, shape, size, notches in the ears, broken tails, etc.), age (can you tell the difference among adults, babies, juveniles?), and sex (can you tell the difference between males and females?).

Does it move much? All the time? Every few minutes? Once or twice an hour? Note the weather: sunny? Cool? Very cool? Very hot? Windy?

Does the animal stay in one small area or move freely? If it stays in one area or its movements seem limited to just a few areas (out of all the possible areas it might go), does it seem to center on certain plants or features (such as rocks or holes)?

What does it do? Eat, dig, fly, clean itself, interact with others of its kind? Hide? Communicate? How do you define each of those activities?

Such exploratory observations give you a feeling for how quickly the animal moves and how far, how easy it is to see its activities, how close you can get to it, and so on. Then you can plan a more realistic and effective study (because you have some idea of when and how to observe the animal), or you might decide to study a different species, because this one is too secretive, too hard to follow, or too active when you cannot be.

"CHUNKING": KINDS OF BEHAVIORS

When you first watch an animal, it can be hard to sort out the different actions you see. As you get to know the species, you begin to identify acts, actions, or behaviors. That practice often is called "chunking," that is, breaking up a stream of information into manageable chunks. The next level is to break manageable chunks into meaningful chunks. Remember, it is essential that you see **what** the animal does. **Why** it does it is quite another question, which can be answered only by careful observation, identification, and recording of what it actually does.

The question of meaningful chunks—what is a meaningful chunk and how do you know—is itself interesting and hugely important. Much behavioral research is flawed by unclear or inappropriate chunking. Often researchers mix chunk levels, interpret or categorize behaviors or actions without enough data, or make unconscious assumptions about chunks.

EXAMPLES

Picking Up Stuff

Suppose we observe a common sparrow. A first chunk level might be a single physical act (the bird picks up something in its bill). Your understanding of that act is enriched when you see <u>what</u> the bird picks up (a peanut or some twigs). And you hit a third chunk level with some analysis of the act, given what was picked up. If the species is unstudied, you cannot interpret the act until you see what happens next. Does the sparrow eat the twigs? Does it eat the peanut? If either happens, you can categorize that act of picking up as food gathering. But you must not <u>assume</u> that picking up stuff is food gathering—you must see the bird eat what it has picked up.

What about those twigs? You might see the bird carry the materials into a tree hole, then emerge empty-beaked. Since it is unlikely that the bird is feeding a tiny horse in there, you might call the activity collecting twigs and grasses. The bird probably is building a nest, but to be very strict about it, until you actually look in the hole and see a nest, you should not make that assumption.

Movement

Let's consider another example. Say the bird sometimes spreads its wings or tail or hops about, moving from one place to another. You may not know why the bird is doing that, but clearly motion or locomotion are taking place. You may see that when the bird is around other sparrows, it spreads its tail or wings but apparently does not change location. Perhaps such motion is a kind of communication, not locomotion. Only by seeing acts over and over, and noting what acts come before and after can you understand what your sparrow is doing. Some acts happen rarely, so they are hard to chunk; sometimes you might see acts happen in a new sequence, which causes you to rethink some previous chunking you did. That is OK; that is what happens when you watch animals.

CATEGORIES

As you chunk things, you can also think about your categories: whether you have left out any, whether some actions should be separated or other actions categorized together. For example, you may decide after watching a bird species for a while that the birds communicate in several ways: by sound, by gestures and body language, by color. Mammals often use all those, plus odors. Fish do not seem to make much use of odors, and most fish seem not to use sounds, but they do use colors (including color changes) and body position to signal to other members of their species. Insects also make use of all these means of communication.

A special kind of communication also occurs between species, most often between animal prey and possible predators. The bright colors of some snakes, frogs, and butterflies advertise poison; the rattle of a rattlesnake is a warning; and some moths "flash" large spots on their wings to startle bird predators.

General categories you can expect from other experiences or work in this curriculum are reproduction (mating, and care of young), feeding, resting, grooming—what else? By what actions does your species accomplish those general categories? How much time does it spend on any activity or category compared to another species? Compared to you?

If you are interested in a particular kind of animal (fish, birds, amphibians, insects), after you have watched for a while, look at a book on the behavior of that kind of animal, to see how other observers have chunked the organism's behavior.

COLLECTING DATA

How long should you watch? What should you note? Do you have to write down <u>everything</u>? Fortunately, no. You sample in some way and note rare or unusual events as they occur.

A DATA TABLE

You already have in mind the chunks you have identified. You already have some question(s) or a hypothesis. Using your chunks, make a data table, perhaps with your chunks across the top (the rows) and space for time down the leftmost column.

Acts	Abbreviations	Acts	Abbreviations
Forage	Fr	Groom self	Gs
Eat	E	Groom other	Go
Fly	F	Vocalize	V
Hop	H	Enter nest hole	Enh
Walk	W	(with or without object)	
Sit	S	Leave nest hole	Lnh
Collect nest material	Cnm	Fight with ____	Fw ____

It also helps to put a space at the top or the bottom for the date, location, page number, and the observer's initials (yours). You might need abbreviations to fit all your chunks across the page—something like this:

Sample Data Table

Date: _____ Place: _____ Observer: _____

Behavior:	Fr	E	F	H	W	S	Cnm	Gs	Go	V	Enh	Lnh	Fw ____
Time:													
10:00													
10:01													
10:02													
10:03													

OR

10:00:00													
10:00:10													
10:00:20													
10:00:30													

Page ____ of ____

Figure 1. Sample data table.

Since you have already spent some time watching your animal, you have decided that hopping and walking are distinct actions; you want to know how many kilocalories per day the sparrow uses, and hopping is energetically more expensive.

"Fight" is another high-level category. Are you sure you can tell the difference between fighting and playing or courtship? Would you call fighting by another name if it were an interaction over food or territory (i.e., competition)? You can make some of those decisions later in the data analysis, but you need chunks to start.

If you are doing an ethogram (a complete inventory of all behaviors performed by the animal, plus the amount of time spent on each), you need to include all your chunks. If you are doing a narrower study, include only the relevant chunks.

Make sure you keep several copies of your abbreviations and their meanings!

AN EXAMPLE: PUMAS

The following list is from an actual study of play and social behavior in three zoo-raised puma cubs.

Behaviors:
Nurse
Wrestle (name of other cub)
Approach (name of other cub or object)

Be approached (name of other cub)
Chase (name of chaser and chased)
Be chased (name of other cub)
Move away from (name of other cub)
Be moved away from (name of other cub)
Jump on (name of cub or object)
Be jumped on (name of other cub)
Jump off (name of cub or object)
Play with object (name)
Rest
Sleep
Walk

Over the 2-month study, the three puma sisters showed significant differences in the amount of time they spent doing most of the things in the list. For example, one cub (Calamity Jane) started most of the chases and wrestling and spent the most time wrestling and the most time nursing. Another cub (Saguaro) was most often chased and spent the least amount of time nursing. The third cub (Susanna) played with the toys in the cage the most. (The study was designed to test the hypothesis that play between two young animals has a predictable pattern, that is, their behaviors occur in predictable statistically significant sequences. The hypothesis was supported by the data. A walking cub is likely to approach or be approached by a second cub, to jump or be jumped on, to wrestle, and to withdraw or to be left. If the first cub withdraws, she is likely to be chased or approached, and the cycle repeats; if the first cub is left by the second, the first cub likely plays with a toy or rests.)

SAMPLES AND SAMPLE FREQUENCY

Researchers generally do not observe and record everything an animal does for a long period of time. Rather, they make detailed observations on only some behaviors or for some periods of time. Your questions will shape how much time you spend collecting data. Following are some possible ways you can plan your schedule.

Choose only certain times of day to observe or a few times throughout the day. (The pumas were most active early and later in the day, so those were good times to watch them.)

An important decision is whether to keep a continuous record of everything done by a single animal or to sample what the animal is doing, say, every 10 or 30 or 60 seconds. Sampling means to take data on a subset of all the animal's actions at some regular time intervals. (One study of lemurs showed no significant differences between data collected at 10-second intervals and those same data analyzed at 60-second intervals, i.e., using only every sixth observation. If there is no difference, how much easier on the observer to record once a minute rather than six times a minute.)

If you are observing a social animal that is part of a group (like the puma cubs), you can collect data on your animal and others, for example, by noting what your individual is doing, say, every 60 seconds, and noting what other members of the group are doing every 5 minutes. Such scanning of the whole group enriches the data on your individual animal by providing some context or background. If you are observing social interactions, you likely will get data on other group members anyway, as they interact with your animal.

Take data only when the animal is within a certain area.

Take data only when the animal is doing certain kinds of things: is near its young, is near others of the same species, is engaging in the behaviors relevant to your question.

NOTES

Make sure you write down enough information that you can make sense of the data later on without having to rely on your memory. Ideally, the notes should make sense to another researcher who was not observing with you. Both these things will be much easier if you use a data table rather than longhand notes. You will also have some longhand notes about things not on your table.

The notes should be readable. Abbreviations can be a huge help in getting a lot of information down quickly, but you have to be able to read them later! If you use abbreviations, be sure to keep copies of them and their meanings in several places.

Note questions to yourself for further exploration (to ask your teacher, to look up in a reference book, to investigate another time).

Make sketches if they make the notes clearer. Do not worry about producing "good" drawings—they should just be meaningful to someone who is watching that kind of creature.

Draw a rough map, including instructions to yourself for finding the place again. Note a couple of really distinct features that you will recognize easily.

AFTER DATA COLLECTION

As soon as you can after the data collection, read over your notes. Do not change what is written, but you may want to add things. For example, make sure all abbreviations are understandable. If you are reminded of things you noticed but did not write down, jot them in the margins or at the end of the day's notes.

Were there things that confused you or that made you want to see more? Are there new questions you want to follow up now or in the future?

Did your observation plan work? Did you have too much to do or too little? Did you need optical instruments, get cold, forget a watch? Note anything that will help you interpret the data you took and get through the next field session.

Try to use what you saw to move your research along. You may get the answer to your question on the first try. More likely, you will learn something that you hoped to see, but also things that you did not expect, cannot make sense of, never imagined. Formulate a hypothesis, make a prediction, set a new goal, revise your schedule.

After you have some or a lot of notes on the behavior you are studying, start writing your report. For suggestions about how to deal with your data and how to represent it, see the **Technique: Data** and the **Technique: Preparing a Presentation**.

IN THE FIELD: MATERIALS

Before you go out, assemble your field supplies:

Notebook, data tables

Pencils (more than one)

Small pencil sharpener (if you are not using mechanical pencils)

Optical equipment (Do you need binoculars? A hand lens?)

Camera (optional)

If you are to be out for a while, make sure you have water. If you will be out for more than a couple of hours, bring some kind of food. Unless you are going out for a short time, be prepared for the weather. Listen to the weather report and make sure you bring appropriate clothing, sunscreen, something to sit on, rain gear, sun hat, and so forth. Remember that on cool days, if you are sitting still, you will get cold, so bring extra clothing. If it is warm and sunny, you will get hot and thirsty faster than you might imagine. Even on a cloudy day, you can get sunburned, so hats and sunscreen are important.

Settle in, become part of the scene, and watch. Enjoy!

TECHNIQUE
DATA

"Data" is the plural form of "datum," a Latin word that means "what is given." In English, "data" essentially means "facts." You have been dealing with data all your lives but probably do not realize it.

WHAT ARE DATA?

Objects exist in the world, regardless of whether humans interact with them or think about them. Data, however, do not exist until humans abstract information about real objects in the world. We create data when we describe real objects.

HOW TO USE THEM

If you want to inform someone about a particular object, you can bring the object to the person (or the person to the object). Alternatively, you can abstract some information about the object and bring those abstracted data to the person. Our example of dragonfly behavior helps demonstrate some of the different forms that data can take.

DRAGONFLY BEHAVIOR: AN EXAMPLE

Imagine sitting by a secluded pond early in the morning. You are fishing, but nothing is biting, so you have plenty of time to watch the world. You notice a twig poking out of the water. Your gaze keeps returning to the twig until, a couple of hours later, you see a large, blue dragonfly land there. You are quite certain that the twig was unoccupied until then—the blue dragonfly is the first creature you have seen all morning. As you watch the insect, you are struck by its beauty. You check your watch—only to discover that you had grabbed a child's wrist thermometer from the kitchen table. It is 20°C when the dragonfly lands on the twig.

A few minutes later, a second dragonfly arrives. This one is red and noticeably smaller than the first dragonfly. It attempts to dislodge the blue dragonfly from the twig but fails. The day is warming up, and you note that the temperature is 21°C. The red dragonfly flies off, but every so often you notice it swooping through the air. Perhaps an hour after the first dragonfly's arrival, a green dragonfly flies by the twig. This one appears to be intermediate in size between the other two. Again, the newcomer attempts—and fails—to dislodge the large blue dragonfly. Glancing at your thermometer, you find that the temperature is now 25°C. Eventually, as the day gets even warmer (you still have not gotten any nibbles, but you are having a great time watching the dragonflies!), the large blue dragonfly takes off and flies into the forest beside the pond. The temperature has now reached 28°C. The small red dragonfly arrives and perches on the stick, but almost immediately the medium-size green one appears. The two insects fly around each other rapidly for a few seconds, then the red one takes off; the green dragonfly has dislodged the red one and assumed the perch.

Impressed by the dragonflies' behavior and acrobatic skills, you are overcome by the urge to discuss the experience with a friend. You gather your fishing gear and rush off—full of data. What types of data did you collect?

TYPES OF DATA

There are three major types of data: categorical (or qualitative or attribute) data, quantitative (or measurement) data, and ranked data. In the dragonfly example, you recorded each of these types of data.

CATEGORICAL DATA

Categorical (or qualitative or attribute) data are used to describe attributes that form discrete and nonoverlapping categories. When you describe a dragonfly as blue, red, or green, you are treating color as categorical data. Each dragonfly can belong to one and only one of the color categories. The categories cannot be ordered in any way or treated as quantitative information. If you were able to observe the dragonflies up close, you could also determine their sex, another example of categorical data, since an individual can be either male or female but not both.

QUANTITATIVE DATA

Quantitative (or measurement) data are measured numerically, according to a specific scale. With the thermometer, you measured the air temperature as each dragonfly arrived or departed—temperature is an example of quantitative data. With an insect net, a ruler, and quick reflexes, you could have caught the dragonflies and measured their lengths, which would have given you a second set of quantitative data.

RANKED DATA

Ranked data are ordered in some fashion, but they are not measured quantitatively. In the dragonfly example, the blue dragonfly arrived first, the red dragonfly arrived second, and the green dragonfly arrived third, so time of arrival is ranked data. (If you had had a watch with you, you could have noted the time of each insect's arrival and treated that as quantitative data.) Similarly, by noting the relative sizes of the dragonflies (large, small, and intermediate), you created a second ranking scheme. Finally, the

423

behaviors of the dragonflies can be ranked: the large blue one was able to retain the perch despite the efforts of the red and green dragonflies. The green one, however, was able to replace the red one. Although you need to collect more data, you can see the beginnings of a ranking of ability to retain the perch: the blue dragonfly is best, the green one is second best, and the red one is last. We typically use ranked data in situations in which we cannot measure a quantity or decide not to do so (if we think that the measurements will add little to your understanding).

DISPERSION OR VARIATION AMONG DATA POINTS

When summarizing a data set that consists of multiple independent data points, most people begin by calculating the mean, or average, of the data points. When we analyze quantitative data, however, it also is crucial to calculate some measure of the dispersion, or spread, of the data. Even though it may be impractical here to explore fully the topic of dispersion in datasets, it is important that we appreciate its importance. (For more information on averages, see Exploration 2 in **Module 2**, **Chapter 7**.)

The simplest description of dispersion is the range, the difference between the highest and the lowest values in a data set. The two data sets listed below have the same mean and the same number of data points. However, the ranges of the two data sets are quite different, since the lengths of the blue dragonflies are much more widely dispersed than those of the red dragonflies.

	LENGTHS OF RED DRAGONFLIES (CM)	LENGTHS OF BLUE DRAGONFLIES (CM)
	2.6	2.3
	2.6	2.4
	2.6	2.5
	2.6	2.6
	2.7	2.7
	2.8	2.8
	2.8	2.9
	2.8	3.0
	2.8	3.1
Mean length	2.7 cm	2.7 cm
Range	0.2 cm	0.8 cm
Number	9	9

When we present quantitative data, we should always give some indication of how much variation exists in the data, even if we say only "Lengths of red dragonflies ranged from 2.6 to 2.8 cm, with a mean of 2.7 cm; lengths of blue dragonflies ranged from 2.3 to 3.1 cm, with a mean of 2.7 cm."

Ecologists typically use statistical measures such as standard deviations and variance to describe dispersion in a data set, but these may be too involved for your first data analyses. Scientific calculators can calculate these measures for small data sets; you may wish to explore their use.

TECHNIQUE
PREPARING A PRESENTATION

For science to be effective and useful, it must be communicated well. That is why scientists write so many articles for their fellow scientists (as well as for the general public) and hold conferences to share their findings.

As part of your doing science, you should learn how to make a good public presentation of a scientific study. Such communication skills will also be useful to you in other contexts throughout your life, so do not feel your efforts are wasted if you do not plan a career in science.

1. **Choose a good title.**
   Your title should be as short as possible, but still let the audience know what you studied. A bit of humor is fine, if you are sure your topic is clear.

   ### Examples
   Testing the hypothesis that height is a good predictor of weight in gorillas
   Variations in daily foraging patterns: Does the early bird always get the worm?

2. **Tell your listeners what you were trying to learn when you began your investigations.**
   You may have been testing a hypothesis, or perhaps just exploring a certain phenomenon. Whatever the case, let your audience know what you hoped to do. If it is relevant, tell your audience about key pieces of background, such as important theories or previous research on the topic. This part of your talk is like the Introduction section of a scientific paper.

   ### Example
   This study began with a question: are height and weight related in gorillas? If they are related, that would be useful for field research, since it is difficult to weigh wild, live gorillas, but it is relatively easy to estimate their heights. Because data on chimpanzees and humans, the closest relatives of gorillas, show that height and weight are closely correlated, we hoped—predicted—that the same might be true for gorillas. Thus, we set out to test the specific hypothesis that height is a good predictor of weight in gorillas.

3. **Tell your listeners the relevant aspects of the methods you employed.**
   You do not want to tell them every single detail of what you did—you do not have time for that. But sketch out your methodology for them. If they want the details, they can read them after you publish your paper. This part of your talk is like the Methods section of a scientific paper.

   ### Example
   We studied captive populations of the mountain gorilla at ten zoos in the United States. In all, we studied seventeen female gorillas and fourteen males. Each individual was measured for height with a standard tape measure and weighed on a Bauhaus 1000 Commercial Scale. The data were analyzed on an Orange IIu computer using the Datanalysister software package.

4. **Tell your listeners the results of the investigation.**

    What major analyses did you perform? Typically your results will be quantitative, that is, they will involve numbers. If possible, present statistical tests to show whether your results were significant (such tests may be beyond the scope of your class, but they are useful to learn and use.

    Prepare visual aids such as graphs and charts to show your results. People absorb information much better if they see patterns as well as hear them. Your visual aids can be on the blackboard, large pieces of paper, overhead projection transparencies, or slides—but they must be clear to all of your audience. Make sure text is large enough to be seen by people in the back of the room. This part of your talk is like the Results section of a scientific paper.

    Example

    We decided to analyze data for the two sexes separately, since it seemed that, on average, male gorillas are much heavier than females. As you can see in Graph 1, the weight of male gorillas ranged from 80 kg to 140 kg and averaged 103 kg. Male height ranged from 1.30 m to 1.63 m, with an average of 1.41 m. We found that as height increased, so did weight. There were, however, several exceptions: Gordon, from the San Diego Zoo, is very heavy for his height.

5. **Interpret your results for your audience.**

    In many ways, this is the most important and most difficult part of your presentation. You need to help your audience understand what your results <u>mean</u> and how they can (and cannot) be used. Discuss any problems you ran into and how you might have improved the project. Also briefly mention directions in which you might follow up this research. This part of your talk is like the Discussion section of a scientific paper.

    Example

    In both sexes we found a close relationship between a gorilla's height and its weight. These results will enable field researchers to estimate gorilla weight from height data (which they can gather relatively easily). The relationship between height and weight is not perfect, however. Several older individuals from two zoos were heavier than younger individuals of the same height. If we pursue this research further, we will study a larger number of gorillas and pay special attention to the role of age in determining weight. We would also like to compare the feeding policies at different zoos, since they may affect gorilla weight.

6. **In all parts of your presentation be brief but clear.**

    Scientific presentations at conferences are often limited to 10 or 15 minutes. These presentations frequently cover the results of many months of study and analysis, so the speakers must make every word and visual aid count. You, too, will have a limited amount of time for your presentation, so do not spend time on unessential information!

7. **Make your visual aids easy to understand.**

    Your graphs, charts, and text visuals can really help your listeners absorb what you are discussing. In addition, do not be afraid to use text aids to emphasize crucial points.

    Example

    Taller gorillas are heavier (and older ones are too!).

TECHNIQUE
CALORIMETRY

This Technique describes a simple, accurate way to determine the energy (calorie) content of a substance. Once you learn this procedure, you can use it to determine the energy content of almost anything that can be burned. Thus, it is exceptionally useful for studies of energy in ecosystems, especially energy stored and transferred through plants, organisms, litter, dung, and so on.

For example, say you know how many members there are in a population and how much and what they eat per day, month, season, whatever. By finding the caloric value of that food and doing a little arithmetic, you have a great deal of information about that population's energy flow and how it fits into its community.

Note that the process of oxidation by combustion is different from digestion as carried out by organisms, which occurs largely by way of enzymatic and chemical oxidation. We are using combustion merely as a way to measure energy content.

RATIONALE AND OVERVIEW

The basic method of calorimetry (determining energy or caloric content by burning something and measuring the heat it produces) is as follows:

1. Dry and weigh the sample.
2. **Burn the sample in a calorimeter (Figure 1) in an atmosphere with sufficient** oxygen.
3. Measure the heat yielded by measuring the change in temperature of a known volume of water.

The first step is to prepare and standardize all samples by drying and weighing them. Drying is especially important for things made up of a lot of water (e.g., lettuce, grass) and less important for "drier" items like seeds and nuts. To compare amounts of energy in different things, we need standard amounts of the stuff. So 1 ounce of lettuce that has been dried for 24 hours at 100°C is comparable to 1 ounce of chicken dried for the same amount of time at the same temperature. (An ounce of undried lettuce would <u>look</u> like much more but actually be less lettuce, since most of it is water. It would not burn well either.)

Burn the samples in an atmosphere with enough oxygen to support combustion, Normal air will do. (Have you ever tried to burn wood or charcoal that was packed tight? Not enough oxygen.)

The last step is to measure the amount of energy released as the burning breaks the bonds of the sample and forms new bonds between the carbon

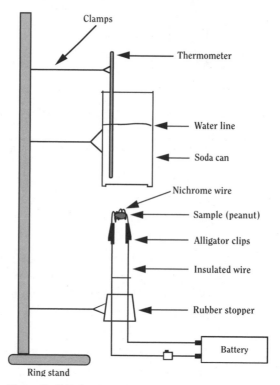

Figure 1. Calorimeter setup.

in the sample and the oxygen in the atmosphere. The released heat raises the temperature of a known amount of water suspended above the flames, by causing the water molecules to move around faster. That increased movement is reflected on the thermometer in the water by an increase in temperature and a higher reading.

The sample is burned under a soda can that contains a known amount of water and a thermometer. The sample can be ignited using a match or a Nichrome wire–battery power system. As the sample burns, the water in the soda can increases in temperature. The "before" and "after" water temperatures show how much energy was in the sample. (Technique from Markow, 1992.)

MATERIALS AND PREPARATION

Safety

> **WARNING**
>
> You will be working with burning matches, burning samples, and perhaps a Nichrome wire–battery ignition system that gets very hot.
>
> DO NOT PERFORM THIS TECHNIQUE IN AN OXYGEN-ENRICHED ATMOSPHERE.
>
> DO NOT ALLOW THE TWO NICHROME WIRES OR ALLIGATOR CLIPS TO TOUCH EACH OTHER.
>
> DO NOT TOUCH ANY BURNING, HEATED, OR RECENTLY BURNING ITEMS WITH BARE FINGERS OR ANYTHING BUT APPROPRIATE TOOLS.
>
> WEAR SAFETY GOGGLES DURING THE PROCEDURE.

In Advance

Prepare samples, if necessary. If you are using wet materials (especially plant materials), dry them in a 100°C oven until they stop losing weight (i.e., have reached a constant weight). For the sample sizes (0.5–1.0 g) used with this version of the calorimetry technique, 24 hours is likely enough time for complete drying. Use samples of 0.5–1.0 g. That amount is easy to weigh and handle and will have enough energy to raise the water temperature noticeably. Measure the mass of the dry sample to 0.01 g. ("Constant weight" means, therefore, that between one weighing and the next there is no change greater than 0.01 g.)

Materials

- **Scale** sensitive to 0.01 g
- **Drying oven**
- **Calorimetry apparatus** (Figure 1), which includes for each setup:

  1 ring stand

  Thermometer

  Soda can

  3 clamps, 1 each for the cork supporting the sample or the Nichrome coil, the soda can with water, and the thermometer
- **Nichrome Wire–battery power system** (described in Table 1) **or matches**

Table 1

Nichrome Wire–Battery Ignition System

ITEM	DESCRIPTION	WHERE WE OBTAINED IT
Ignition coil	12- to 15-cm coil of 22-gauge Nichrome wire	Edmund Scientific; cost approx. $20 per roll
Wire	12-gauge household electrical wire	Hardware store
Alligator clips		Hardware or electronics store
Battery	7.2 V, 1.2 amp hour NiCad battery pack	Radio Shack P/N 23-230; cost approx. $15
Recharger	NiCad battery recharger (120 V AC @ 10 amp in, 7.2 V DC @ 0.4 amp out)	Radio Shack P/N 23-231A, cost approx. $10

NOTE: Recharging the battery

The battery can deliver 1.2 amp hour before needing a recharge. Thus, it will need to be recharged after about (1.2 amp hour) / (8 amp × 1 hour/60 minutes) = 10 minutes of use. The battery can be recharged fully in 4–5 hours with an AC recharger.

- **Samples**, dried and weighed
- **Goggles**
- **Tongs or tweezers**
- **Oven mitt**
- **Fireproof work surface** (laboratory bench or heat-resistant pad)

Procedure

1. **Prepare the samples.**

   Dry all samples to a constant weight. Use sample sizes of 0.5–1.0 g.

2. **Decide which method you will use to burn the sample: with matches or with a Nichrome wire and a battery.**

   a. **Matches.** Materials that burn easily (e.g., paper, wood, peanuts) can be lit with a match. Use paper matches since they do not contribute much heat to the final total of match plus sample. (How can you calculate the heat contributed by the match alone? Just run the experiment without a sample, note the change in water temperature, and subtract that amount from the temperature change of the match plus sample.)

   Mount the sample on a wire (or paper clip) loop stuck into a cork or rubber stopper (Figure 2).

   b. **Nichrome wire–battery ignition system.** A somewhat more elegant approach is to ignite the sample with a hot coil of Nichrome wire (Figure 3). We used a 12- to 15-cm length of 22-gauge Nichrome wire, wrapped into a coil with 3–10 turns. You can wrap the wire directly around a sample or force the sample between the coils. Use a NiCad battery pack (normally used to power radio-controlled toy cars) to heat the coil to an orange-yellow heat (approximately 900–1,100°C), which will take only a few seconds. Samples that are easy to ignite will burst into flame in 5–10 seconds and then continue to burn on their own. **Turn off the coil once the sample is burning.**

   Less flammable samples will burn better if the coil is left hot until the sample is completely burned. Doing that, however, seriously affects the results because the heat added by the coil is considerable and must be subtracted from the total. For example, heating the coil draws approximately 8 amps from the battery, with about a 4 volt drop across the coil,

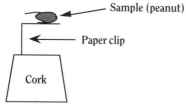

Figure 2. Mounting of sample for ignition with matches.

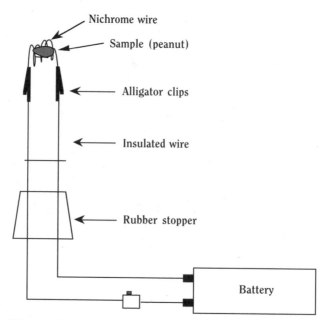

Figure 3. Mounting of sample for ignition with Nichrome coil.

so the coil consumes about 8 amps × 4 volts = 32 watts = 32 joules/sec = 8 cal/sec. If we estimate 1 minute of coil use, the coil produces about 500 calories (assuming all the electrical energy consumed by the coil is released as heat). That is a significant portion of the heat generated by burning the sample and needs to be accounted for in calculating sample caloric values.

Samples that do not liquefy or fall apart when they burn (e.g., both green and dry leaves) can be ignited and burned within the coil, using the coil itself to support the sample. For messier samples (e.g., sugar), use a ceramic crucible to contain the sample and the residue that remains after burning. Oils, fats, and waxes can be burned with a wick, although the combustion of the wick must be taken into account.

3. **Burning the sample.**
    Burn the sample under a soda can that contains 200 ml of water (see Figure 1). For the most effective heat transfer, the sample should be burned 1–2 cm below the bottom of the can. If the flames lap up the sides of the can, increase the distance between the sample and the can. For maximum efficiency, the flame should cover, but not extend beyond the bottom of the can.

    Ignite the sample using a match or a Nichrome coil, as discussed in step 2. It may be important to take into account the heat contributed by the match or the Nichrome. (How can you account for that extra heat? Simply run a control experiment: Run the apparatus without a sample, using the ignition method alone. Then subtract those results from the results of an experiment that used a sample.)

    Measure the initial and the final temperatures of the water with a thermometer to determine the quantity of heat transferred from the burning sample to the water. We place our thermometer about 2 cm from the bottom of the can. Be aware that the temperature of the water may not be uniform—we found that the water at the top of the can was up to 1°C warmer than that at the bottom. Stir the water to eliminate that source of error. (Uneven water temperature could introduce an error of 0.5°–1.0°C/19.1 = 2%–5% in the measurement of heat released.)

4. **Record your data.**
    Keep track of the following data in your notebook: sample name, dry weight of sample before and after burning, temperature of water in the soda can before and after burning, whether you used matches or Nichrome wire as the power source, and distance between sample and soda can. Can you think of anything else? You might find it useful to lay out a data table if you will be burning several samples.

5. **Data calculations.**
    See the examples that follow.

6. **Evaluating the results.**
    The results are about 72% of the expected caloric value of peanuts, based on the 6.0 kcal/g listed on the peanut wrapper and the USDA Handbook, which estimates that roasted peanuts contain 5.9 kcal/g. Markow's paper suggests and our experience confirms that efficiencies of 70–90% are readily obtainable with this technique.

Example: Burning a Peanut with a Match

A roasted salted peanut (with the salt wiped off with a damp towel) was burned 1.5 cm below the bottom of the soda can. Two paper matches were used to ignite the peanut, which burned for about 1 minute. Room temperature was about 25°C.

The water in the soda can changed temperature as follows: (final temperature) − (initial temperature) = 41.6° − 22.5°C = 19.1°C.

The amount of peanut consumed is also calculated "before" and "after": (initial peanut weight) − (final peanut weight) = 0.97g − 0.10g = 0.87g, which means that, by weight, 90% of the peanut was burned.

Example: Data Calculation

The energy released in terms of kcal is calculated using both the temperature and weight data. Remember, it takes 1 calorie of energy to raise the temperature of 1 g of water 1°C. And 1 g of water equals 1 ml. Since our calorimeter (the soda can) contains 200 g of water, each increase of 1°C requires an input of 200 calories. In this experiment, the temperature rose 19.1°C, so the amount of energy that was taken up by the calorimeter is

19.1 × 200 calories = 3,800 calories (3.8 kcal)

The two matches together weighed 0.11 g, and about 0.03 g (2.7%) of their mass burned. Assuming that the matches are cardboard (cellulose), their caloric value is 4 kcal/g. Thus, the match burning contributed 4,000 cal/g × 0.03 g = 120 cal.

Total calories of the sample, therefore, are 3,800 cal − 120 cal, which is a 3% difference. So the total energy from the peanut itself is about 3,680, or, rounding up, 3,700.

How much energy is in a gram of the sample? In the end, only 0.87 g of the peanut was burned. How many calories are there per gram of peanut? With a little algebra, we can find the heat released per unit mass:

= 3,700 cal/0.87 g

= 4,252.9 cal/g, or 4.2 kcal/g

Example: Burning a Peanut with the Nichrome Wire–Battery Ignition

Used the same setup using the wire coil. Turned on the coil for 10 seconds to ignite the peanut, which burned on its own for about 1 minute.

The water in the soda can changed temperature as follows: (final temperature) − (initial temperature) = 36.0° − 26.5°C = 9.5°C.

The amount of peanut consumed is also calculated "before" and "after": (initial peanut weight) − (final peanut weight) = 0.48g − 0.04g = 0.44g. By weight, 92% of the peanut was burned.

The Nichrome coil contributed about 8 cal/sec × 10 sec = 80 cal to the heat measured.

Heat released = (1 cal g^{-1} °C^{-1}) × (200 g water) × (9.5°C) = 1,900 cal
Heat released per unit mass = 1,900 cal/0.44 g = 4,300 cal/g = 4.3 kcal/g

This result is about 71% of that expected for peanuts. The Nichrome coil probably contributed about 4% (80 cal/1900 cal) of the heat measured. So results are similar to those obtained using matches to ignite the sample.

REFERENCES

Markow, Peter. 1992. "Calorimetry in a Nutshell: Peanut Pyrotechnics." The Science Teacher (September): 54–59.

TECHNIQUE
CARBONOMETRY

This Technique describes a simple, accurate way to determine the carbon content of a substance. Once you learn this procedure, you can use it to determine the content of almost anything that can be burned. It is exceptionally useful for studies of carbon in ecosystems, especially how it is stored and transferred through plants, organisms, litter, dung, and so on.

Note that the process of oxidation by combustion is different from digestion as carried out by organisms, which occurs largely by way of enzymatic and chemical oxidation. We are using combustion merely as a way to measure energy content.

RATIONALE AND OVERVIEW

The basic method of carbonometry (determining carbon content) is as follows:

1. Dry and weigh the sample.

2. Burn the sample in a container that provides an atmosphere with sufficient oxygen; we recommend a 6-gal spring-water bottle or jug.

3. Measure the carbon dioxide yielded. We recommend that this be done using a diffusion tube, such as those manufactured by Dräger® or Sensidyne®, which indicates the concentration of carbon dioxide (CO_2) in the air in parts per million (ppm).

The first step is to prepare and standardize all samples by drying and weighing them. Drying is especially important for things made up of a lot of water (e.g., lettuce, grass) and less important for "drier" items like seeds and nuts. To compare amounts of energy in different things, we need standard amounts of the stuff. So 1 ounce of lettuce that has been dried for 24 hours at 100°C is comparable to 1 ounce of chicken dried for the same amount of time at the same temperature. (An ounce of undried lettuce would look like much more but actually be less lettuce, since most of it is water. It would not burn well either.)

In the carbonometry apparatus (Figure 1), the sample is burned in a large plastic bottle, which collects the gases produced by the burning. Note that the burning part of this equipment is the same we used for the technique of calorimetry. (For instructions on building that apparatus, refer to the **Technique: Calorimetry**.) Ignite the sample using a match or a Nichrome wire–battery power system.

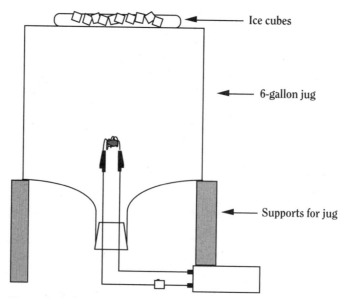

Figure 1. Carbonometry apparatus.

As the sample burns, the amount of carbon dioxide in the bottle increases. By knowing the weight difference of the sample before and after burning and the amount of carbon dioxide present in the bottle before and after burning, we can calculate the carbon content per gram of dry weight.

MATERIALS AND PREPARATION

Safety

> You will be working with burning matches, burning samples, and perhaps a Nichrome wire–battery ignition system that gets very hot.
> **DO USE THIS TECHNIQUE WITHOUT ADULT SUPERVISION.**
> **DO NOT PERFORM THIS TECHNIQUE IN AN OXYGEN-ENRICHED ATMOSPHERE.**
> **DO NOT ALLOW THE TWO NICHROME WIRES OR ALLIGATOR CLIPS TO TOUCH EACH OTHER.**
> **DO NOT TOUCH ANY BURNING, HEATED, OR RECENTLY BURNING ITEMS WITH BARE FINGERS OR ANYTHING BUT APPROPRIATE TOOLS.**
> **WEAR SAFETY GOGGLES DURING THE PROCEDURE.**

In Advance

Prepare the samples, if necessary. If you are using wet materials (especially plant materials), dry them in a 100°C oven until they stop losing weight (i.e., have reached a constant weight). For the sample sizes (0.5–1.0 g) used with this version of the carbonometry technique, 24 hours is likely enough time for complete drying. Use samples of 0.5–1.0 g. That amount is easy to weigh and handle and will have enough energy to raise the water temperature noticeably. Measure the mass of the dry sample to 0.01 g. ("Constant weight" means, therefore, that between one weighing and the next there is no change greater than 0.01 g.)

Materials

- **Scale** sensitive to 0.01 g
- **Drying oven**
- **Calorimetry apparatus** without the soda can or the thermometer; one setup for each group of 3–5 students
- **Nichrome wire–battery power system** (described in Table 1) **or matches**

Table 1   ## Nichrome Wire–Battery Ignition System

ITEM	DESCRIPTION	WHERE WE OBTAINED IT
Ignition coil	12- to 15-cm coil of 22-gauge Nichrome wire	Edmund Scientific; cost approx. $20 per roll
Wire	12-gauge household electrical wire	Hardware store
Alligator clips		Hardware or electronics store
Battery	7.2 V, 1.2 amp hour NiCad battery pack	Radio Shack P/N 23-230; cost approx. $15
Recharger	NiCad battery recharger (120 V AC @ 10 amp in, 7.2 V DC @ 0.4 amp out)	Radio Shack P/N 23-231A, cost approx. $10

NOTE: Recharging the battery
The battery can deliver 1.2 amp hour before needing a recharge. Thus, it will need to be recharged after about (1.2 amp hour) / (8 amp × 1 hour/60 minutes) = 10 minutes of use. The battery can be recharged fully in 4–5 hours with an AC recharger.

- **Samples**, dried and weighed
- **Goggles**
- **Tongs or tweezers**
- **Oven mitt**
- **Fireproof work surface** (laboratory bench or heat-resistant pad)
- **Carbonometry apparatus** (described in Table 2)

Table 2.   ## Materials for Carbonometry Apparatus

ITEM	DESCRIPTION	WHERE WE OBTAINED IT
Plastic have to buy one	Plastic, empty, 6-gal water container (not tinted)	Costs probably $10–15 if you bottle, preferably clear
Stopper	Rubber stopper (No. 8)	Lab supply catalog
CO_2 detector	Dräger CO_2 diffusion tube	Dräger 500/a-D carbon dioxide diffusion tube P/N 8101381; approx. $40 per pack of 10. We ordered from BGI Inc., 58 Guinan St., Waltham, MA 02154, Tel. 617-891-9380.

Procedure

1. **Prepare the samples.**

   Dry all samples to a constant weight. Use sample sizes of 0.5–1.0 g.

2. **Decide which method you will use to burn the sample: matches or a Nichrome wire–battery power system.**

   a. **Matches.** Materials that burn easily (e.g., paper, wood, peanuts) can be lit with a match. Use paper matches since they do not contribute much carbon to the final total of the match plus the sample. (How can you calculate the carbon contributed by the match alone? Just run the experiment without a sample and compare the results with those from the match plus the sample.)

   Mount the sample on a wire (or paper clip) loop stuck into a cork or rubber stopper (Figure 2).

   b. **Nichrome wire–battery ignition system.** A somewhat more elegant approach is to ignite the sample with a hot coil of Nichrome wire (Figure 3). We used a 12- to 15-cm length of 22-gauge Nichrome wire, wrapped into a coil with 3–10 turns. You can wrap the wire directly around a sample or force the sample between the coils. Use a NiCad battery pack (normally used to power radio-controlled toy cars) to heat the coil to an orange-yellow color (approximately 900–1,100°C), which will take only a few seconds. Samples that are easy to ignite will burst into flame in 5–10 sec and then continue to burn on their own. **Turn off the coil once the sample is burning.**

   Samples that do not liquefy or fall apart when they burn (e.g., both green and dry leaves) can be ignited and burned within the coil, using the coil itself to support the sample. For "messier" samples (e.g., sugar), use a ceramic crucible to contain the sample and the residue that

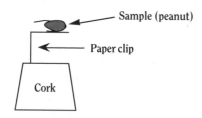

Figure 2. Mounting of sample for ignition with matches.

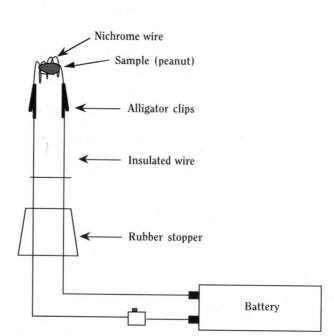

Figure 3. Mounting of sample for ignition with Nichrome coil.

remains after burning. Oils, fats, and waxes can be burned with a wick, although the combustion of the wick must be taken into account).

3. **Record your data.**
Keep track of the following data in your notebook: sample name, dry weight of sample before and after burning, whether you used matches or Nichrome wire as your power source, and the CO_2 reading from the diffusion tube. Can you think of anything else?

You might find it useful to lay out a data table if you will be burning several samples.

4. **Placing the sample.**
Set up the sample in the inverted water bottle (see Figure 1) so the sample is approximately 20 cm above the neck of the jug, to encourage free air flow to the burning sample. Mount the sample on the rubber stopper so you can seal the sample inside the bottle. Place a tray of ice cubes on top of the container during burning to prevent the top from becoming too warm and to encourage convection in the jug.

5. **The actual burning: Ignition.**
Ignite the sample using a match or a Nichrome coil, as discussed in step 2. It may be important to take into account the carbon contributed by the match or the Nichrome. (How can you account for the extra carbon? Simply run a control experiment: run the apparatus without a sample, using the ignition method alone. Then subtract those results from the results of an experiment using a sample plus the ignition method.)

If you are using a match, light the sample and then lower the container over the burning sample. If you are using the Nichrome coil, seal the container before you ignite the sample.

NOTE: A 6-gal water bottle is large enough to contain ample O_2 for the combustion of at least 1 g of material. The jug contains 6 gal, or 22.7 l, of air. Of that, 21%, or 4.8 l is O_2. Burning 1 g of fat will consume approximately 2 l of O_2, which is about 40% of the available oxygen.

6. **Keeping track of the burning time.**
Burning 0.3–0.5 g of material takes 1–2 min for fast-burning materials, such as paper, and as long as 8 min for slower-burning materials, such as candles.

7. **Inserting the CO_2 tube.**
Once the sample has stopped burning, open the container briefly to insert a CO_2 diffusion tube, then reseal the bottle. Opening the container undoubtedly results in some loss of the combustion gases, which is probably a small but significant source of error. Unfortunately, we have not found a practical way to avoid opening the container to insert the detector tube.

If your plastic container is clear, you can watch the color change progress as the CO_2 diffuses through the length of the diffusion tube. Leaving the tube in the bottle for 15–30 min usually is sufficient to react nearly half of the CO_2 tube.

8. **The tube and the data.**
The tubes can be read to about one significant figure (an uncertainty of

about 10–20% per reading). Typical readings correspond to 1–3% CO_2. (That compares to 700–900 ppm, or 0.07–0.09%, for ambient indoor CO_2 levels, a low-enough level that we can ignore the CO_2 present in the container before burning.) To clean out the carbonometer jug between runs, flush it (with water or room air) to remove the combustion gases.

9.   **Data calculation.**
     See the examples that follow and Table 3.

Example: Burning a Candle

We burned a birthday candle for approximately 8 min. Approximately 5 cm of the candle length was burned.

15-min Dräger tube readings

CO   25 parts per million per hour (ppm-hr) for 0.25 hr = 100 ppm = 0.01%
         0.01% × 22.7 liters / (24.5 l/mole @ 25°C) × 12 gC/mole = 0.001 gC

CO_2   7,000 ppm-hr / 0.25 hr = 28,000 ppm = 2.8%
         2.8% × 22.7 liters / (24.5 l/mole @ 25°C) × 12 gC/mole = 0.31 gC

30-min Dräger tube readings

CO   40 ppm-hr / 0.5 hr = 80 ppm = 0.008%
         0.008% × 22.7 liters / (24.5 l/mole @ 25°C) × 12 gC/mole = 0.001 gC

CO_2   12,000 ppm-hr / 0.5 hr = 24,000 ppm = 2.4%
         2.4% × 22.7 liters / (24.5 l/mole @ 25°C) × 12 gC/mole = 0.27 gC

Less than 1% of the carbon released is in the form of carbon monoxide.

The sample is weighed after burning. The weight difference between before and after burning is used to calculate the carbon content per gram of dry weight. (Remember that we are using dry samples.)

(initial candle weight) – (final candle weight) = 1.04 g – 0.69 g = 0.35 g

Carbon content = 0.27–0.31 gC / 0.35 g = 77–89% carbon

This result agrees well with the values of 80–82% taken from the literature and calculated from the molecular formula for wax.

Example: Burning a Paper Towel

We burned a piece of paper towel for approximately 1 min.

30-min Dräger tube readings

CO   250 ppm-hr / 0.5 hr = 500 ppm = 0.05%
         0.05% × 22.7 liters / (24.5 l/mole @ 25°C) × 12 gC/mole = 0.006 gC

CO_2   9,000 ppm-hr / 0.5 hr = 18,000 ppm = 1.8%
         1.8% × 22.7 liters / (24.5 l/mole @ 25°C) × 12 gC/mole = 0.20 gC

A small fraction (3%) of the carbon released is in the form of carbon monoxide.

Again, the sample is weighed after burning, and the difference between before and after weights allows us to calculate the carbon content per gram of dry weight of the sample.

(initial paper weight) – (final paper weight) = 0.61 g

Carbon content = 0.20 gC / 0.61 g = 33% carbon

This result is near, but significantly different from, the value of 44% calculated from the molecular formula for cellulose. The paper may have resorbed moisture from the air while we were preparing our setup, so the values are lower than predicted for cellulose. Also, the paper towel may contains binders and finishes, which might affect its carbon content.

Table 3 **Translation of CO_2 Diffusion Results into Grams of Carbon (gC)**

TUBE EXPOSED FOR 15 MINUTES

5-Gallon Jug CO_2 ppm-hr	gC	6-Gallon Jug CO_2 ppm-hr	gC
500	0.02	500	0.02
1,000	0.04	1,000	0.04
2,000	0.07	2,000	0.09
3,000	0.11	3,000	0.13
4,000	0.15	4,000	0.18
5,000	0.19	5,000	0.22
7,000	0.26	7,000	0.31
10,000	0.37	10,000	0.44
15,000	0.56	15,000	0.67
20,000	0.74	20,000	0.89

TUBE EXPOSED FOR 20 MINUTES

5-Gallon Jug CO_2 ppm-hr	gC	6-Gallon Jug CO_2 ppm-hr	gC
500	0.01	500	0.02
1,000	0.03	1,000	0.03
2,000	0.06	2,000	0.07
3,000	0.08	3,000	0.10
4,000	0.11	4,000	0.13
5,000	0.14	5,000	0.17
7,000	0.20	7,000	0.24
10,000	0.28	10,000	0.34
15,000	0.42	15,000	0.51
20,000	0.56	20,000	0.67

TUBE EXPOSED FOR 30 MINUTES

5-Gallon Jug CO_2 ppm-hr	gC	6-Gallon Jug CO_2 ppm-hr	gC
500	0.01	500	0.01
1,000	0.02	1,000	0.02
2,000	0.04	2,000	0.04
3,000	0.06	3,000	0.07
4,000	0.07	4,000	0.09
5,000	0.09	5,000	0.11
7,000	0.13	7,000	0.16
10,000	0.19	10,000	0.22
15,000	0.28	15,000	0.33
20,000	0.37	20,000	0.44

TUBE EXPOSED FOR 60 MINUTES

5-Gallon Jug CO_2 ppm-hr	gC	6-Gallon Jug CO_2 ppm-hr	gC
500	0.00	500	0.01
1,000	0.01	1,000	0.01
2,000	0.02	2,000	0.02
3,000	0.03	3,000	0.03
4,000	0.04	4,000	0.04
5,000	0.05	5,000	0.06
7,000	0.06	7,000	0.08
10,000	0.09	10,000	0.11
15,000	0.14	15,000	0.17
20,000	0.19	20,000	0.22

TECHNIQUE
DESCRIBING AND COMPARING COMMUNITIES

This Technique presents some ways to describe and analyze communities or local associations of species. Community ecology is a complicated and controversial discipline, but it is a fascinating way to see ecological interactions at a more accessible scale than an ecosystem. We focus on ways to describe and analyze biological diversity. Who lives where, how many of them, and how many we might reasonably expect.

Two fundamental activities are necessary for describing communities: identifying what is there and counting. Everything else is based on those two tasks. They can be pretty challenging, however, and even counting can be harder than you might think!

Communities come in many sizes, and while the term implies an identifiable entity, it can be used flexibly (some might say "loosely").

For example, we can speak of a "stream bank community," meaning the characteristic vegetation along the stream bank in a particular location. We might then speak of the "birds of the stream bank community." On the other hand we can speak of the "bird community of the oak-hickory forest" or the "amphibian community." The common theme is frequent, perhaps predictable, associations of species—plant, animal, or both. In what follows, we discuss basic indexes for community description. Bear in mind, though, that the ways of taking data on plant species in a community are different from ways of censusing insect or reptile diversity. Such practical matters of natural history will shape the studies you might do.

The measures we address are richness, diversity, and similarity.

SPECIES RICHNESS

The basic information we need about a community is how many species are present (in the study area).

Establish the area within which you will collect data. As you travel through the area, note any species you encounter. If the study area is very large, you may wish to sample it rather than try to visit and catalog every square meter.

If you have comparable information from elsewhere, a simple species list can be revealing, since species live in characteristic habitats, have associations with other species, and tolerances and intolerances of various kinds. Further, your list may raise interesting questions when compared with the species list of a comparable or contrasting plot of the same size. If on one hectare of forest in Ecuador, you find as many tree species as are found in all of North America (as is quite possible), you have reason to suspect that the ecosystems differ in some important respects. Just what causes such differences is, of course, a matter of great interest and intense study.

If you are interested in describing diversity, the simple list of species is only a starting point. To carry your description further, keep track of the number of <u>individuals</u> of each species. For very numerous or very mobile species, such as grasses or gnats, you may need to settle for estimates or standardized sampling techniques (number of individuals along a transect or in some manageable, small unit of area).

Example

See Figures 1 and 2. Each figure represents a plot with a small number of plant species present. Take a census of each plot. Name the species or merely label them somehow.

1. How many species are present on each plot?
2. How many individuals of each species are present on each plot?

Are the communities similar or different?

Arrange the species lists in descending order of number of individuals. What is the total number of individuals?

Your species lists for the two communities might be the same, but the numbers of individuals of each species are quite different. Assuming that each species has other species associated with it (e.g., animals that eat its fruit or leaves or use it for shelter), that may mean that the animal (including microbial) elements of the community are quite different. It may also suggest that the soil, moisture, or other physical characteristics of the site are quite different. To differentiate among those factors or to decide whether the communities are similar, more data are needed.

DIVERSITY

Now we consider not only how many species are on a site but how many individuals of each species are present.

First, we need the following raw data:

- the species list
- the number of individuals of each species encountered
- the total number of individuals of all species

Once we have this information, there are several ways to calculate diversity. Usually, various bits of information are combined to yield a single number, an index, that sums up the diversity information for a study site. Like the species list, we can compare the index with indexes from other sites. We focus on one common index, the Shannon-Weaver (also known as the Shannon-Wiener) diversity index, often represented by H' for short.

Figures 1 through 6 show some imaginary plant communities that we will census and compare. Note that these sample plots are all of the same size. You will learn best if you do the counting and calculating yourself. All the calculations can be done with pencil, paper, and a calculator for doing

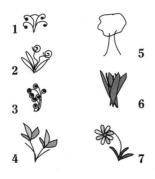

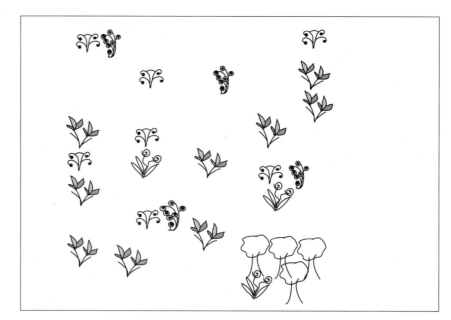

Figure 1. Community A

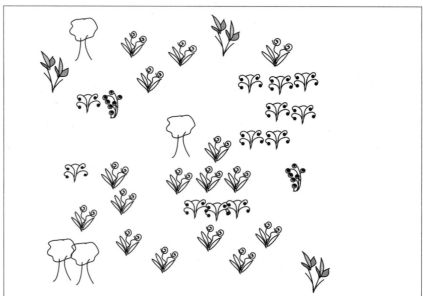

Figure 2. Community B

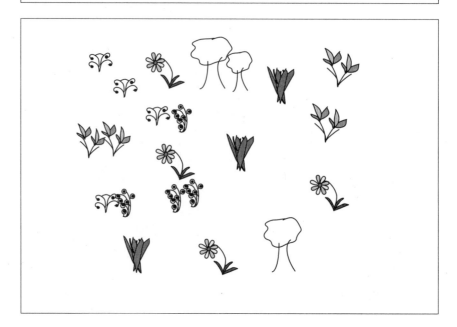

Figure 3. Community C

442

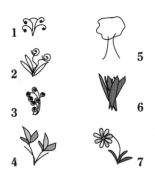

Figure 4. Community D

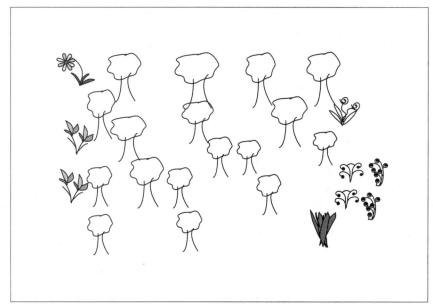

Figure 5. Community E

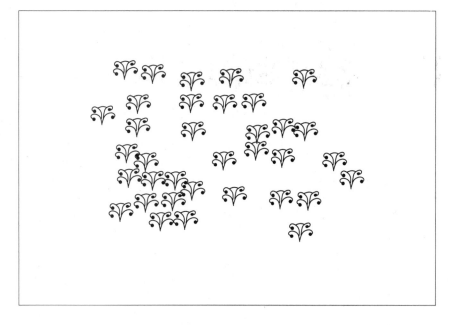

Figure 6. Community F

logarithms, although a spreadsheet makes things easier. At the end of this Technique is a sample spreadsheet for the examples.

The calculation uses the number of individuals of each species present in the sample (e.g., species 1), the number of individuals of all species, the ratio of those two numbers, and the logarithm of the ratio. (It is customary to use the natural log, ln, or $\log_{10}$.)

Thus, for each species:

1. Divide the number of individuals of species 1 by the number of individuals of all species.

2. Find the log of that number.

3. Now multiply the number calculated for step 1 by the log calculated in step 2.

4. Repeat steps 1–3 for each species represented, then add all the results.

5. Multiply the total from step 4 by –1.

In formal terms, the Shannon-Weaver index is:

$$H' = -\Sigma p_i (\ln p_i)$$

or

$$H' = -\Sigma p_i (\log p_i)$$

where p_i is the proportion of each species i in the total sample of individuals.

Use the communities in Figures 1–6 and compare two or more species i. For help with the method, see the worked out example at the end of this Technique.

SIMILARITY

Even though a whole region is identified as belonging to a general biome type (e.g., "Northern Hardwood Forest"), within such a region are many types of ecosystems, with many types of communities. Sometimes it is easy to tell that there is little or no similarity. For example, we do not expect the lichen community on oak trees in New Hampshire to have much in common with the stream-bottom invertebrate community in the same region.

It is not always so easy to tell how different or similar two communities are, even using species lists, a diversity index, and information on which species tend to associate with which other species.

One simple step beyond comparing two communities on the basis of their diversity indexes is to compare their composition directly. Again, various indexes are used for this kind of comparison, but the simplest and most widespread is Jacard's index of similarity.

To calculate the similarity of two communities, X and Y, we need to know the following:

- which species are in X and how many species there are (let's call that number X)

- which species are in Y and how many species there are (let's call that number Y)

- how many species are in common, that is, how many species occur in both X and Y (let's call that number c)

Then we can calculate the Jacard's index as follows:

$$\frac{X + Y - c}{X + Y}$$

Example

Using the formula for Jacard's index, calculate the similarity between community A (Figure 1) and itself. The result shows you the index value you get for two identical communities.

Then compare the community A with some of the other communities in Figures 2–6, to see how the results differ. The communities shown here are very simple ones, but the process is the same. Compare your results with those shown in Table 2.

Once you find out that there are some differences, the next level of questions start, for example, what difference do the differences make? Why are there such differences?

Table 1 **Community Data from Schematic Communities in Figures 1–6**

Community A

SPECIES	n	i/N equals p_i	$\ln p_i$	$p_i \times \ln p_i$
1	7	0.26	−1.35	−0.35
2	3	0.11	−2.20	−0.24
3	4	0.15	−1.91	−0.28
4	9	0.33	−1.10	−0.37
5	4	0.15	−1.91	−0.28
Total individuals	27 = N			
		Shannon-Weaver		−1.53

Community B

SPECIES	n	i/N	$\ln p_i$	$p_i \times \ln p_i$
1	12	0.32	−1.13	−0.37
2	16	0.43	−0.84	−0.36
3	2	0.05	−2.92	−0.16
4	3	0.08	−2.51	−0.20
5	4	0.11	−2.22	−0.24
Total individuals	37 = N			
		Shannon-Weaver		−1.33

Species called i, with i = 1 through however many species are in the community.

n = number of individuals counted for each species i

N = total individuals of all species

i/N = proportion of all species made up by individuals of species i (that is the same as p_i)

p_i = proportion of all species made up by individuals of species i

ln = log normal

CONTINUED

Community C

SPECIES	n	i/N	$\ln p_i$	$p_i \times \ln p_i$
1	4	0.18	−1.70	−0.31
3	4	0.18	−1.70	−0.31
4	4	0.18	−1.70	−0.31
5	3	0.14	−1.99	−0.27
6	3	0.14	−1.99	−0.27
7	4	0.18	−1.70	−0.31
Total individuals	22 = N			
			Shannon-Weaver	−1.78

Community D

SPECIES	n	i/N	$\ln p_i$	$p_i \times \ln p_i$
4	15	0.79	−0.24	−0.19
7	4	0.21	−1.56	−0.33
Total individuals	19 = N			
			Shannon-Weaver	−0.51

Community E

SPECIES	n	i/N	$\ln p_i$	$p_i \times \ln p_i$
1	2	0.08	−2.56	−0.20
2	1	0.04	−3.26	−0.13
3	2	0.08	−2.56	−0.20
4	2	0.08	−2.56	−0.20
5	17	0.65	−0.42	−0.28
6	1	0.04	−3.26	−0.13
7	1	0.04	−3.26	−0.13
Total individuals	26 = N			
			Shannon-Weaver	−1.25

Community F

SPECIES	n	i/N	$\ln p_i$	$p_i \times \ln p_i$
1	35	1.00	0.00	0.00
Total individuals	35 = N			
			Shannon-Weaver	0.00

CONTINUED

Species called i, with i = 1 through however many species are in the community.

n = number of individuals counted for each species i

N = total individuals of all species

i/N = proportion of all species made up by individuals of species i (that is the same as p_i)

p_i = proportion of all species made up by individuals of species i

ln = log normal

Hypothetical Community G

SPECIES	n	i/N	$\ln p_i$	$p_i \times \ln p_i$
1	2	0.10	−2.30	−0.23
2	2	0.10	−2.30	−0.23
3	2	0.10	−2.30	−0.23
4	2	0.10	−2.30	−0.23
5	2	0.10	−2.30	−0.23
6	2	0.10	−2.30	−0.23
7	2	0.10	−2.30	−0.23
8	2	0.10	−2.30	−0.23
9	2	0.10	−2.30	−0.23
10	2	0.10	−2.30	−0.23
Total individuals	20 = N			
			Shannon-Weaver	−2.30

Table 2 Coefficient of Similarity (Jacard's Index) for Several Pairs of Communities in Figures 1–6

	COMPARED WITH COMMUNITY					
COMMUNITY	A	B	C	D	E	F
A	1	1.00	0.57	0.17	0.714	0.2
B	1	1.00	0.57	0.17	0.714	
C	1	0.57	1.00	0.30	0.54	

Acknowledgments and credits (*continued* from p. iv)

Module 2, Unit 2, Chapter 1
Unit title page: Courtesy of Michael S. Quinton; **Pg. 127:** From Leonard B. Radinsky (1987: Fig. 17.3 [c]). *The Evolution of Vertebrate Design*. Chicago: University of Chicago Press. © University of Chicago Press; **Pp. 132–133:** Figures from THE VERTEBRATE BODY, Sixth Edition by Alfred Sherwood Romer and Thomas S. Parsons, copyright © 1986 by Saunders College Publishing, reproduced by permission of the publisher (Figs. 55, 57, 60); and, From A. S. Romer 1959. *The Vertebrate Story*. Chicago: University of Chicago Press. © University of Chicago 1959. (Pp. 240, 265)

Module 2, Unit 2, Chapter 2
Pg. 142: From Knut Schmidt-Nielsen (1990: Fig. S.11). *Animal Physiology: Adaption and Environment*. Cambridge, UK: Cambridge University Press. Reprinted with the permission of Cambridge University Press.

Module 2, Unit 2, Chapter 4
Animal Cards: Topi, Wildebeest: Courtsey of Jonathan Kingdon. © by Jonathan Kingdon 1982.

Module 2, Unit 2, Chapter 5
Pg. 190: From "The Energetics of Bird Flight," Vance Tucker. Copyright © 1969 by Scientific American, Inc. All rights reserved.

Module 2, Unit 2, Chapter 6
Pg. 200: CALVIN AND HOBBES © Watterson. Reprinted with permission of UNIVERSAL PRESS SYNDICATE. All rights reserved; **Fig. 4:** Courtesy of C. Ladd Prosser (Prosser 1973: Fig. 9-31).

Module 2, Unit 3, Chapter 1
Figs. 2, 3: Adapted from "Forest Succession," Henry S. Horn. Copyright © 1975 by Scientific American, Inc. All rights reserved.

Module 2, Unit 3, Chapter 2
Fig. 7: (Adapted from) COMMUNITIES AND ECOSYSTEMS by Whittaker, © 1975. Reprinted by permission of Prentice-Hall, Inc., Upper Saddle River, NJ. (Fig. 4.10); **Figs. 6 [a–e] and 8:** From Christen Raunkiaer (1934: Figs. 1–4, 6, 7). The Life Forms of Plants and Statistical Plant Geography: Being the Collected Papers of C. Raunkiaer. Oxford, UK: Clarendon Press, by permission of Oxford University Press.

Technique: Introduction to Research
Fig. 2: From: STATISTICS: CONCEPTS AND CONTROVERSIES 2/E by David S. Moore © 1985 by W. H. Freeman and Company. Used with permission. (Fig. 1-2)